Level 1

¡Avancemos!

Cuaderno práctica por niveles
Teacher's Edition

HOLT McDOUGAL
a division of Houghton Mifflin Harcourt

ISBN-13: 978-0-618-75101-3
ISBN-10: 0-618-75101-7
Internet: www.holtmcdougal.com

3 4 5 6 7 8 9 10 0982 15
4500531602

TABLE OF CONTENTS

TO THE STUDENT:

Cuaderno práctica por niveles provides activities for practice at different levels of difficulty. Leveled vocabulary and grammar activities cover the entire content of each lesson of your student book. Other activity pages practice the content of the lesson while targeting a specific skill, such as listening. Within most categories of practice there are three pages, each at a different level of difficulty (A, B, and C). The A level is the easiest and C is the most challenging. The different levels of difficulty (A, B, C) are distinguished by the amount of support you're given. A level activities usually give you choices, B level activities often call for short answers to be written, and C level activities require longer answers.

The following sections are included in the **Cuaderno** for each lesson:

- **Vocabulario**
  Each page in this section has three activities that practice the lesson vocabulary.

- **Gramática**
  This section follows the same pattern as the **Vocabulario** section and reinforces the grammar points taught in each lesson.

- **Gramática**
  Follows the same pattern as the Vocabulario section and reinforce the grammar points taught in each lesson.

- **Integración**
  Each of these pages requires you to gather information from two different sources and respond to a related question. The source material is always presented in two different formats: written and spoken.

- **Escuchar**
  Each page in this section has two audio passages, each followed by a short activity. The passages allow you to practice your oral comprehension of Spanish.

- **Leer**
  This section contains short readings accompanied by **¿Comprendiste?** and **¿Qué piensas?** questions.

- **Escribir**
  In this section you are asked to write a short composition. A pre-writing activity will help you prepare to write your composition.

- **Cultura**
  Activities in this section focus on the cultural information found throughout each lesson.

TO THE TEACHER:

Cuaderno práctica por niveles is referenced in the student edition and addresses the individual needs of students. Leveled vocabulary and grammar activities cover the entire content of each lesson of the student edition. Other activity pages practice the content of the lesson while targeting a specific skill, such as listening. Within most categories of practice there are three pages, each at a different level of difficulty (A, B, and C). The A level is the easiest and C is the most challenging. As an additional study tool, the workbook contains lesson bookmarks that include the **En resumen** vocabulary list and abbreviated grammar explanations.

The following sections are included in the **Cuaderno** for each lesson:

- **Vocabulario**
  Each page in this section has three activities that practice the lesson vocabulary.

- **Gramática**
  This section follows the same pattern as the **Vocabulario** section and targets a specific grammar point taught in the lesson.

- **Integración**
  Each of these pages requires that students gather information from two different sources and respond to a related question. The source material is always presented in two different formats: written and spoken.

- **Escuchar**
  Each page in this section has two audio passages, each followed by a short activity. The passages allow students to gain practice and increase their comprehension of spoken Spanish.

- **Leer**
  This section contains short readings accompanied by ¿**Comprendiste?** and ¿**Qué piensas?** questions.

- **Escribir**
  Each page in this section has a preparatory activity that helps students organize their ideas before they complete the writing task.

- **Cultura**
  Activities in this section practice recall and analysis of the cultural information found throughout each **lección**.

Vocabulario A

Level 1, pp. 32-36

> ¡AVANZA! **Goal:** Talk about activities.

1 Put an X next to each activity that you do in your Spanish classroom.

1. _____ andar en patineta

2. __X__ leer un libro

3. __X__ estudiar

4. _____ comprar un helado

5. __X__ aprender el español

2 Talk about what you like to do. Complete the following sentences with a word or expression from the vocabulary.

1. A ti ¿qué _____te gusta_____ hacer?

2. A mí me gusta montar en _____bicicleta_____ .

3. Me gusta preparar la _____comida_____ .

4. Los sábados me gusta _____alquilar_____ un DVD.

3 Ask the following people if they like to do the activities in parentheses.

modelo: Camila (dibujar): **Camila, ¿te gusta dibujar?**

1. Felipe (tocar la guitarra) Felipe, ¿te gusta tocar la guitarra? _____

2. Mayra (hablar por teléfono) Mayra, ¿te gusta hablar por teléfono? _____

Vocabulario B

> **Goal:** Talk about activities.

1 Describe what you like to do. Choose the best word or expression from the vocabulary.

1. Después de las clases me gusta (<u>practicar</u> / escuchar) deportes.

2. Me gusta más escuchar (bicicleta / <u>música</u>).

3. ¿Te gusta (<u>escribir</u> / jugar) correos electrónicos?

4. A mí me gusta (descansar / <u>mirar</u>) la televisión.

2 Look at the images below. Then, write what they are under the appropriate category.

Comer	**Beber**
1. pizza	**1.** agua
2. helado	**2.** jugo
3. galletas	**3.** refresco
4. fruta	

3 Answer the following questions in complete sentences.

1. ¿Te gusta más escuchar música o leer un libro?

Answers will vary: **Me gusta más escuchar música.**

2. ¿Te gusta practicar deportes después de las clases?

Answers will vary: **Sí, (No, no) me gusta practicar deportes después de**

las clases.

3. ¿Qué te gusta hacer más, alquilar un DVD o andar en patineta?

Answers will vary: **Me gusta más alquilar un DVD.**

4. ¿Qué te gusta hacer más, pasear o trabajar?

Answers will vary: **Me gusta más pasear.**

Vocabulario C

| ¡AVANZA! | **Goal:** Talk about activities. |

1 **¿Qué te gusta hacer?** Complete these sentences using the appropriate words from the vocabulary.

1. Después de las clases me gusta ___escuchar___ música.

2. Los sábados y domingos no me gusta estudiar o hacer ___la tarea___ .

3. Antes de practicar deportes me gusta beber ___agua/jugo___ .

4. Los sábados me gusta ___pasar___ un rato con los amigos.

2 Make a list of six things that you like or do not like to eat and drink.

Comer

modelo: (No) Me gusta comer **papas fritas.**

1. *Answers will vary:* **Me gusta comer fruta.**
2. **No me gusta comer galletas.**
3. **Me gusta comer helado.**

Beber

1. *Answers will vary:* **Me gusta beber agua.**
2. **No me gusta beber refrescos.**
3. **Me gusta beber jugo.**

3 Write two sentences about what you like to do, and two sentences about what you do not like to do during Saturday and Sunday. Use **Me gusta...** and **No me gusta...**

Answers will vary: **Los sábados y domingos me gusta pasar un rato con los amigos. También me gusta mirar la televisión y descansar. No me gusta hacer la tarea. Me gusta más escuchar música.**

Gramática A *Subject Pronouns and* ser

Level 1, pp. 37-41

> **¡AVANZA!** **Goal:** Use the subject pronouns and the verb **ser**.

1 Some friends talk about themselves. Complete the sentences using the subject pronouns from the box.

Ustedes	Tú	Yo	Ella	Nosotros

1. _____Tú_____ eres estudiante.
2. _____Ella_____ es de Colombia.
3. _____Nosotros_____ somos de México.
4. _____Ustedes_____ son de Argentina.
5. _____Yo_____ soy de España.

2 Underline the correct form of the verb ser in parentheses to tell where everyone is from.

1. Yo (<u>soy</u> / son) de Miami.
2. Tú (<u>eres</u> / es) de Honduras.
3. Nosotros (sois / <u>somos</u>) de Los Ángeles.
4. ¿Usted (<u>es</u> / son) de Buenos Aires, señor Calvo?
5. ¿Ustedes (<u>son</u> / sois) de España, chicos?

3 Write the correct form of the verb **ser** to complete the sentences and tell where everyone is from.

1. Mi amiga _____es_____ de Nueva York.
2. Yo _____soy_____ de Los Ángeles.
3. Tú _____eres_____ de Boston.
4. Sonia _____es_____ de Miami.
5. Nosotros _____somos_____ de Estados Unidos.
6. Ustedes _____son_____ de Estados Unidos.

Gramática B *Subject Pronouns and* **ser**

> ¡AVANZA! **Goal:** Use the subject pronouns and the verb **ser**.

1 Choose the correct subject pronoun to talk about where people are from.

1. __b__ somos de Buenos Aires.

   a. Yo   **b.** Nosotros   **c.** Ustedes   **d.** Él

2. __c__ son de México.

   a. Él   **b.** Tú   **c.** Ellas   **d.** Usted

3. __a__ son de Valencia.

   a. Ellos   **b.** Yo   **c.** Ella   **d.** Tú

4. __c__ eres de Valladolid.

   a. Él   **b.** Usted   **c.** Tú   **d.** Ellos

2 Two friends talk about where they are from. Complete the dialog using the verb **ser** .

Claudia: Yo **1.** __soy__ de Panamá. Y tú, ¿de dónde **2.** __eres__ ?

Andrés: Yo **3.** __soy__ de Colombia, pero mi hermano **4.** __es__ de Costa Rica y mis padres **5.** __son__ de Venezuela.

Claudia: Una amiga también **6.** __es__ de Venezuela. ¿De dónde **7.** __son__ tus amigos?

Andrés: ¡De muchos países!

3 Tell where the following people are from. Use the correct subject pronouns. Write your answers in complete sentences.

modelo: María y Patricia (Panamá): **Ellas son de Panamá.**

1. Leila y Javier (Colombia)

   Ellos son de Colombia.

2. Susana (Nueva York)

   Ella es de Nueva York.

3. Marcos (República Dominicana)

   Él es de la República Dominicana.

Gramática C *Subject Pronouns and* **ser**

> **¡AVANZA!** **Goal:** Use the subject pronouns and the verb **ser**.

1 Write the correct form of the verb **ser**.

1. ¿Tú _____*eres*_____ de Bariloche?
2. ¿Profesora Loreto, usted _____*es*_____ de Texas?
3. Mis hermanas y yo _____*somos*_____ de Nicaragua.
4. ¿Tú y tus padres _____*son*_____ de Puerto Rico?

2 Ask where these people are from and then write the correct answer.

modelo: Carmela / Bolivia

¿De dónde es Carmela? (Ella) es de Bolivia.

1. Señora Luna y señora Varita / Honduras

¿De dónde son la señora Luna y la señora Varita? Ellas son de Honduras.

2. Vicente / Perú

¿De dónde es Vicente? Él es de Perú.

3. Señor González / Cuba

¿De dónde es el señor González? Él es de Cuba.

4. tú / México

¿De dónde eres tú? Yo soy de México.

3 Write about where you and people you know are from. Use three different subject pronouns.

1. *Answers will vary:* **Yo soy de Uruguay.**
2. *Answers will vary:* **El amigo de mi papá es de Irlanda.**
3. *Answers will vary:* **Los amigos de mi hermana son de Estados Unidos.**

Gramática A *The verb gustar*

> **¡AVANZA!** **Goal:** Express what people like to do using the verb **gustar**.

1 **¿Qué les gusta hacer?** Complete these sentences by underlining the correct pronoun in parentheses.

1. A ellas (<u>les</u> / le) gusta escribir correos electrónicos.

2. A nosotros (<u>nos</u> / les) gusta aprender el español.

3. A ustedes (<u>les</u> / le) gusta pasar un rato con los amigos.

4. ¿ A ti (<u>te</u> / les) gusta trabajar los sábados y domingos?

5. A mí (te / <u>me</u>) gusta pasar un rato con los amigos.

2 Complete the sentences with an appropriate form of **gustar** and the correct pronoun.

1. A mis amigas no _____les gusta_____ comer papas fritas.

2. A Napoleón _____le gusta_____ pasar un rato con los amigos.

3. ¿A ellas _____les gusta_____ tocar la guitarra?

4. A mí _____me gusta_____ estudiar.

5. ¿A ustedes _____les gusta_____ alquilar un DVD?

6. A ti _____te gusta_____ comprar fruta.

3 Look at the drawings and write complete sentences to say what these people enjoy doing.

1.   2.   3.

1. A ellos <u>les gusta descansar / leer.</u>

2. A ella <u>le gusta jugar al fútbol.</u>

3. A él <u>le gusta comer (helado).</u>

Gramática B *The verb gustar*

> **¡AVANZA!** **Goal:** Express what people like to do using the verb **gustar**.

1 To tell what people enjoy doing, choose the correct expression from the word box.

a. A nosotros	**b.** A Paulina	**c.** A ustedes	**d.** A ti

1. __a__ nos gusta preparar la comida.
2. __d__ te gusta más andar en patineta.
3. __b__ le gusta montar en bicicleta.
4. ¿ __c__ no les gusta escuchar música?

2 Write sentences with the following words in order to say what each person enjoys or doesn't enjoy doing. Use the verb **gustar**.

1. A Marcos y Marisela / comer papas fritas A Marcos y Marisela **les gusta** comer

   papas fritas.

2. ¿A ustedes / preparar la comida? ¿A ustedes **les gusta** preparar la comida?

3. A mis amigas y a mí / practicar deportes A mis amigas y a mí **nos gusta** practicar

   deportes.

4. ¿A ti / pasear los sábados? ¿A ti **te gusta** pasear los sábados?

3 Answer the questions in complete sentences using **a + pronoun**.

modelo: ¿Le gusta comer pizza a Juan?

   Sí, (No) **a él** (no) **le gusta** comer pizza.

1. ¿Le gusta tocar la guitarra a la maestra?

   Answers will vary: Sí, (No) a ella (no) le gusta **tocar la guitarra.**

2. ¿Les gusta comer fruta a ustedes?

   Answers will vary: Sí, (No) a nosotros (no) nos gusta comer fruta.

3. ¿Te gusta beber jugo?

   Answers will vary: Sí, (No) a mí (no) me gusta beber jugo.

4. ¿Les gusta leer libros a ellas?

   Answers will vary: Sí, (No) a ellas (no) les gusta leer libros.

Gramática C *The verb gustar*

Level 1, pp. 42-44

> ¡AVANZA! **Goal:** Express what people like to do using the verb **gustar**.

1 **¿Qué cosas no les gusta hacer?** Write an appropriate subject pronoun to complete each sentence.

1. A _____nosotros(as)_____ no nos gusta comprar refrescos.

2. A _____mí_____ no me gusta hacer la tarea.

3. A _____ti_____ no te gusta comer galletas.

4. A ___ustedes / ellos(as)___ no les gusta pasear.

2 Complete the sentences using the verb **gustar** + **infinitive** to tell what people like and dislike doing.

1. A mí _____me gusta alquilar_____ un DVD.

2. A nosotros _____nos gusta mirar_____ la televisión.

3. A Martín y a Sofía no _____les gusta hacer_____ la tarea después de las clases.

4. ¿A usted _____le gusta beber_____ jugo de naranja?

5. A Carlos no _____le gusta jugar_____ al fútbol.

3 Write three questions and answers about people you know and the activities they enjoy. Follow the model.

modelo: ¿Qué **les gusta hacer** a Susana y a ti? **A Susana y a mí nos gusta** jugar al fútbol.

1. *Answers will vary: ¿Qué le gusta hacer a Leonardo? A Leonardo le gusta*

   aprender el español.

2. *Answers will vary: ¿Qué les gusta hacer a Alejandro y Andrés? A Alejandro*

   y Andrés les gusta descansar los sábados.

3. *Answers will vary: ¿Qué les gusta hacer a Rebeca y a ti? A Rebeca y a mí*

   nos gusta preparar la comida.

Integración: Hablar

Sofía's homework was to create a Web page that includes what she likes and dislikes doing on Saturdays. But wait! Sofía does not include the things she dislikes, and her mother mentions those during a voice mail she left for Sofía's teacher.

Fuente 1 Leer

Read what Sofía likes to do on Saturdays...

Mi nombre es: Sofía Marcano

Fecha: 23 de noviembre

Los sábados me gusta tocar la guitarra y escuchar música. Me gusta pasar un rato con los amigos. Me gusta montar en bicicleta, ¡ah! y también me gusta mucho descansar. Me gusta hacer muchas actividades los sábados.

Fuente 2 Escuchar   *CD 01 track 02*

Listen to what Sofía's mother says about her. Take notes.

_____

_____

Hablar

What activities does Sofía like and dislike doing on Saturdays?

modelo: Los sábados, a Sofía le gusta... Pero a Sofía no le gusta...

Answers will vary: **Los sábados, a Sofía le gusta montar en bicicleta.**

Pero a Sofía no le gusta preparar la comida.

Integración: Escribir

Lisa, your new pen pal in Uruguay, is very organized. She wrote an email to you saying what she likes to do on weekdays. She preferred to tell you all the fun things she likes doing on weekends by recording herself in a video message.

Fuente 1 Leer
Read Lisa's e-mail...

> De: Lisa   A: David
> Tema: Me gusta hacer...
>
> Me llamo Lisa y soy de Montevideo, Uruguay. Soy organizada. Me gusta hacer cosas todos los días después de las clases. Los lunes, me gusta hacer la tarea; los martes, me gusta alquilar un DVD; los miércoles y los jueves, me gusta hacer más tarea. Hoy es viernes, y los viernes me gusta mucho escribir correos electrónicos y hablar por teléfono.
>
> ¡Adiós!
>
> Lisa

Fuente 2 Escuchar   *CD 01 track 04*
Listen to what Lisa says about her weekend activities. Take notes.

_____

_____

_____

Escribir
Explain what Lisa likes to do each day of the week.

modelo: Los lunes a Lisa le gusta...
Los martes a Lisa le gusta...
Los sábados a Lisa le gusta...

Answers will vary:

Los lunes a Lisa le gusta hacer la tarea.

Los martes a Lisa le gusta alquilar un DVD.

Los miércoles a Lisa le gusta hacer más tareas.

Los jueves a Lisa le gusta hacer más tarea.

Los viernes a Lisa le gusta escribir correos electrónicos.

Los sábados a Lisa le gusta pasear y pasar un rato con los amigos.

Los domingos a Lisa le gusta hacer muchas actividades.

Escuchar A

¡AVANZA! **Goal:** Listen to find out what Carolina and her friends like to do and where they are from.

1 Listen to the conversation about what these friends like to do. Match each name with the appropriate picture.

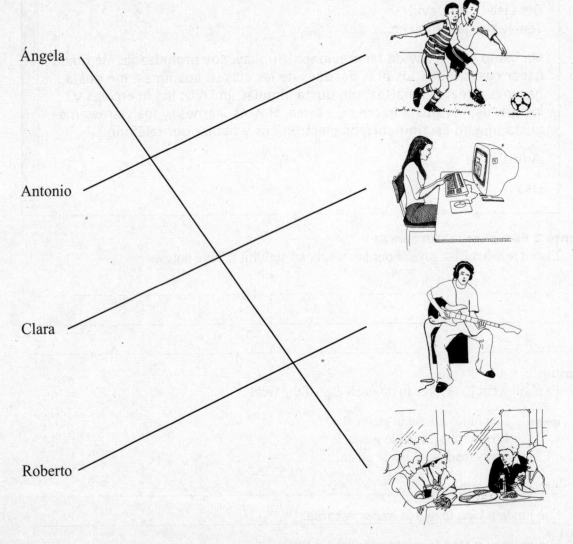

Ángela

Antonio

Clara

Roberto

2 Listen to each person say what she or he likes to do. Then read each statement below and say if it is true **(cierto)** or false **(falso)**.

C (F) **1.** A Carolina le gusta escuchar música antes de las clases.

(C) F **2.** A Carlos y a Carlota les gusta practicar deportes después de las clases.

(C) F **3.** A Norberto le gusta preparar la comida.

C (F) **4.** A Gabriel le gusta hacer la tarea los sábados y los domingos.

Escuchar B

 Goal: Listen to find out what Carolina and her friends like to do and where they are from.

1 Listen to each statement and take notes. Then complete the sentences with the activities they like to do.

1. A Carlos y a Carlota les gusta _____practicar_____ deportes.

2. A Carolina le gusta _____escuchar_____ música.

3. A Gabriel le gusta _____correr_____ .

4. A Norberto le gusta _____preparar_____ la comida.

2 Listen to the conversation and take notes. Then complete the following sentences based on what you heard.

de México	de Honduras
de Estados Unidos	de Chile

1. Ricardo _____es de Honduras_____ .

2. Laura _____es de Estados Unidos_____ .

3. Los amigos de Laura _____son de Chile_____ .

4. Felipe y Julia _____son de México_____ .

Escuchar C

 Goal: Listen to find out what Carolina and her friends like to do and where they are from.

1 **¿Qué les gusta hacer?** Listen to the conversation between two friends. Take notes and then complete the sentences.

1. A Ricardo ____le____ gusta más _____escuchar música_____ .

2. A Laura ____le____ gusta ____montar en bicicleta____ después de la escuela.

3. A Ricardo ____le____ gusta más _____pasear_____ y correr después de la escuela.

4. A Laura ____le____ gusta dibujar y a Ricardo ____le____ gusta más _____escuchar_____ música.

2 Listen to each person's statement. Take notes and then answer the questions in complete sentences.

1. ¿Qué le gusta a Gabriel?

   A Gabriel le gusta correr.

2. ¿Qué no le gusta a Gabriel?

   A Gabriel no le gusta trabajar los sábados.

3. ¿De dónde es Gabriel?

   Gabriel es de Miami (Estados Unidos).

4. ¿De dónde es Carlota?

   Carlota es de Bogotá (Colombia).

5. ¿Qué no le gusta hacer a Carlota?

   A Carlota no le gusta hacer la tarea.

Leer A

DIA DE ACTIVIDADES CON AMIGOS

¿Te gusta...

❋ *pasar un rato con los amigos*

❋ *dibujar*

❋ *escuchar música*

❋ *tocar la guitarra*

❋ *practicar deportes?*

Actividades después de las clases _____

¿Comprendiste? Did you understand the reading? Answer the following questions true **(cierto)** or false **(falso)**.

Ⓒ F **1.** El día de actividades es para practicar deportes.

C Ⓕ **2.** El día de actividades es para pasear con amigos.

Ⓒ F **3.** El día de actividades es para tocar la guitarra.

C Ⓕ **4.** Las actividades son antes de las clases.

¿Qué piensas?

1. ¿A ti te gusta pasar un rato con los amigos?

Answers will vary: **Sí (No, no) me gusta pasar un rato con los amigos.**

2. ¿Qué te gusta hacer en el día de actividades con amigos?

Answers will vary: **Me gusta tocar la guitarra y practicar deportes.**

3. ¿Qué otras (*others*) actividades te gustan?

Answers will vary: **Me gusta leer libros y preparar la comida.**

Leer B

¡Buenos días! Me llamo Graciela y soy de la ciudad de Panamá, en la República de Panamá. Es un país muy bonito. Mi escuela es muy buena. Se llama Instituto Cultural. Me gusta estudiar. Muchos estudiantes son internacionales. Mi amigo Juan es de Lima, Perú. A Juan le gusta jugar al fútbol. A mi me gusta más andar en patineta. Mi amiga Silvia es de Buenos Aires, Argentina. A ella le gusta dibujar y leer. A nosotros nos gusta pasar un rato con los amigos y escuchar música o mirar la televisión. Los sábados nos gusta alquilar DVDs y comprar pizzas.

¿Comprendiste?

Did you understand the reading? Complete the following sentences.

1. A Graciela le gusta _____estudiar_____ .

2. Juan es de _____Perú_____ .

3. A los amigos de Graciela les gusta _____escuchar música_____ .

4. Los sábados les gusta __alquilar DVDs/comprar pizza__ .

5. A Silvia le gusta _____dibujar_____ .

¿Qué piensas?

1. ¿De dónde eres?

   Answers will vary: **Soy de Kalamazoo. Soy de Estados Unidos.**

2. ¿De dónde es el (la) maestro (a) de español?

   Answers will vary: **El (la) maestro (a) de español es de Cuba.**

3. ¿Qué les gusta hacer a ustedes los sábados y domingos?

   Answers will vary: **A nosotros nos gusta montar en bicicleta y descansar**

   los sábados y domingos.

Leer C

Me llamo Valeria: ¿Qué nos gusta hacer?

Lucas es de Nicaragua. *A Lucas le gusta escribir y leer libros. También le gusta comer helado los domingos por la tarde. Lucas es mi amigo. A nosotros nos gusta alquilar un DVD los sábados y practicar deportes después de las clases.*

Araceli es de México. *A ella le gusta preparar la comida. A mí me gusta comer la comida que ella prepara. A Araceli y a mí nos gusta comprar y comer helado los domingos. También nos gusta hacer la tarea después de las clases.*

Simón es de Texas, Estados Unidos. *A él le gusta aprender el español en la escuela. A nosotros nos gusta estudiar el español después de las clases. También le gusta andar en patineta y comer helado los sábados y domingos.*

¿Comprendiste?

Did you understand the reading? Answer the following questions in complete sentences.

1. ¿De dónde son Lucas, Araceli y Simón?

   Lucas es de Nicaragua, Araceli es de México y Simón es de Estados Unidos.

2. ¿Qué les gusta hacer a Valeria y a Lucas los sábados?

   A Valeria y a Lucas les gusta alquilar un DVD

   los sábados.

3. ¿Qué le gusta hacer a Araceli? ¿Qué le gusta comer a Valeria?

   A Araceli le gusta preparar la comida y a Valeria le gusta comer la comida

   que Araceli prepara.

4. ¿Qué les gusta hacer a Valeria y a Simón después de las clases?

   A Valeria y a Simón les gusta estudiar español después de las clases.

5. ¿Qué les gusta a todos?

   A todos les gusta comer helado los domingos.

¿Qué piensas?

1. ¿A ti te gusta comer helado? ¿Qué te gusta comer?

   Answers will vary: **Sí, (No, no) me gusta comer helado. Me gusta comer pizza**

   y fruta.

2. ¿Qué actividades les gusta hacer a ti y a tus amigos después de las clases?

   Answers will vary: **A nosotros nos gusta hacer la tarea, practicar**

   deportes y hablar por teléfono.

Escribir A

> **¡AVANZA!** **Goal:** Write about activities that you like and don't like to do.

Step 1

Make a list of four activities you like and don't like to do. *Answers will vary:*

correr _____

estudiar _____

bailar _____

andar en patineta _____

Classify your list in the chart.

Me gusta...	No me gusta...
1. estudiar	**1.** bailar
2. andar en patineta	**2.** correr

Step 2

Write four sentences using the information above about what you like to do .

Answers will vary: **Los martes me gusta estudiar. Los sábados y domingos me gusta andar en patineta. Los jueves no me gusta bailar. No me gusta correr los viernes.**

Step 3

Evaluate your writing using the information in the table.

Writing Criteria	Excellent	Good	Needs Work
Content	Your sentences state four things that you like and don't like to do.	Your sentences state three things that you like and don't like to do.	Your sentences state less than three things that you like and don't like to do.
Communication	Most of your responses are clear.	Some of your responses are clear.	Your message is not very clear.

Escribir B

> **¡AVANZA!** **Goal:** Write about activities that you and others like and don't like to do.

Step 1

Make a list of three things your friend likes to do, and three things she/he doesn't like to do.

Nombre de mi amigo(a): _____ *Answers will vary:* **Ana**

Le gusta…	No le gusta…
1. *Answers will vary:* **correr**	**1.** *Answers will vary:* **dibujar**
2. *Answers will vary:* **comer helado**	**2.** *Answers will vary:* **andar en patineta**
3. *Answers will vary:* **jugar al fútbol**	**3.** *Answers will vary:* **mirar la televisión**

Step 2

Write a paragraph about what your friend likes and doesn't like to do.

Answers will vary: **A mi amiga Ana le gusta comer helado, correr y jugar al fútbol. A ella no le gusta mirar la televisión, andar en patineta y dibujar.**

Step 3

Evaluate your writing using the information in the table.

Writing Criteria	Excellent	Good	Needs Work
Content	You state six things your friend likes and doesn't like to do.	You state four or five things that your friend likes and doesn't like to do.	You state fewer than four things that your friend likes and doesn't like to do.
Communication	Most of your responses are clear.	Some of your responses are clear.	Your message is not very clear.
Accuracy	You make few mistakes in grammar and vocabulary.	You make some mistakes in grammar and vocabulary.	You make many mistakes in grammar and vocabulary.

Escribir C

> ¡AVANZA! **Goal:** Write about activities that you and others like and don't like to do.

Step 1

Fill in the chart with information about yourself. *Answers will vary:*

Me gusta...	1. practicar deportes	2. leer libros	3. pasar un rato con los amigos
No me gusta...	1. correr	2. andar en patineta	3. bailar
Soy de...	La Habana, Cuba		

Step 2 Now write a short letter to a pen pal with the information from above.

> *Answers will vary:*¡Hola! Me llamo Eduardo y soy de La Habana, Cuba. A mí me gusta practicar deportes y leer libros, pero no me gusta correr y no me gusta andar en patineta. Los sábados me gusta pasar un rato con los amigos y alquilar un DVD.

Step 3

Evaluate your writing using the information in the table.

Writing Criteria	Excellent	Good	Needs Work
Content	Your letter includes what you like and don't like to do.	Your letter includes most of what you like and don't like to do	Your letter does not include what you like and don't like to do.
Communication	Your letter is clear and easy to follow.	Parts of your letter are clear and easy to follow.	Your letter is not very clear.
Accuracy	You make few mistakes in grammar and vocabulary.	You make some mistakes in grammar and vocabulary.	You make many mistakes in grammar and vocabulary.

Cultura A

> **¡AVANZA!** **Goal:** Review cultural information about the Hispanic community in the United States.

1 **United States** Read the following statements about the United States and answer *true* or *false*.

Ⓣ F **1.** There are almost 40 million Hispanics in the United States.

T Ⓕ **2.** The city with the largest Hispanic population in the United States is San Francisco.

Ⓣ F **3.** Xavier Cortada is a Cuban American artist.

Ⓣ F **4.** San Antonio's oldest neighborhood is called La Villita.

2 **In the community** Complete the following sentences with a word from the box.

Calle Ocho	Freedom Tower
Hispanic Heritage Month	Fiesta San Antonio

1. The ___Hispanic Heritage Month___ celebrates the cultural diversity of Americans.

2. ___Calle Ocho___ is famous for its Cuban restaurants, cafés, and shops.

3. The ___Fiesta San Antonio___ honors the heroes of the Álamo.

4. The ___Freedom Tower___ is the building that houses the Cuban-American Museum.

3 **Los Premios Juventud** Write a few lines to describe **los Premios Juventud.** Then, if you were to vote for some nominees, who would you choose? Write a name for each category listed below.

_____

_____

_____

Best Actor: *Answers will vary:* **Antonio Banderas** _____

Best Actress: *Answers will vary:* **Salma Hayek** _____

Best Female Vocalist: *Answers will vary:* **Jennifer Lopez** _____

Best Male Vocalist: *Answers will vary:* **Juanes** _____

Best Sports Player: *Answers will vary:* **Samy Sosa** _____

Cultura B

Level 1, pp. 52-53

> **¡AVANZA!** **Goal:** Review cultural information about Hispanic communities in the United States.

1 **Awards** Complete the following sentences with the words from the box.

teens	Spanish-language	actors	Juanes	Juventud

1. Los Premios ____Juventud____ are awarded in Miami.

2. ____Teens____ nominate and vote for their favorite artists.

3. ____Juanes____ was a past nominee.

4. The event is shown on _Spanish-language_ television.

5. The winners of these awards can be famous sports stars, singers, and ____actors____.

2 **In the U. S.** Choose a multiple-choice item to complete the following sentences.

1. The number of Hispanics living in the United States is __a__

   a. 40 million   **b.** 20 million   **c.** 30 million

2. The Fiesta San Antonio honors the heroes of the Álamo and the Batalla de __b__

   a. San Jorge   **b.** San Jacinto   **c.** San Luis

3. The street in Miami renowned for its Cuban restaurants, cafés, and shops is called __b__

   a. Calle Siete   **b.** Calle Ocho   **c.** Calle Nueve

4. Miami's Cuban American Museum is located in the __c__

   a. University of Miami   **b.** public library   **c.** Freedom Tower

3 **Describing art** Look at the picture of Xavier Cortada's *Music* on page 44 of your book. Describe it. What feelings does it evoke? What message do you think the artist wants to convey?

Answers will vary: **The painting has many bright colors and different**

instruments. At the bottom of the painting, there are designs that look

like waves. It makes me think of music and rhythm. I think the artist

wants to share his pride in his musical heritage.

_____

_____

Nombre _____ Clase _____ Fecha _____

Cultura C

Level 1, pp. 52-53

 Goal: Review cultural information about Hispanic communities in the United States.

1 **Celebrities** Do you know where the following celebrities come from? Write the name of the country of origin of each person listed below.

Name	Where is he/she from?
Juanes	Colombia
Gael García Bernal	México
Jennifer Lopez	Estados Unidos

2 **Hispanic community in the U. S.** Answer the following questions.

1. What is San Antonio's oldest neighborhood called? San Antonio's oldest

neighborhood is called La Villita.

2. What do people celebrate in the United States between September 15 and October 15?

From September 15 to October 15 people in the United States celebreate

Hispanic Heritage Month.

3. What is something that influences Xavier Cortada's artwork?

His Cuban heritage influences his artwork.

3 **Los Premios Juventud** Create a poster advertising **Los Premios Juventud.** Your poster should explain what the event is and where it is held. Also include a date and time for the event.

Answers will vary, but posters should include a brief description of the event,
a date/time, and the location (Miami).

UNIDAD 1 • Vocabulario A
Lección 2

Vocabulario A

Level 1, pp. 56–60

> ¡AVANZA! **Goal:** Describe yourself and others.

1 **¿Cómo eres?** Match the adjective in the first column with an adjective that means the opposite in the second column.

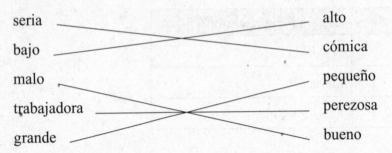

seria — alto

bajo — cómica

malo — pequeño

trabajadora — perezosa

grande — bueno

2 Describe these people by completing the following sentences with an adjective from the word bank.

estudiosa	atlética	organizado	artístico

1. A Julio le gusta dibujar. Julio es ___artístico___ .

2. A Julieta le gusta estudiar. Julieta es ___estudiosa___ .

3. El señor Gustavo no es desorganizado; es muy ___organizado___ .

4. A la señora Ponce le gusta practicar deportes; es muy ___atlética___ .

3 **¿Cómo eres tú?** Make a list of words that describe your personality and then write one sentence using them. Follow the model.

modelo: Lista de palabras: ___cómica, joven, baja, pelo castaño___

Oración: **Soy cómica, joven, baja y tengo pelo castaño**.

1. Lista de palabras: *Answers will vary:* **inteligente, guapa, artística, pelo rubio.**

2. Oración: *Answers will vary:* **Yo soy inteligente, guapa, artística y tengo pelo rubio.**

Vocabulario B

> **¡AVANZA!** **Goal:** Describe yourself and others.

1 **¿Cómo son?** Choose the word or expression from the vocabulary that best describes the people in the following sentences.

1. A Samuel no le gusta trabajar los domingos. Es un chico (<u>perezoso</u> / trabajador).

2. A Rebeca y a Marta no les gusta hacer la tarea. No son estudiantes muy (simpáticas / <u>buenas</u>).

3. Gustavo tiene pelo (estudioso / <u>castaño</u>).

4. La clase de español tiene tres estudiantes. Es una clase (grande / <u>pequeña</u>).

2 **¿Quién es?** Choose the word from the word bank that best completes each sentence.

1. A Víctor le gusta estudiar. Es un _____estudiante_____ muy bueno.

2. La señora García es una _____persona_____ muy buena.

3. Arturo tiene una _____amiga_____ muy guapa. Se llama Beatriz.

4. Al señor Gómez le gusta pasar un rato con los amigos. Es un _____hombre_____ muy simpático.

estudiante
persona
amiga
hombre

3 **¿Cómo son ustedes?** Write two complete sentences describing yourself and one of your friends. Follow the model.

modelo: Yo soy alto y tengo pelo castaño.

Mi amigo Daniel es grande y tiene pelo rubio.

1. _Answers will vary:_ **Yo soy bajo y tengo pelo rubio.**

2. _Answers will vary:_ **Mi amigo Luis es grande y tiene pelo castaño.**

Vocabulario C

> **¡AVANZA!** **Goal:** Describe yourself and others.

1 Choose the correct word to complete each description.

1. Anita es una chica muy (guapa / un poco / malo).

2. Danilo es (trabajador / un poco / amigo) desorganizado.

3. Aníbal, Darío, Facundo y Sergio son (guapo / un poco / todos) estudiantes.

4. Diana y Adela tienen pelo (rubio / pelirrojas / viejo).

2 **¿Cómo son?** Look at each drawing and write a complete sentence that describes the people in them. The first one is done for you.

1. **modelo:** La mujer es vieja.

2. *Answers will vary:* **El chico es atlético.** _____

3. *Answers will vary:* **La chica es joven.** _____

4. *Answers will vary:* **El chico es desorganizado.** _____

3 **Te presento a…** Complete this dialog. Each friend introduces another friend to someone else. Each friend should describe herself and say what she likes to do.

Antonia: ¡Hola Patricia! Ella es mi amiga Begoña. Es de España.

Patricia: Encantada. Begoña, ¿te gusta mirar la televisión o correr? Me gusta correr porque soy muy atlética.

Begoña: *Answers will vary:* **Me gusta dibujar porque soy artística.** _____

Antonia: *Answers will vary:* **Yo soy perezosa porque no me gusta trabajar.** _____

Patricia: *Answers will vary:* **Soy muy organizada y un poco seria.** _____

Gramática A   *Definite and Indefinite Articles*

Level 1, pp. 61–65

> ¡AVANZA! **Goal:** Use definite and indefinite articles to identify people and things.

1 Match the noun on the left with the correct indefinite article on the right.

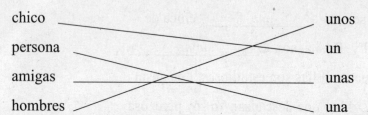

chico   unos

persona   un

amigas   unas

hombres   una

2 **¿Qué les gusta comer?** Underline the correct article in parentheses to complete the sentences describing what these people like to eat.

1. A Eva le gustan (<u>las</u> /unos) galletas.

2. A Sebastián y Celestino les gustan más (una / <u>las</u>) papas fritas.

3. A nosotros nos gusta beber (<u>el</u> / los) refresco.

4. ¿A usted le gusta (unas / <u>la</u>) pizza?

5. ¿A ustedes les gustan (<u>unos</u> / unas) helados?

3 Use the verb **ser** to describe what these people are like in three complete sentences. You may use the adjectives from the box.

> organizado(a)   simpáticos(as)   atléticos(as)   perezosos(as)   trabajador(a)

modelo: Mis padres **son muy trabajadores**.

Los futbolistas (*Answers will vary:* **son muy atléticos.**) _____

Pablo y Luis (*Answers will vary:* **son muy simpáticos.**) _____

El maestro (*Answers will vary:* **es muy organizado.**) _____

Gramática B *Definite and Indefinite Articles*

UNIDAD 1 • Gramática B
Lección 2

> **¡AVANZA!** **Goal:** Use definite and indefinite articles to identify people and things.

1 **Somos…** Write **un, una, unos,** or **unas** to complete the sentences.

Hola, me llamo Dolores y soy **1.** _____una_____ chica de

La Habana. Las amigas, Isabel y Rosita, son **2.** _____unas_____

personas muy inteligentes y buenas. Ellas son estudiosas. Les gusta

más leer **3.** _____un_____ libro que descansar. Yo soy perezosa.

Me gusta más alquilar **4.** _____un_____ DVD. Nuestros

vecinos (*Our neighbors*), el señor Valdés y el señor León, son **5.**

_____unos_____ señores artísticos. Les gusta mucho dibujar.

2 Change each noun from singular to plural. Then, write the appropriate plural definite article for each. Follow the model.

modelo: una persona
dos **personas**
las personas

1. un amigo

_____cuatro amigos_____
_____los amigos_____

2. una mujer

_____ocho mujeres_____
_____las mujeres_____

3. un hombre

_____siete hombres_____
_____los hombres_____

3 **¿Cómo es?** These friends are different. Tell how. Use **ser.** Follow the model.

modelo: María / estudiante organizada   Katy / chica desorganizada

María es una estudiante organizada. Katy es una chica desorganizada.

1. Roberto / hombre trabajador   Alejandro /chico perezoso

Roberto es un hombre trabajador. Alejandro es un chico perezoso.

2. Julia / mujer alta   Guadalupe / chica baja

Julia es una mujer alta. Guadalupe es una chica baja.

Gramática C *Definite and Indefinite Articles*

> **¡AVANZA!** **Goal:** Use definite and indefinite articles to identify people and things.

❶ Fill in the blanks with a correct definite or indefinite article.

1. Nosotros somos ____unos / unas / los / las____ estudiantes de Buenos Aires.

2. Ellos son _____unos / los_____ amigos de Gisela.

3. Ustedes son _____unas_____ personas estudiosas e inteligentes.

4. Tú eres _____un_____ hombre de Valladolid.

❷ Rewrite these sentences changing the words underlined to the plural.

1. Él es <u>un hombre</u> de Bariloche.

Ellos son unos hombres de Bariloche.

2. ¿<u>Ella</u> es <u>la amiga</u> de Texas?

¿Ellas son las amigas de Texas?

3. Me gusta beber <u>el jugo</u>.

Me gusta beber los jugos.

4. ¡<u>Tú</u> eres <u>un estudiante atlético</u>!

¡Ustedes son unos estudiantes atléticos!

❸ Write three sentences describing people you know. Use the verb **ser** and the indefinite articles **un, una, unos, unas.**

1. *Answers will vary:* **Leandro es un chico de Albania muy inteligente.**

2. *Answers will vary:* **Unos amigos de papá son muy artísticos.**

3. *Answers will vary:* **Una amiga de mamá es muy simpática.**

Gramática A *Noun-Adjective Agreement*

> **¡AVANZA!** **Goal:** Use adjectives with nouns.

❶ Underline the adjective in parentheses that agrees with the noun on the left.

1. las chicas (bajos / <u>bajas</u>)

2. una persona (<u>buena</u> / bueno)

3. un estudiante (<u>trabajador</u> / trabajadora)

4. los hombres (ancianas / <u>ancianos</u>)

❷ Write the correct ending that completes these adjectives. Remember to match the gender and number of the noun.

1. A Eva le gusta comer unas galletas buen<u>as</u>   .

2. A Samuel y a Carlos les gusta dibujar. Son unos chicos artístic<u>os</u>   .

3. Natalia es una chica guap<u>a</u>   .

4. ¿A ustedes les gusta comer las pizzas grand<u>es</u>   ?

5. Ignacio e Isabela son unos estudiantes organizad<u>os</u>   .

❸ Complete these sentences with an appropriate adjective. Use different adjectives in each sentence. Follow the model.

> **modelo**   David es un chico **trabajador** porque le gusta trabajar los sábados y domingos.

1. El señor Moreno es un maestro de español muy *Answers will vary:* **bueno**   .

2. Nosotros somos los estudiantes más *Answers will vary:* **inteligentes**   del señor

Unamuno.

3. Vosotros sois estudiantes buenos porque sois *Answers will vary:* **estudiosos**   .

4. La señora Márquez es una maestra muy *Answers will vary:* **organizada**   .

Gramática B *Noun-Adjective Agreement*

> **¡AVANZA!** **Goal:** Use adjectives with nouns.

1 We are all different. Choose the correct adjective that best completes these sentences about different people.

1. Nosotros somos unos estudiantes __c__ .

  a) guapo   **b)** guapa   **c)** guapos

2. A él le gusta pasar un rato con amigos porque es __c__ .

  a) simpáticas   **b)** simpáticos   **c)** simpático

3. Vosotros sois unas personas __a__ .

  a) inteligentes   **b)** inteligente

4. Las chicas de la clase de la señora García son muy __b__ .

  a) trabajador   **b)** trabajadoras   **c)** trabajadores

2 Write the correct form of an adjective to complete the following sentences:

1. A los amigos les gusta leer y hacer la tarea. Son *Answers will vary:* **estudiosos** .

2. María y Carla son unas mujeres *Answers will vary:* **organizadas** .

3. Los chicos no son altos, son ___ *Answers will vary:* **bajos** .

4. Las mujeres no son viejas, son ___ *Answers will vary:* **jóvenes** .

3 In three complete sentences, describe the people you see in the drawings below.

1. *Answers will vary:* **El chico es atlético y alto.**

2. *Answers will vary:* **Las chicas son artísticas.**

3. *Answers will vary:* **Una chica tiene pelo rubio.**

Gramática C *Noun-Adjective Agreement*

> **¡AVANZA!** **Goal:** Use adjectives with nouns.

❶ Change each phrase from plural to singular. Follow the model.

> **modelo:** las personas inteligentes
>
> **la persona inteligente**

1. los chicos atléticos _____ el chico atlético _____

2. las mujeres trabajadoras _____ la mujer trabajadora _____

3. los hombres pelirrojos _____ el hombre pelirrojo _____

❷ Complete these descriptions with the appropriate word.

1. Miguel es _____ atlético _____ porque le gusta practicar deportes.

2. Elisa es buena estudiante porque _____ hace la tarea. _____.

3. Laura es muy _____ buena _____ porque no es mala.

4. Mario es un chico muy _____ organizado _____ porque no es desorganizado.

❸ In complete sentences, describe three of your friends. Say where each one is from, what each one looks like, and write two adjectives that describe them. Follow the model.

> **modelo:** Andrea es de Texas. Andrea es una chica alta y tiene pelo rubio. Andrea
> es atlética.

1. *Answers will vary:* **Lucía tiene pelo castaño. Es de Nueva York. Es muy**

   guapa. Lucía es simpática.

2. *Answers will vary:* **Jorge tiene pelo negro. Es de Honduras. Jorge**

   es cómico.

3. *Answers will vary:* **Manuel es de la República Dominicana. Él es bajo y**

   grande. Manuel es muy inteligente.

Integración: Hablar

Arthur moved from Denver, Colorado, to Mexico City. He is going to study Spanish for a year abroad at a local High School. The high school's principal is very happy because Arthur is a talented soccer player who can help the school's soccer team win the city championship. Arthur writes about himself for the high school newspaper. The Principal introduces Arthur to everybody at the first soccer match of the year.

Fuente 1 Leer

Read what Arthur wrote in the school's newspaper...

¡HOLA!

Me llamo Arthur. Arturo en español. Yo soy de los Estados Unidos. Soy de Colorado. En Colorado hace frío y nieva.
Soy atlético y me gusta practicar deportes .
También me gusta jugar al fútbol. Soy inteligente pero un poco desorganizado.

Fuente 2 Escuchar   *CD 01 track 12*

Listen to the principal's description of Arthur over the loudspeaker before his first soccer game. Take notes.

_____

_____

_____

_____

Hablar

What is Arthur like? Describe his personality and appearance.

modelo: Arthur es... Y también es... Pero no es...

Answers will vary: **Arthur es alto y pelirrojo. También le gusta jugar al**

fútbol. Es inteligente y atlético, pero un poco desorganizado.

Es muy simpático.

Integración: Escribir

Level 1, pp. 69–71
WB CD 01 Track 13

Escuela González, a soccer foundation in Ecuador, is looking for international participants for its programs. On their Web page there is a letter from the director of the foundation who is looking for volunteers.

Fuente 1 Leer

Read the letter from the director.

> ¡Hola! Me llamo Gustavo González y soy el director de la Escuela González. La escuela tiene muchas personas trabajadoras. ¿Te gusta practicar deportes? La escuela tiene seis maestros de fútbol de lunes a viernes y nueve maestros los sábados y domingos. Tenemos clases de hombres y mujeres, y también tenemos clases de chicos y chicas.

Fuente 2 Escuchar   *CD 01 track 14*

Listen to the audioclip of a testimonial from Escuela González's Web site. Take notes.

_____

_____

_____

Escribir

Why would you choose Escuela González to learn soccer? Remember to include information from both the Web page and the audioclip for your answer.

Modelo: Escuela González tiene... También, es...

Answers will vary: **Escuela González tiene mucho para aprender. Tiene**

maestros buenos y clases de chicos. También, la Escuela González es

grande y organizada y los maestros son simpáticos.

_____

_____

_____

Escuchar A

 Goal: Listen to students at an international school as they describe themselves and each other.

1 Listen to each statement and take notes. Then choose who fits each description below.

_a_ **1.** trabajador(a)

_c_ **2.** estudioso(a)

_b_ **4.** artístico(a)

a. Claribel
b. Gustavo
c. Mario

2 Listen to each person describe him/herself. Then read each statement below and say if it is true **(Cierto)** or false **(Falso)**.

Ⓒ F **1.** Julio y Araceli son unos chicos simpáticos.

Ⓒ F **2.** Araceli es una chica artística.

Ⓒ F **3.** A Julio le gusta jugar al fútbol.

C Ⓕ **4.** A Julio le gusta dibujar.

Nombre _____ Clase _____ Fecha _____

Escuchar B

¡AVANZA! **Goal:** Listen to students at an international school as they describe themselves and each other.

1 Listen and then draw a line from the people to the adjectives that describe them.

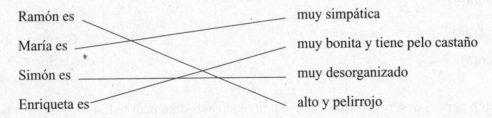

Ramón es   muy simpática

María es   muy bonita y tiene pelo castaño

Simón es   muy desorganizado

Enriqueta es   alto y pelirrojo

2 Listen to how each person is described. Then complete the following sentences.

1. Iván es _____ pelirrojo _____ .

2. Nancy es _____ muy estudiosa _____ .

3. Melvin es _____ inteligente y serio _____ .

4. Iván y Melvin son _____ muy simpáticos _____ .

Nombre _____ Clase _____ Fecha _____

Escuchar C

 Goal: Listen to students at an international school describe themselves and   each other.

1 Listen to the dialog and then write three adjectives to describe each of the following people:

1. La señora Guadalupe: *Answers will vary:* **baja, inteligente, organizada,**

joven, guapa

2. Mauricio: *Answers will vary:* **desorganizado, perezoso, cómico, muy**

simpático

3. Marta y Tania: *Answers will vary:* **pelo castaño, buenas, inteligentes, bonitas**

2 Take notes while you listen to the conversation. Then answer the questions in complete sentences.

1. ¿Cómo es Esperanza?

Esperanza es alta, bonita y estudiosa.

2. ¿Quiénes son estudiosas?

Diana y Luisa son estudiosas.

3. ¿Quién tiene pelo rubio?

Diana tiene pelo rubio.

4. ¿Cómo es Luisa?

Luisa es pelirroja y baja.

5. ¿Cómo eres tú?

Answer may vary: **Soy alta(o) y cómica (o).**

Leer A

> **Goal:** Read how people describe themselves and others.

¡Hola! Me llamo Rocío. Tengo pelo rubio y soy estudiosa. El señor Cruz, es un poco viejo y es muy bueno. Nora y Lidia, son muy inteligentes. Les gusta mucho leer. Nora tiene un hermano. Se llama Norberto. Es bajo. Nora es alta y tiene pelo rubio, pero su hermano es pelirrojo. Nora, Norberto y Lidia son simpáticos.

¿Comprendiste?

Answer the following questions true (**Cierto**) or false (**Falso**).

C (F) **1.** A Rocío no le gusta estudiar.

C (F) **2.** El señor Cruz es joven.

(C) F **3.** Las amigas de Rocío son chicas muy inteligentes.

C (F) **4.** Norberto es un chico alto.

(C) F **5.** Norberto, Nora y Lidia son simpáticos.

¿Qué piensas?

1. ¿Tienes pelo castaño?

Answers will vary: **Sí, (No, no) tengo pelo castaño.**

2. ¿Cómo son tus amigos(as)?

Answers will vary: **Mi amigo es cómico. Mi amiga es artística.**

3. ¿Eres un chico o una chica organizado(a)?

Answers will vary: **Sí, (No, no) soy un(a) chico(a) organizado(a).**

4. Describe a un amigo.

Answers will vary: **Mi amigo José es alto.**

Leer B

> **¡AVANZA!** **Goal:** Read how people describe themselves and others.

¡Hola! Me llamo Pedro. Tengo pelo castaño. Rafael tiene pelo rubio. Laura y Raquel tienen pelo castaño. Son muy altas, también son muy inteligentes. La persona de pelo rubio es muy perezosa, seria y un poco mala.

¿Comprendiste?

Answer the following questions in complete sentences, based on the information in the reading.

1. ¿Cómo es Rafael?

   Answers will vary: **Rafael es muy perezoso, serio y un poco malo. Rafael**

   tiene pelo rubio.

2. ¿Cómo son Laura y Raquel?

   Answers will vary: **Laura y Raquel son muy altas y muy**

   inteligentes.

3. ¿Es Rafael trabajador?

   Answers will vary: **No, Rafael es perezoso.**

¿Qué piensas?

1. ¿Cómo eres tú?

   Answers will vary: **Soy un(a) chico(a) organizado(a).**

2. ¿Te gustan las personas rubias?

   Answers will vary: **Sí, (No, no) me gustan las personas rubias.**

3. ¿Te gustan las personas altas?

   Answers will vary: **Sí, (No, no) me gustan las personas altas.**

Goal: Read how people describe themselves and others.

¡Hola! Somos estudiantes. Yo me llamo Alberto y soy de España. Tengo unos amigos de los Estados Unidos y otros (*others*) de Colombia. La maestra es una mujer joven de Paraguay. Yo soy una persona organizada y un estudiante bueno porque me gusta estudiar. A Andrés no le gusta hacer la tarea, pero es muy artístico. A él le gusta dibujar. Felipe es un poco desorganizado, pero es muy simpático. Sandro es un estudiante bueno y es muy atlético. Le gusta correr y jugar al fútbol. Andrés tiene pelo castaño y es alto. Felipe es grande y tiene pelo rubio. Yo soy pelirrojo y un poco bajo. ¡Todos somos amigos muy simpáticos!

¿Comprendiste?

Answer the following questions in complete sentences.

1. ¿Cómo es la maestra?

La maestra es una mujer joven de Paraguay.

2. ¿Es Alberto un estudiante bueno? ¿Por qué?

Sí, Alberto es un estudiante bueno porque le gusta estudiar y es organizado.

3. ¿Cómo es Andrés?

Andrés es artístico.

4. ¿Cómo es Felipe?

Felipe es un poco desorganizado pero es muy simpático.

¿Qué piensas?

1. ¿Son los chicos buenos amigos? ¿Por qué? (Why?)

Answers will vary: **Los chicos son amigos porque todos son muy simpáticos.**

2. ¿Cómo son los amigos de tu (*your*) clase?

Answers will vary: **Los amigos de la clase son atléticos y muy simpáticos.**

Escribir A

¡AVANZA! **Goal:** Write descriptions of people you know.

Step 1

Write the name of one person you admire. Then, make a list of adjectives that describe him or her.

1. **Nombre:** *Answers will vary:* **José**

2. **¿Cómo es?:** *Answers will vary:* **pelo castaño, organizado, inteligente, alto, atlético**

Step 2

Refer back to your list in Step 1, and write two sentences about the person you chose and one sentence about why (s)he is that way.

Answers will vary. **José tiene pelo castaño y es alto. José es organizado,**

inteligente y atlético. José es atlético porque le gusta jugar al fútbol.

Step 3

Evaluate your writing using the information in the table.

Writing Criteria	Excellent	Good	Needs Work
Content	You have included three sentences to write your description about the person you chose.	You have included two sentences to write your description about the person you chose.	You have included one or less sentences to write your description about the person you chose.
Communication	Most of your description is clear.	Some of your desription is clear.	Your description is not very clear.
Accuracy	You make few mistakes in grammar and vocabulary.	You make some mistakes in grammar and vocabulary.	You make many mistakes in grammar and vocabulary.

Nombre _____ Clase _____ Fecha _____

Escribir B

> ¡AVANZA! **Goal:** Write descriptions of people you know.

Step 1

Fill out this chart with information about yourself.

Nombre	*Answers will vary:* **Lucía**
Soy	*Answers will vary:* **artística**
No soy	*Answers will vary:* **perezosa**
Tengo	*Answers will vary:* **pelo castaño**
Me gusta	*Answers will vary:* **tocar la guitarra**

Step 2

Now, tell why you chose the words above to describe yourself. Write three complete sentences about yourself. Follow the model.

modelo: Soy una estudiante buena porque me gusta hacer la tarea. No soy perezosa porque me gusta trabajar. Me gusta tocar la guitarra porque soy artística.

Answers will vary: **Las personas artísticas y trabajadoras son buenas. Yo**

soy una persona artística y buena.

Step 3

Evaluate your writing using the information in the table.

Writing Criteria	Excellent	Good	Needs Work
Content	You have included three sentences in your explanation.	You have included two sentences in your explanation.	You have included one of fewer sentences in your explanation.
Communication	Most of your explanation is clear.	Some of your explanation is clear.	Your explanation is not very clear.
Accuracy	You make few mistakes in grammar and vocabulary.	You make some mistakes in grammar and vocabulary.	You make many mistakes in grammar and vocabulary.

Escribir C

> **¡AVANZA!** **Goal:** Write descriptions of people you know.

Step 1

List one person you know. Then, write as many nouns, adjectives and other expressions as you can to describe him or her.

Nombre: *Answers will vary:* **Francisco**

Es deportista, guapo y bueno

Tiene pelo castaño.

Le gusta practicar deportes y tocar la guitarra.

Step 2

Now, in four sentences, tell why you like the person you chose in Step 1. Begin your paragraph with "Me gusta…" and the name of the person you described.

Answers will vary: **Me gusta Francisco porque es deportista y**

guapo. Me gusta Francisco porque me gustan las personas artísticas,

buenas, y simpáticas.

Step 3

Evaluate your writing using the information in the table.

Writing Criteria	Excellent	Good	Needs Work
Content	You have included four sentences to write your explanation.	You have included three sentences to write your explanation.	You have included two or less sentences to write your explanation.
Communication	Most of your explanation is clear.	Some of your explanation is clear.	Your explanation is not very clear.
Accuracy	You make few mistakes in grammar and vocabulary.	You make some mistakes in grammar and vocabulary.	You make many mistakes in grammar and vocabulary.

Nombre _____ Clase _____ Fecha _____

Cultura A

Level 1, pp. 76–77

 Goal: Review the importance of the Hispanic community in the United States.

1 **The United States** Complete the following sentences with one of the multiple choice phrases.

1. This city has the highest percentage of Latinos (77%) in the United States. __c__

  a. San Antonio   **b.** Houston   **c.** El Paso

2. Miami's Little Havana is home to the famous __a__

  a. Calle Ocho   **b.** Calle Nueve   **c.** Calle Cuatro

3. One of San Antonio's main attractions is __b__

  a. the Freedom Tower   **b.** the Paseo del Río   **c.** the Cuban American Museum

2 **Florida and Texas** Complete the following sentences.

1. Carmen Lomas Garza is a painter who grew up in _____Texas_____.

2. _____Cascarones_____ are eggshells filled with confetti.

3. Many people go to __Calle Ocho/Little Habana__ in Miami to enjoy Cuban sandwiches and mango juice.

4. It is possible to hear _____mariachi_____ music played in San Antonio's El Mercado.

3 **Regional cuisine** Fill out the chart below to list typical dishes or ingredients of Tex-Mex and Mexican cuisine. Then, describe the foods you listed. Have you ever eaten any of these dishes (or dishes made with these ingredients)? Tell where you have eaten them and whether or not you like the dish. (Answers will vary. See below.)

Tex-Mex	Mexican
Answers will vary: **fajitas**	corn tortillas
crispy tacos	black beans

Answers will vary: _____

_____

_____

_____

Cultura B

 Goal: Review the importance of the Hispanic community in the United States.

1 **The United States** Read the following sentences and answer *true* or *false*.

T (F) **1.** Tex-Mex is a mix of Mexican and Cuban food.

T (F) **2.** *Cascarones* are eggshells filled with rice.

(T) F **3.** **Chile con carne** is a Tex-Mex dish.

(T) F **4.** Black beans are typical of traditional Mexican cuisine.

(T) F **5.** The Alamo is located in San Antonio.

2 **Popular places** Write where you can find the following places.

Places to visit	In which city are they located?
Little Havana	en Miami
The Paseo del Río	en San Antonio
Calle Ocho	en Miami
La Villita	en San Antonio

3 **Cascarones** Write a simple, step-by-step guide for making *cascarones.* Tell what they are, how to make them, and what to do with them.

Answers will vary: Cascarones are eggshells that are painted and filled with

confetti. They are commonly used at Easter and also at some parties. To make

cascarones, you should first carefully remove the egg yolks and egg whites.

When the eggshells are all empty, fill them up with confetti. Then paint the

eggshells. You can give a cascarón to a friend or break one over his or her

head for good luck.

Nombre _____ Clase _____ Fecha _____

Cultura C

Level 1, pp. 76–77

¡AVANZA! **Goal:** Review the importance of the Hispanic community in the United States.

1 **Hispanic culture** Complete the following sentences.

1. ___Cascarones___ are eggshells filled with confetti.

2. Carmen Lomas Garza is a painter who grew up in ___Texas___ .

3. The Paseo del Río and the Alamo are located in ___San Antonio___ .

4. Little Havana is located in ___Miami___ .

2 **In the U. S.** Answer the following questions about the Hispanic community in the United States.

1. Where in the United States can you hear mariachi music?

   You can hear mariachi music played in San Antonio's El Mercado.

2. What is Tex-Mex food? Give two examples.

   Tex-Mex food is a mix of Mexican and Texan cuisine. **Nachos** and **fajitas** are

   two examples.

3. Where is Calle Ocho located and what can people do there?

   Calle Ocho is located in Miami's Little Havana. Some things people can do

   there include: shop, eat Cuban sandwiches, and drink mango juice.

3 **Visiting San Antonio** Write a postcard to a friend describing a trip to San Antonio. What did you see and do there? What foods did you try?

   Answers will vary: Hi Eddie! I'm having fun in San Antonio. I took a tour of the

   Alamo and then I went to El Mercado to shop and listen to mariachi music.

   Last night, I walked along the Paseo de Río and went to a Tex-Mex

   restaurant. I ordered fajitas and chile con carne. See you soon!

_____

_____

_____

_____

_____

_____

Unidad 1, Lección 2
Cultura C

¡Avancemos! 1
Cuaderno: Práctica por niveles

Comparación cultural: Me gusta...

Lectura y escritura

After reading the paragraphs about how José, Manuel, Martina, and Mónica describe themselves and their favorite activities, write a short paragraph about yourself. Use the information on your personal chart to write sentences and then write a paragraph that describes yourself.

Step 1

Complete the personal chart describing as many details as you can about yourself.

Categoría	Detalles
país de origen	
descripción física	
personalidad	
actividades favoritas	
comidas favoritas	

Step 2

Now take the details from your personal chart and write a sentence for each topic on the chart.

_____

_____

_____

_____

_____

_____

_____

Comparación cultural: Me gusta...

Level 1, pp. 78–79

Lectura y escritura (continued)

Step 3

Now write your paragraph using the sentences you wrote as a guide. Include an introduction sentence and use the verbs **ser** and **gustar** to write about yourself.

_____

_____

_____

_____

_____

_____

_____

Checklist

Be sure that…

☐ all the details about yourself from your chart are included in the paragraph;

☐ you use details to describe, as clearly as possible, the activities you like the most;

☐ you include new vocabulary words and the verbs **ser** and **gustar.**

Rubric

Evaluate your writing using the rubric below.

Writing criteria	Excellent	Good	Needs Work
Content	Your paragraph includes many details about yourself.	Your paragraph includes some details about yourself.	Your paragraph includes little information about yourself.
Communication	Most of your paragraph is organized and easy to follow.	Parts of your paragraph are organized and easy to follow.	Your paragraph is disorganized and hard to follow.
Accuracy	Your paragraph has few mistakes in grammar and vocabulary.	Your paragraph has some mistakes in grammar and vocabulary.	Your paragraph has many mistakes in grammar and vocabulary.

Comparación cultural: Me gusta...

Compara con tu mundo

Now write a comparison about yourself and one of the three students from page 79. Organize your comparison by topics. First, compare where you are from, then your personality and physical description, and lastly your favorite activities and food.

Step 1

Use the chart to organize your comparison by topics. Write details for each topic about yourself and the student you chose.

Categoría	Mi descripción	La descripción de _____
país de origen		
descripción física		
personalidad		
actividades favoritas		
comidas favoritas		

Step 2

Now use the details from your personal chart to write a comparison. Include an introduction sentence and write about each topic. Use the verbs **ser** and **gustar** to describe yourself and the student you chose.

_____

_____

_____

_____

_____

_____

_____

Nombre _____ Clase _____ Fecha _____

Vocabulario A

Level 1, pp. 86-90

¡AVANZA! **Goal:** Talk about daily schedules.

1 What are your classes this year? Read the following list and mark with an X next to each subject you are taking. *Answers will vary.*

1. ____ el español   7. ____ la historia
2. ____ el inglés   8. ____ las matemáticas
3. ____ el arte   9. ____ las ciencias

2 **¿A qué hora son las clases?** Look at Wednesday's class schedule and complete the sentences with the time each class meets.

Horario de clases	
Hora	**miércoles**
8:30	historia
9:15	inglés
10:00	español
12:50	ciencias

1. La clase de historia es *a las ocho y media* .
2. La clase de inglés es *a las nueve y cuarto* .
3. La clase de español es *a las diez de la mañana* .
4. La clase de ciencias es *a la una menos diez* .

3 In a complete sentence, answer the following questions about yourself:

1. ¿A qué hora es la clase de matemáticas?

   Answers will vary: **La clase de matemáticas es a las nueve y media.**

2. ¿Cuántos exámenes hay en la clase de español?

   Answers will vary: **Hay cinco exámenes en la clase de español.**

Vocabulario B

> ¡AVANZA! **Goal:** Talk about daily schedules.

1 Choose the correct word or phrase in parentheses to complete each sentence.

1. Hay (<u>veinticuatro</u> / veintiún) horas en un día.

2. Hay (setenta / <u>sesenta</u>) minutos en una hora.

3. Tengo que estudiar para (<u>sacar una buena nota</u> / sacar una mala nota).

4. Estudiar a las diez de la noche es estudiar (<u>tarde</u> / temprano).

5. El maestro tiene que (aprender / <u>enseñar</u>) el español.

6. La estudiante tiene que (llegar/ <u>contestar</u>) la pregunta.

2 Look at María's schedule and tell when she has the following classes. Use the words in the box.

Hora	lunes	martes	miércoles	jueves	viernes
8:30	historia	historia	historia	historia	historia
10:15	matemáticas	matemáticas	matemáticas	matemáticas	matemáticas
12:00	inglés	español	ciencias	español	español

1. ¿La clase de historia?

   <u>todos los días</u>

2. ¿La clase de arte?

   <u>nunca</u>

3. ¿La clase de ciencias?

   <u>de vez en cuando</u>

> todos los días
> de vez en
> cuando
> nunca
> muchas veces

3 Describe your schedule of morning classes in complete sentences. Follow the model:

modelo: A las siete y media de la mañana tengo clase de inglés. La clase de matemáticas es a las nueve. A las once tengo clase de arte.

Answers will vary: **La clase de ciencias es a las nueve y la clase de inglés**

es a las diez y cuarto.

_____

Vocabulario C

Level 1, pp. 86-90

┌───┐
│ **¡AVANZA!** **Goal:** Talk about daily schedules.   │
└───┘

1 Describe what you have to do in each class in order to get a good grade. Use complete sentences. Answers will vary:

1. (la clase de español) *En la clase de español tengo que tomar apuntes.*

2. (la clase de matemáticas) *En la clase de matemáticas tengo que contestar las preguntas.*

3. (la clase de ciencias) *En la clase de ciencias tengo que estudiar.*

4. (la clase de inglés) *En la clase de inglés tengo que usar la computadora.*

2 Answer the following questions with complete sentences:

1. ¿Te gusta usar la computadora en la clase de español?

Answers will vary: **Sí me gusta usar la computadora en la clase de español.**

2. ¿Te gusta hablar en la clase de español?

Answers will vary: **Sí me gusta hablar en la clase de español.**

3. ¿Te gusta dibujar en la clase de arte?

Answers will vary: **No, no me gusta dibujar en la clase de arte.**

4. ¿A qué hora es tu clase de matemáticas?

Answers will vary: **La clase de matemáticas es a la una y veinte de la tarde.**

5. ¿Te gusta leer libros en la clase de inglés?

Answers will vary: **Sí me gusta leer libros en la clase de inglés.**

6. ¿Cómo es el(la) maestro(a) de ciencias?

Answers will vary: **La maestra de ciencias es inteligente.**

3 Describe your schedule of afternoon classes in complete sentences. Explain what you like to do in each class.

Answers will vary: **La clase de ciencias es a la una y la clase de**

matemáticas es a las dos y media de la tarde. Me gusta contestar las

preguntas de la maestra y me gusta usar la computadora.

_____

_____

Gramática A *The Verb* **tener**

> **¡AVANZA!** **Goal:** Use **tener** to say what people have and have to do.

1 Underline the correct form of **tener** that completes the sentence.

1. Nosotros (tienen / <u>tenemos</u>) patinetas.

2. Tú (<u>tienes</u> / tengo) una computadora.

3. Laura y Tomás (tiene / <u>tienen</u>) clase a las nueve y cuarto.

4. Yo (tiene / <u>tengo</u>) mucha tarea de ciencias.

2 Complete the following sentences with an expression of frequency from the word bank:

nunca	siempre	de vez en cuando	mucho

1. Rodrigo y Trina son muy inteligentes; _____*siempre*_____ les gusta contestar las preguntas del maestro.

2. No me gusta sacar una mala nota; tengo que estudiar _____*mucho*_____ .

3. Teresa es muy perezosa; _____*nunca*_____ le gusta hacer la tarea.

4. La clase de inglés es muy fácil; tenemos tarea _____*de vez en cuando*_____ .

3 **Para sacar una buena nota en el examen...** Look at the drawings and write two complete sentences about what the following people have to do.

1. **2.** **3.**

1. <u>Él tiene que estudiar.</u>

2. <u>Ella tiene que usar la computadora.</u>

3. <u>Ellos tienen que hacer la tarea.</u>

Gramática B *The Verb tener*

> **¡AVANZA!** **Goal:** Use **tener** to say what people have and have to do.

1 Choose the form of **tener** that best completes each sentence.

1. Javier __d__ clase de español los martes a las once menos cuarto.

    a. tienen   **b.** tienes   **c.** tenemos   **d.** tiene

2. Muchas veces, Raúl y Aída __b__ que tomar apuntes en la clase de historia.

    a. tiene   **b.** tienen   **c.** tenemos   **d.** tienes

3. Lorena, Paloma y yo __c__ que trabajar los sábados y domingos.

    a. tenéis   **b.** tengo   **c.** tenemos   **d.** tienen

4. Carolina, ¿tú __c__ un lápiz?

    a. tiene   **b.** tengo   **c.** tienes   **d.** tenéis

2 Tell what the following people have to do in order to get good grades. Write complete sentences.

    modelo: Jorge / tomar apuntes (siempre)
                 Jorge siempre tiene que tomar apuntes.

1. María Elena y Nora / estudiar (mucho)

    María Elena y Nora tienen que estudiar mucho.

2. nosotros / usar la computadora (siempre)

    Nosotros siempre tenemos que usar la computadora.

3. yo / hablar con la maestra (de vez en cuando)

    Yo tengo que hablar con la maestra de vez en cuando.

4. Alejandro / hacer la tarea (muchas veces)

    Muchas veces Alejandro tiene que hacer la tarea.

5. tú / leer el libro / (todos los días)

    Tú tienes que leer el libro todos los días.

3 Write three sentences to explain what you have to do in Spanish class today.

    Answers will vary: **Tengo que tomar apuntes. Tengo que hablar con la**

    maestra. Tengo que leer.

Gramática C   *The Verb Tener*

¡AVANZA!   **Goal:** Use **tener** to say what people have and have to do.

---

1   Write the correct form of the verb **tener**.

1. Manuel y Norberto _____ tienen _____ un examen de ciencias mañana.

2. Yo _____ tengo _____ que estudiar todos los días para el examen de historia.

3. Nosotros siempre _____ tenemos _____ que tomar apuntes en la clase de inglés.

4. Muchas veces Nadia _____ tiene _____ que trabajar los sábados.

2   Answer the following questions in complete sentences.

1. ¿A qué hora y qué días tienes clase de español?

Answers will vary: **Tengo clase de español los lunes y miércoles a las once**

menos cuarto.

2. ¿Qué tienes que hacer para sacar buenas notas?

Answers will vary: **Para sacar buenas notas tengo que tomar apuntes y**

estudiar mucho.

3. ¿Qué tienes que hacer siempre en la clase de español?

Answers will vary: **Tengo que ir a clase siempre.**

_____

4. ¿Cuántas clases tienes los martes?

Answers will vary: **Los martes tengo cuatro clases.**

_____

3   Write four sentences about what you have to do in a regular week at school. Use expressions of frequency.

Answers will vary: **Los martes siempre tengo clase de arte. Todos los días**

tengo que estudiar o hacer la tarea. Tengo que tomar apuntes muchas

veces por día. De vez en cuando llego a clase tarde.

_____

_____

Gramática A *Present tense of –ar verbs*

> **¡AVANZA!** **Goal:** Use the present tense to say what people do.

1 Underline the verb that best completes each sentence below.

1. Sara (<u>mira</u>/ miran / miro) la televisión por la tarde.

2. Alicia y yo (escucho / <u>escuchamos</u> / escucha) música todos los días.

3. Muchas veces, tú (contestamos / contesta/ <u>contestas</u>) las preguntas.

4. Ustedes (trabaja / trabajamos / <u>trabajan</u>) todos los días.

2 Complete the following sentences with the appropriate form of the verb in parentheses.

1. Todos los días, Sandra, Eduardo y yo _____tocamos_____ la guitarra. (tocar)

2. Sandra y sus amigas _____dibujan_____ por las tardes. (dibujar)

3. Yo _____contesto_____ las preguntas del maestro. (contestar)

4. Sandra, tú siempre _____llegas_____ temprano a casa. (llegar)

3 Write complete sentences to say what each person is doing. Follow the model:

modelo: nosotros / estudiar mucho: Nosotros estudiamos mucho.

1. tú / siempre / tomar apuntes

Tú siempre tomas apuntes. _____

_____

2. Fernando y Clara / casi nunca / montar en bicicleta

Fernando y Clara casi nunca montan en bicicleta. _____

_____

3. Yaliza y yo / nunca / sacar malas notas

Yaliza y yo nunca sacamos malas notas. _____

_____

4. Usted / enseñar matemáticas

Usted enseña matemáticas. _____

_____

Gramática B *Present Tense of –ar Verbs*

> ¡AVANZA! **Goal:** Use the present tense to say what people do.

---

① Sandra and Eduardo do many things. Choose the verb that best completes each sentence.

1. Sandra __d__ televisión por la tarde.

  a. miras **b.** miran **c.** miramos **d.** mira

2. Eduardo __c__ música todos los días.

  a. escuchan **b.** escuchas **c.** escucha **d.** escuchamos

3. Eduardo y Sandra casi nunca __b__ por la tarde.

  a. descansas **b.** descansan **c.** descanso **d.** descansamos

4. Yo siempre __b__ un DVD.

  a. alquila **b.** alquilo **c.** alquilas **d.** alquilan

② Write the correct form of the verbs in parentheses to complete the following conversation.

Sandra: Hola, Eduardo. ¿**1.** _____descansas_____ (descansar) en la tarde?

Eduardo: Nunca. Mis amigos y yo siempre **2.** _____tocamos_____ (tocar) la guitarra. ¿Y tú?

Sandra: Yo **3.** _____practico_____ (practicar) deportes casi todas las tardes.

¿Tú **4.** _____estudias_____ (estudiar) en la mañana o en la tarde?

Eduardo: En la tarde **5.** _____monto_____ (montar) en bicicleta.

6. _____Estudio_____ (Estudiar) en la mañana, a las seis.

③ Answer the following questions in complete sentences.

1, ¿Preparas la comida todos los días?

Answers will vary: **Sí, preparo la comida todos los días.** _____

2. ¿Estudias mucho en la clase de español?

Answers will vary: **Sí, estudio todos los días en la clase de español.** _____

3. ¿Miras la televisión después de las clases?

Answers will vary: **Sí, miro la television después de las clases.** _____

Gramática C *Present Tense of –ar Verbs*

> **¡AVANZA!** **Goal:** Use the present tense to say what people do.

1 Complete these sentences with the correct form of the verb **llegar**.

Martín y yo **1.** _____llegamos_____ a la escuela antes de las ocho.

Somos estudiantes en la escuela de Miami. Martín siempre

2. _____llega_____ temprano a clase, pero yo casi siempre

3. _____llego_____ tarde porque hablo mucho con los amigos. Y

tú, ¿ **4.** _____llegas_____ tarde o temprano a clase?

2 Look at the drawings below and write what each person is doing.

1.  **2.**  **3.**  **4.**

1. Soraya y yo Soraya y yo hablamos por teléfono. _____

2. Manuel Manuel usa la computadora. _____

3. los maestros Los maestros enseñan (la clase de ciencias). _____

4. yo Yo preparo la comida. _____

3 Write four sentences describing what you do after school.

Answers will vary: **Después de las clases voy a la biblioteca. Paso un rato**

con

_____

los amigos. Miro la televisión. Después de hacer la tarea, preparo

_____

la comida.

_____

_____

_____

_____

Integración: Hablar

Level 1, pp. 99-101
WB CD 01 track 21

The Rodríguez' go to a family summer camp in México. There are many recreational and educational activities, and kids and parents need to come to terms with their schedules. The parents and kids want to participate in different activities, but they also want to be together. Señora Rodríguez calls the camp's Automated Information Center to get help with everybody's schedules.

Fuente 1 Leer

Read the ad for the family summer camp...

CAMPAMENTO FAMILIAR GUADALAJARA

HAY ACTIVIDADES TODOS LOS DÍAS.

- Los lunes, miércoles y viernes tenemos clases de la historia y el arte de México. Las clases son de hombres y mujeres. Son de las nueve y media a las diez y cuarto de la mañana.

- ¿Les gusta practicar deportes? Los martes y jueves tenemos fútbol de hombres y mujeres, de las diez y cuarto a las once de la mañana.

El horario del sábado y domingo es muy bueno; siempre hay actividades de grandes y pequeños ¿La familia tiene chicos y chicas? ¿Tienen preguntas? **El número de teléfono es 723-888-2479.**

Fuente 2 Escuchar   *CD 01 track 22*

Listen to the students' schedule recorded on the automated information center. Take notes.

_____

_____

_____

Hablar

How are the kids' schedules different from the parents'? Include information from both the camp ad and the automated information center in your answer.

modelo: Los hombres y mujeres tienen actividades en la...El horario de los chicos y chicas...Pero los sábados y domingos...

Answers will vary: **Los hombres y mujeres tienen actividades en la mañana.**

Los chicos y chicas tienen clases de guitarra a las dos y

diez. Pero los sábados y domingos hay actividades de grandes y pequeños.

Integración: Escribir

Level 1, pp. 99-101
WB CD 01 track 23

Joaquín writes an editorial about his history teacher. He describes him in such good terms that now everybody calls señor Ortiz's office to get into his class. Señor Ortiz records an automated answer with frequently asked questions.

Fuente 1 Leer

Read Joaquín's editorial in the school's newspaper about his history teacher...

El señor Ortiz: un maestro de historia muy bueno

En la clase de historia me gusta aprender. ¿Por qué? Porque el señor Ortiz es bueno. Él siempre contesta las preguntas de los estudiantes. A veces la tarea es difícil. Pero soy organizado y tomo apuntes todos los días. Tengo que sacar una buena nota, porque me gusta aprender con el señor Ortiz.

Fuente 2 Escuchar   *CD 01 track 24*

Listen to señor Ortiz's recorded message. Take notes.

_____

_____

_____

_____

Escribir

What do you need to do to get a good grade in señor Ortiz's history class?

modelo: Tengo que ser organizado y también tengo que llegar temprano, nunca llegar tarde. De vez en cuando está bien, pero no siempre.

Answers will vary: **Tengo que ser organizado y tomar apuntes todos los días.**

También tengo que llegar temprano, nunca llegar tarde. De vez en cuando

está bien, pero no siempre. _____

_____

_____

_____

_____

Escuchar A

Level 1, pp. 106-107
WB CD 01 tracks 25-26

> **¡AVANZA!** **Goal:** Listen to find out about the activities that some kids do.

1 Listen to Pablo and take notes. Then, read each sentence and answer **cierto** (true) or **falso** (false).

C (F) **1.** El examen de ciencias es el martes.

C (F) **2.** Claudia nunca saca buenas notas.

(C) F **3.** A Pablo no le gusta estudiar.

(C) F **4.** Pablo y sus amigos siempre tocan la guitarra.

C (F) **5.** Hoy, Pablo llega tarde.

2 Listen to Adriana and take notes. Then, complete the sentences below.

1. Adriana es muy _____inteligente_____.

2. A Saúl no le gusta _____estudiar_____.

3. A Saúl le gusta más _____practicar deportes_____.

4. Saúl necesita ____sacar una buena nota____ el viernes.

5. Hoy, Saúl _____estudia_____ con Adriana.

Escuchar B

Level 1, pp. 106-107
WB CD 01 tracks 27-28

¡AVANZA! **Goal:** Listen to find out about the activities that some kids do.

1 Listen to Luciana talk about different people. Take notes. Then match the activities below with the correct name in the box.

1. Monta en bicicleta. __c__

2. Tiene que sacar una buena nota en la clase de ciencias. __d__

3. Enseña la clase de ciencias. __b__

4. Tienen un examen de ciencias el viernes. __a__

a. Luciana y Rubén
b. la señora Burgos
c. Luciana
d. Rubén

2 Listen to Rubén and take notes. Then, write about what people are doing in complete sentences. *Answers will vary.*

1. La señora Burgos enseña (ciencias). _____

2. Nosotros estudiamos (matemáticas). _____

3. Rubén necesita sacar una buena nota. _____

4. Ellas toman (muchos) apuntes. _____

Escuchar C

¡AVANZA! **Goal:** Listen to find out about the activities that some kids do.

1 Listen to señora Domínguez and take notes. Then, complete the following sentences.

1. Los estudiantes de la señora Domínguez casi siempre _____sacan buenas notas_____ .

2. Los estudiantes llegan _____temprano_____ a clase.

3. De vez en cuando, Mercedes no _____estudia_____ mucho.

4. Todos los estudiantes de la señora Domínguez _____practican deportes_____ .

5. Los chicos nunca _____llegan tarde_____ a casa.

2 Listen to señora Pérez describe her class. Then answer the questions below in complete sentences.

1. ¿Cómo son los estudiantes de la señora Pérez?

Los estudiantes de la señora Pérez son inteligentes.

_____

2. ¿Llegan tarde a clase?

No, ellos no llegan tarde a clase.

_____

3. ¿Qué tiene que hacer Iván?

Él tiene que estudiar con un amigo o una amiga de clase.

_____

4. ¿Quién (who) toma muchos apuntes?

Daniela y Beatriz toman muchos apuntes.

_____

Leer A

¡AVANZA! **Goal:** Read about what students do and what they have to do.

En la clase de ciencias hay muchos estudiantes. A Irene siempre le gusta estudiar y hacer la tarea. En todos los exámenes saca cien. Pablo nunca estudia y no le gusta tomar apuntes. En los exámenes saca cuarenta, cincuenta y treinta. Muchas veces, a Sandra le gusta hacer la tarea. En los exámenes saca noventa, cuarenta y cien. A Eduardo a veces le gusta estudiar y hacer la tarea. En los exámenes saca noventa, noventa y noventa. A Javier nunca le gusta leer libros. En los exámenes saca cuarenta, cincuenta y cuarenta. Todos los estudiantes son diferentes y me gusta enseñar ciencias a todos.

¿Comprendiste?

Read the note from señor Ortiz. Then, read each sentence and answer **cierto** (true) or **falso** (false).

Ⓒ   F   **1.** Irene siempre saca buenas notas.

Ⓒ   F   **2.** De vez en cuando, Sandra saca una mala nota.

C   Ⓕ   **3.** En todos los exámenes, Javier saca buenas notas.

C   Ⓕ   **4.** Muchas veces, Pablo saca una buena nota.

Ⓒ   F   **5.** Eduardo nunca saca una mala nota.

¿Qué piensas?

1. ¿Piensas que Javier tiene que estudiar más?¿Por qué?

Sí, pienso que Javier tiene que estudiar más porque saca malas notas.

_____

_____

2. ¿Tú sacas buenas notas en la clase de ciencias?

Answers will vary: **Sí, (No, no) saco buenas notas en la clase de ciencias.**

_____

_____

Leer B

> **¡AVANZA!** **Goal:** Read about what students do and what they have to do.

Señores Rodríguez,

Soy la maestra de ciencias y Javier es estudiante en la clase. Javier saca malas notas en los exámenes de ciencias. Él siempre toma apuntes en clase y prepara la tarea todos los días, pero necesita estudiar más. A Javier no le gusta contestar preguntas en clase. Es inteligente pero no trabaja mucho en clase. Por favor, necesitan hablar con Javier antes del exaámen en mayo.

Señora Burgos

¿Comprendiste?

Read the letter Javier's teacher has written to his parents. Then, complete the following sentences:

1. Javier saca _____ malas notas _____ en ciencias.

2. Javier siempre _____ toma apuntes _____ en clase.

3. Javier _____ prepara _____ la tarea todos los días.

4. Javier _____ necesita _____ estudiar más.

5. Javier no _____ trabaja _____ mucho en la clase.

¿Qué piensas?

1. ¿Necesitas estudiar mucho en todas las clases? Explica.

   Answers will vary: **Sí, tengo que estudiar mucho porque necesito sacar una**

   buena nota.

   _____

2. ¿En qué clases no tomas apuntes?

   Answers will vary: **No tomo apuntes en la clase de matemáticas.**

   _____

   _____

Leer C

> **¡AVANZA!** **Goal:** Read about what students do and what they have to do.

Mario:	¡Hola Leonor! ¿Cómo estás?
Leonor:	Bien. ¿Tienes que llegar a clase temprano?
Mario:	Sí. La clase de español es a las ocho y diez de la mañana.
Leonor:	¿Qué tienes que hacer después de las clases?
Mario:	Después de las clases tengo que hacer la tarea. Necesito leer un libro de inglés. ¿Y tú?
Leonor:	Yo tengo que tocar la guitarra. Tengo una clase de música a las cinco y media. Toco la guitarra casi todos los días.
Mario:	También dibujo o escucho música en la tarde.
Leonor:	Mario, ¡son las ocho menos diez!
Mario:	¡Tengo que ir a clase! Adiós.
Leonor:	¡Hasta luego!

¿Comprendiste?

Read the conversation between two friends, Mario and Leonor. Then, answer **cierto** (true) or **falso** (false).

Ⓒ F **1.** Mario tiene que ir temprano a la clase de español.

C Ⓕ **2.** Leonor toca la guitarra de vez en cuando.

C Ⓕ **3.** A Mario le gusta mucho tocar la guitarra.

Ⓒ F **4.** Leonor tiene que ir a la clase de música por la tarde.

C Ⓕ **5.** Mario dibuja y toca música.

¿Qué piensas?

1. ¿Qué tienes que hacer antes de las clases?

Answers will vary: **Tengo que practicar deportes antes de las clases.**

2. ¿Qué tienes que hacer después de las clases?

Answers will vary: **Después de las clases tengo que hacer la tarea.**

Escribir A

> **¡AVANZA!** **Goal:** Write about your daily schedule.

Step 1

Write Carolina's schedule in order in the chart using the list in the box. Write the class times in numbers.

nueve menos diez: ciencias	diez y cuarto: español	doce y media: historia	dos y diez: arte

Hora	8:50	10:15	12:30	2:10
Lunes	ciencias	español	historia	arte

Step 2

Write three sentences telling when Carolina has class on Monday.

Answers will vary: **Carolina tiene clase de ciencias a las nueve menos**

diez de la mañana. Carolina tiene clase de español a las diez y cuarto.

Carolina tiene clase de historia a las doce y media.

Step 3

Evaluate your writing using the information in the table.

Writing Criteria	Excellent	Good	Needs Work
Content	You included three sentences telling when Carolina has class on Monday.	You included two sentences telling when Carolina has class on Monday.	You include one sentence telling when Carolina has class on Monday.
Communication	Most of your message is organized and easy to follow.	Parts of your message are organized and easy to follow.	Your message is disorganized and hard to follow.
Accuracy	You make few mistakes in grammar and vocabulary.	You make some mistakes in grammar and vocabulary.	You make many mistakes in grammar and vocabulary.

Escribir B

> **¡AVANZA!** **Goal:** Write about your your daily schedule.

Step 1

Write out in words the times of the classes in Laura's schedule:

Hora	lunes	martes	miércoles	jueves
8:30 *ocho y media*	matemáticas	historia	matemáticas	matemáticas
11:15 *once y cuarto*	ciencias	ciencias	historia	ciencias
1:20 *una y veinte*	español			español

Step 2

Look at Laura's schedule and write about her week at school:

Answers will vary: **Laura tiene clase de historia a las ocho y media y a las once y cuarto. Tiene clase de matemáticas tres veces por semana. Tiene clase de ciencias los lunes, los martes y los jueves. Los lunes tiene clase de matemáticas, de ciencias y clase de español.**

Step 3

Evaluate your writing using the information in the table.

Writing Criteria	Excellent	Good	Needs Work
Content	You have described Laura's schedule at school completely.	You have described most of Laura's schedule at school.	You have not described much of Laura's schedule at school.
Communication	Most of your response is clear.	Some of your response is clear.	Your message is not very clear.
Accuracy	You make few mistakes in grammar and vocabulary.	You make some mistakes in grammar and vocabulary.	You make many mistakes in grammar and vocabulary.

Escribir C

 Goal: Write about your daily schedule.

Step 1

Read what Julio says and write his class schedule in order. Write the subjects and times of the classes in the table below.

Julio: Los lunes, miércoles y viernes tengo clase de matemáticas a las doce y cuarto de la tarde. Los martes y jueves tengo clase de español a las nueve y media de la mañana. Los lunes y miércoles tengo clase de inglés a las ocho menos diez de la mañana. Tengo clase de ciencias los martes y jueves a las dos y veinte de la tarde.

Hora	lunes	martes	miércoles	jueves	viernes
7:50	inglés		inglés		
9:30		español		español	
12:15	matemáticas		matemáticas		matemáticas
2:20		ciencias		ciencias	

Step 2

Using Julio's schedule above, and the words **siempre, muchas veces, de vez en cuando,** write about what Julio has to do in three of his classes.

Answers will vary: **En clase de matemáticas, siempre tiene que tomar apuntes. En clase de español, tiene que contestar preguntas muchas veces. En clase de inglés tiene que tomar apuntes de vez en cuando.**

Step 3

Evaluate your writing using the information in the table.

Writing Criteria	Excellent	Good	Needs Work
Content	You described what Julio has to do in three classes.	You described what Julio has to do in two classes.	You described what Julio has to do in one class.
Communication	Most of your message is organized and easy to follow.	Parts of your message are organized and easy to follow.	Your message is disorganized and hard to follow.
Accuracy	You make few mistakes in grammar and vocabulary.	You make some mistakes in grammar and vocabulary.	You make many mistakes in grammar and vocabulary.

Cultura A

> ¡AVANZA! **Goal:** Review cultural information about Mexico.

1 **Mexican culture** Choose the multiple choice item that completes each sentence.

1. The currency of Mexico is the _b_

   a. Mexican dollar **b.** Mexican peso **c.** Mexican bolívar

2. A **zócalo** is a _a_

   a. town square **b.** garden **c.** temple

3. Three typical Mexican foods are _c_

   a. pizzas, pasta and sausages **b.** hamburgers, French fries, and malts **c.** tortillas, tacos, and enchiladas

2 **Mexico** Choose the correct word to complete the following sentences.

1. UNAM is Mexico's largest (airport / <u>university</u>).

2. The pyramid of Kukulcán was used as a (tomb / <u>temple</u>).

3. Salma Hayek is a Mexican (<u>actress</u> / writer).

4. The Jardín Principal in San Miguel de Allende, Mexico is a (temple / <u>park</u>).

5. It is common for students in Mexico to wear (jeans / <u>uniforms</u>) to school.

3 **Arte mexicano** Look at the image from the mural on page 97 of your book. Who painted it, and what ideas does it reflect? Describe what you see in the mural.

Answers will vary. _____

_____

_____

_____

_____

Cultura B

> ¡AVANZA! **Goal:** Review cultural information about Mexico.

1 **Mexico** Read the following statements about Mexico and circle *true* or *false*.

T (F) **1.** The capital of Mexico is San Luis.

(T) F **2.** Tacos are an example of typical Mexican food.

T (F) **3.** The Mexican currency is the euro.

(T) F **4.** Diego Rivera created many murals reflecting Mexico's history.

(T) F **5.** Mexico has the largest Spanish-speaking population in the world.

T (F) **6.** Only private school students in Mexico wear uniforms.

2 **Identify places** Match each place with the corresponding description.

The pramid of Kukulcán   One of the oldest universities in
                                          Latin America

The **Jardín Principal**   Used as a temple

UNAM

Chichén Itzá   A town square or plaza

zócalo   A park located in San Miguel de Allende

                                          An ancient Mayan city

3 **School requirements** Write a comparison of your school and the Colegio Americano in Guadalajara, Mexico. What subjects do you have to study at school? What do you have to do to graduate from high school? How is this similar or different from the requirements at the Colegio Americano?

Answers will vary.
_____
_____
_____
_____
_____
_____
_____

UNIDAD 2
Lección 1 • Practice A

Cultura C

¡AVANZA! **Goal:** Review cultural information about Mexico.

1 **Mexico** Complete the following sentences.

1. The _____peso_____ is the official currency of Mexico.

2. The _____pyramid_____ of Kukulcán was used as a temple.

3. _____Uniforms_____ are commonly worn by students in Mexican schools.

4. The ___Universidad Nacional Autónoma___ de México has almost 270,000 students.

5. Many Mexican cities have town squares known as _____zócalos_____

2 **Mexican culture** Answer the following questions about Mexico.

1. What can you do in the **Jardín Principal** in San Miguel de Allende?

You can stroll through the Jardín Principal and listen to live music.

2. What languages, other than Spanish, are spoken in Mexico?

Maya and other indigenous languages.

3. What appears on the walls of the library at UNAM?

A mosaic showing the cultural history of Mexico.

3 **A visit to Mexico** There are many interesting places to visit in Mexico. Write a paragraph about the following places in Mexico: Parque San Miguel de Allende, the Mayan city of Chichén Itzá, and the Universidad Nacional Autónoma de México (UNAM). Describe each place and then tell which place you would like to visit and why.

Answers will vary. _____

_____

_____

_____

_____

_____

_____

Vocabulario A

> ¡AVANZA! **Goal:** Talk about your school.

① Marcela needs to go to science class. Indicate what she would put in her backpack by placing an X next to the words.

1. _____ el escritorio
2. __X__ el lápiz
3. __X__ el cuaderno
4. _____ el pizarrón
5. __X__ la calculadora

6. __X__ la pluma
7. __X__ el papel
8. _____ la silla
9. _____ la puerta
10. _____ el mapa

② Raúl and Graciela are at school. Complete the following sentences with the appropriate word from the box.

1. Raúl practica muchos deportes los lunes. Hoy es martes y él está

   _____cansado_____ .

2. El maestro escribe en el pizarrón. Él necesita

   _____tiza_____ y _____un borrador_____ .

3. Graciela necesita leer un libro. Ella está en _____la biblioteca_____ .

4. Pasar un rato con amigos en la cafetería es _____divertido_____ .

5. Hoy hay un examen de matemáticas muy difícil. Los estudiantes están

   _____nerviosos_____ .

la biblioteca
nerviosos
tiza
divertido
cansado
un borrador

③ List three items you have in your backpack for your morning classes.

En la mochila tengo:

Answers will vary: **un cuaderno, un lápiz y una calculadora.**

_____

_____

_____

_____

Vocabulario B

> **¡AVANZA!** **Goal:** Talk about your school.

1 The following students are at school. Choose the word that best completes the sentence:

1. Raúl está __c__ porque tiene examen de ciencias. Es muy difícil.

    a. contento   **b.** interesante   **c.** nervioso   **d.** aburrido

2. Cristina necesita libros de ciencias. Ella está en __d__ .

    a. el gimnasio   **b.** el pasillo   **c.** el baño   **d.** la biblioteca

3. Muchos estudiantes compran refrescos en __b__ .

    a. casa   **b.** la cafetería   **c.** la biblioteca   **d.** el baño

4. Susana tiene mucha tarea; está muy __b__ .

    a. aburrida   **b.** ocupada   **c.** difícil   **d.** tranquila

5. La clase de música no es aburrida porque el maestro es __a__ .

    a. interesante   **b.** emocionada   **c.** enojado   **d.** deprimido

2 Roberto is the opposite of his friend Lorena. Complete the following sentences.

1. Cuando Roberto está deprimido, o triste, Lorena está _____ contenta _____ .

2. Lorena es divertida, pero Roberto es _____ aburrido _____ .

3. Cuando Roberto está nervioso, Lorena está _____ tranquila _____ .

4. Cuando Lorena tiene tarea fácil, Roberto tiene tarea _____ difícil _____ .

3 Answer the following questions about yourself and your classroom in complete sentences.

1. ¿Cómo estás cuando sacas una buena nota?

Answers will vary: **Yo estoy contento(a) cuando saco una buena nota.**

2. ¿Cómo estás cuando tienes un examen difícil?

Answers will vary: **Yo estoy nervioso(a) cuando tengo un examen difícil.**

3. ¿Cuántas ventanas hay en tu clase?

Answers will vary: **Hay cuatro ventanas en mi clase.**

Vocabulario C

¡AVANZA! **Goal:** Talk about your school.

1 Margarita and Marcelo are at school. Complete the following text using the words from the box.

Margarita y Marcelo compran refrescos en **1.** _____la cafetería_____

de la escuela. Luego, leen libros en **2.** _____la biblioteca_____

para el examen de ciencias del viernes. El examen no es

3. _____fácil_____ , es difícil. Por eso, Marcelo está

4. _____nervioso_____ . Margarita no está nerviosa, ella está

muy **5.** _____tranquila_____ porque siempre saca buenas notas en

ciencias. A Margarita le gusta mucho estudiar ciencias porque es

6. _____interesante_____ .

tranquila
la biblioteca
interesante
la cafetería
fácil
nervioso

2 Complete the following sentences describing a school.

1. En la escuela de El Valle, hay _____un gimnasio_____ para practicar deportes.

2. Los estudiantes dibujan en _____el pizarrón_____ con la tiza.

3. No hay _____un reloj_____ en la clase. ¿Qué hora es?

4. Antes de las clases, los estudiantes están en _____el pasillo_____ .

5. Cuando hay problemas muy difíciles en la clase de matemáticas, usamos

_____una calculadora_____ .

3 You have just transferred to a new school. Send an e-mail to your best friend and describe what it looks like and your feelings about it.

Answers will vary: **La escuela es interesante. De vez en cuando es aburrido pero, cuando paso un rato en la cafetería con mis amigos, estoy muy contento. Me gusta la clase de arte, es emocionante. Cuando tengo un examen, siempre estoy nervioso, pero estoy tranquilo cuando saco una buena nota. ¿Cómo es en tu escuela?**

Gramática A *The Verb estar*

> **¡AVANZA!** **Goal:** Use the verb **estar** to talk about location and condition.

1 Cristina and Sergio are talking in the hall. Re-create their conversation below.

Hola, Sergio. ¿Cómo _____estás_____ ? (están / estás)

Hola Cristina. _____Estoy_____ un poco nervioso. (Estamos / Estoy)

¿Por qué _____estás_____ nervioso? (estás / estoy)

_____Estoy_____ nervioso por el examen de ciencias. (Estoy / Están) Es difícil.

No, es fácil. Yo _____estoy_____ tranquila. (estamos / estoy) En mi cuaderno tengo

todos los apuntes. ¿Dónde _____está_____ tu cuaderno? (está / están)

_____Está_____ en mi mochila, encima de mi escritorio. (Estoy / Está)

2 Write the correct form of **estar** to complete the description of where these people are.

1. Sarita _____está_____ en la clase de inglés.

2. Yo _____estoy_____ en la biblioteca.

3. Ana, Claudia y yo _____estamos_____ en la cafetería.

4. ¿Dónde _____están_____ Sarita y Pablo?

5. El señor Ramírez _____está_____ en la oficina del director.

3 Write questions about Guillermo and his friends. Follow the model.

modelo: Guillermo está en la oficina. ¿Está Guillermo en la oficina?

Jorge está en el pasillo. ¿Está Jorge en el pasillo? _____

Luisa está muy contenta. ¿Está Luisa muy contenta? _____

Ramón está nervioso. ¿Está Ramón nervioso? _____

Gramática B *The Verb estar*

> **¡AVANZA!** **Goal:** Use the verb **estar** to talk about location and condition.

1 Choose the correct form of the verb to complete the following statements about location.

1. Mi cuaderno __c__ encima de mi escritorio.

   a. estás   **b.** están   **c.** está   **d.** estamos

2. Las ventanas __b__ al lado de la puerta.

   a. estamos   **b.** están   **c.** estoy   **d.** está

3. Milagros y yo __d__ detrás de la puerta.

   a. estoy   **b.** estás   **c.** están   **d.** estamos

4. La calculadora __b__ dentro de la mochila.

   a. están   **b.** está   **c.** estás   **d.** estoy

2 Write sentences to describe some people at school.

1. El maestro / estar en la oficina del director.

   El maestro está en la oficina del director.

2. Los estudiantes / estar en la cafetería / al lado de la biblioteca.

   Los estudiantes están en la cafetería, al lado de la biblioteca.

3. El director / estar ocupado.

   El director está ocupado.

4. ¿Estar / (tú) cansado?

   ¿Estás (tú) cansado?

3 Esteban has answered his friend's e-mail. Write questions for his responses.

1. ¿La oficina del director está cerca del gimnasio?

   Sí, la oficina del director está cerca del gimnasio.

2. ¿Estás muy nervioso?

   No, no estoy muy nervioso.

3. ¿El director está enojado?

   No, el director no está enojado.

Gramática C *The Verb estar*

> **¡AVANZA!** **Goal:** Use the verb **estar** to talk about location and condition.

UNIDAD 2 • **Gramática C**
Lección 2

1 Write complete sentences to find out about the following people in Spanish class.

1. Claudia y yo / estar / cerca de la puerta

Claudia y yo estamos cerca de la puerta.

2. La maestra / estar / contenta

La maestra está contenta.

3. Los estudiantes / estar / ocupados

Los estudiantes están ocupados.

4. tú / estar / delante de Ana

(Tú) estás delante de Ana.

5. yo / estar / detrás de Miguel

(Yo) estoy detrás de Miguel.

2 Complete the following questions with the correct form of **estar** and the subject. Then, answer each question in complete sentences.

1. ¿ _____ Estás _____ nervioso(a) cuando tienes un examen? (estar / tú)

Sí, (No,) cuando tengo un examen (no) estoy nervioso(a).

2. ¿ ___ Están los estudiantes ___ contentos cuando sacan buenas notas?
(estar / los estudiantes)

Sí, (No,) los estudiantes (no) están contentos cuando sacan buenas notas.

3. ¿ ___ Están los baños ___ cerca de la biblioteca? (estar / los baños)

Answers will vary: **Los baños están cerca de la biblioteca.**

3 Write three sentences describing people, places, and things at your school. Use the verb **estar** in each of your sentences.

Answers will vary: **Los baños de la escuela están cerca del gimnasio. Los**

maestros siempre están muy ocupados. Los estudiantes están

nerviosos porque los exámenes son muy difíciles.

Gramática A *The Verb ir*

> **¡AVANZA!** **Goal:** Use the verb **ir** to say where you and others are going.

❶ **¿Adónde van?** Choose the verb that best completes each sentence below.

1. ¿Adónde (<u>va</u> / vamos) Sandra?

2. Nosotras (<u>vamos</u> / van) al gimnasio.

3. ¿Cuándo (vas / <u>van</u>) Sergio y tú a la cafetería?

4. Tú (va / <u>vas</u>) a la clase de inglés los lunes y miércoles.

5. Yo (va / <u>voy</u>) a la biblioteca.

❷ Write three complete sentences using the information in the boxes below.

Cristina Sandra y yo Tú	ir a	la biblioteca el gimnasio la clase de arte

1. *Answers will vary:* **Sandra y yo vamos a la biblioteca.**

2. *Answers will vary:* **Cristina va al gimnasio.**

3. *Answers will vary:* **Tú vas a la clase de arte.**

❸ Answer the following questions in complete sentences.

1. ¿Adónde vas los lunes a las 8:30 de la mañana?

   Answers will vary: **Los lunes a las 8:30 de la mañana voy a la clase de**

   inglés.

2. ¿Adónde vas los lunes a las 3:30 de la tarde?

   Answers will vary: **Los lunes a las 3:30 de la tarde voy a practicar deportes.**

Gramática B *The Verb ir*

| ¡AVANZA! | **Goal:** Use the verb **ir** to say where you and others are going. |

1 Three students are going to Spanish class. Complete the text below with words from the box.

| voy | van | vamos | va |

Sarita, Cristina y yo **1.** _____vamos_____ a la clase de español. Lucía

también **2.** _____va_____ a la clase de español. A mí me gusta,

pero es un poco difícil. Ustedes **3.** _____van_____ a la clase de

español los lunes y miércoles. **4.** Yo _____voy_____ a la clase de

español los martes y jueves.

2 Write complete sentences about the following students.

1. Ana y Sandra / ir / a la cafetería.

Ana y Sandra van a la cafetería.

2. ¿Cuándo ir / Claudia y yo / al gimnasio?

¿Cuándo vamos Claudia y yo al gimnasio?

3. (Yo) / ir / a la clase de música.

(Yo) voy a la clase de música.

4. Ustedes / ir / a España / mañana por la noche.

Ustedes van a España mañana por la noche.

3 Complete the dialogue by answering Nora's questions

Nora: ¿Vas a la clase de inglés en la mañana o en la tarde?

Tú: *Answers will vary: Voy a la clase de inglés en la tarde.*

Nora: ¿Cuándo vas a la cafetería?

Tú: *Answers will vary: Voy a la cafetería a las dos de la tarde.*

Nora: ¿Adónde vas después de comer?

Tú: *Answers will vary: Después de comer voy al gimnasio.*

Gramática C

¡AVANZA! **Goal:** Use the verb **ir** to say where you and others are going.

1 Complete the sentences with the correct form of **ir**.

1. Todos los días, yo _____ voy _____ a la escuela.

2. ¿Adónde _____ vamos _____ Sergio y yo cuando estudiamos?

3. Yo _____ voy _____ a la escuela cerca de mi casa.

4. Ustedes _____ van _____ a Colombia el miércoles.

5. ¿Adónde _____ vas _____ tú a las ocho de la mañana?

2 These students are at school. Put the sentence in the correct order using the correct form of the verb **ir**.

1. Sandra y Pablo / gimnasio (ir)

   Sandra y Pablo van al gimnasio.

2. yo / todos los días / a la escuela (ir)

   Yo voy todos los días a la escuela.

3. Sandra, Sarita y yo / ¿Adónde / en la tarde? (ir)

   ¿Adónde vamos Sandra, Sarita y yo en la tarde?

4. todas las tardes / tú / a la biblioteca (ir)

   Tú vas a la biblioteca todas las tardes.

3 Write an e-mail to one of your friends at school about plans you have with another friend. Be sure to explain where you are going.

Answers will vary:

David:

Mañana temprano voy a la clase de historia. Después voy a la cafetería

con Sandra. Estoy emocionado. Tenemos que hablar mucho. Ella es

interesante y muy divertida. Me gusta. Y tú, ¿adónde vas mañana?

Miguel

UNIDAD 2
Lección 2 • Gramática C

Integración: Hablar

It's the first day of class at Escuela Monterrey, in Mexico. Señor Amador, the doorman, is handing out welcome flyers to all students. Then, the principal welcomes everybody over the loudspeaker and gives information about school supplies.

Fuente 1 Leer
Read the school's handout for students...

DÍA UNO EN LA ESCUELA MONTERREY

¡Hola! Soy el señor Amador. Siempre estoy en la puerta de la escuela. Siempre estoy contento. Los estudiantes tienen mucho que hacer. Las clases son muy interesantes y el gimnasio es grande. La cafetería es pequeña; a todos les gusta. Cuando estás en clase, siempre necesitas un cuaderno, un lápiz y una pluma. Pero, ¿cuándo necesitas la calculadora y el mapa? Escucha a la directora. Ella habla todos los días a las ocho y diez. Necesitas llegar temprano siempre y escuchar a la directora.

Fuente 2 Escuchar   *CD 01 track 32*
Listen to the principal's loudspeaker message. Take notes.

_____

_____

_____

_____

Hablar
You need to bring many things to school but, when exactly do you need these things? Remember to include information from both señor Amador's handout and the principal's message in your answer.

Modelo: Todos los días hay clases y necesito... Pero cuando no hay clases de...

Answers will vary: **Todos los días hay clases y necesito llegar temprano.**

Necesito tener el cuaderno y el lápiz en la mochila. Pero cuando no hay

clase de matemáticas, no necesito la calculadora.

Integración: Escribir

Level 1, pp.123-125
WB CD 01 track 33

A group of students has created posters to start an afterschool club. They want to help fellow students who are feeling bored. They want to convince everybody to join the club, so they put an ad in their school radio station.

Fuente 1 Leer

Read the poster the students created.

¿ESTÁS ABURRIDO?

SOMOS EL CLUB DE "LOS DIVERTIDOS".
TENEMOS ACTIVIDADES INTERESANTES
PARA TODOS.

¿CUÁNDO?
TODOS LOS MARTES Y JUEVES
A LAS CUATRO Y CUARTO

¿DÓNDE?
EN EL GIMNASIO
DE LA ESCUELA

¿QUIÉN?
¡TODOS LOS ESTUDIANTES DE LA ESCUELA!

Fuente 2 Escuchar   *CD 01 track 34*

Listen to the school radio ad. Take notes.

_____

_____

_____

Escribir

Then answer this question: You have to convince your friend to join the club. What can you say? Remember to include information from both the poster as well as the radio ad in your answer.

modelo: ¡Hola! ¿Estás aburrido? Hay...

Answers will vary: **¡Hola! ¿Estás aburrido? Hay actividades para todos en**

el club "Los Divertidos". Están en el gimnasio todos los martes y jueves a

las cuatro y cuarto. Es muy divertido.

Escuchar A

> **Goal:** Listen to find out what the kids are doing and what they like to do.

1 Listen to Sandra. Match each person with his or her description.

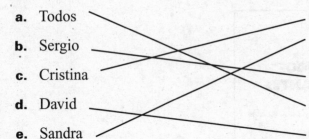

a. Todos — siempre está contenta.

b. Sergio — le gusta la clase de ciencias.

c. Cristina — está muy tranquilo.

d. David — compran refrescos y hablan.

e. Sandra — le gusta escuchar música.

2 Listen to Miguel. Then, read each sentence and answer **cierto** *(true)* o **falso** *(false)*.

Ⓒ F **1.** El pasillo está cerca de la biblioteca.

C Ⓕ **2.** Tomás está muy nervioso.

C Ⓕ **3.** A Elena no le gusta leer.

C Ⓕ **4.** Mario es aburrido.

Ⓒ F **5.** A Mario le gusta escuchar música.

Escuchar B

> **¡AVANZA!** **Goal:** Listen to find out what the kids are doing and what they like to do.

1 Listen to Sergio. Then complete the sentences below.

1. Los chicos van al pasillo que está al lado _____del gimnasio_____.

2. Los chicos van a _____la cafetería_____ y compran refrescos.

3. El pasillo está _____cerca_____ de la biblioteca.

4. Los amigos de Sergio son _____divertidos_____.

5. Los amigos de Sergio nunca están _____aburridos_____.

2 Listen to Pablo. Then, answer the questions in complete sentences.

1. ¿Qué tiene que hacer Carolina?

   Carolina siempre tiene que estudiar. _____

   _____

2. ¿Qué actividades practican los amigos de Pablo?

   Los amigos de Pablo practican deportes y escuchan música. _____

   _____

   _____

Escuchar C

| ¡AVANZA! | **Goal:** Listen to find out what the kids are doing and what they like to do. |

1 Listen to David and take notes. Then, complete the sentences.

1. A David le gusta _____escuchar música_____ .

2. David está contento porque _toca la guitarra con amigos_ .

3. El pasillo está _____cerca de la biblioteca_____ .

4. Los amigos de David son _____divertidos_____ .

5. _____Sandra_____ tiene libros dentro de la mochila.

2 Listen to Fabián and take notes. Then, answer the questions in complete sentences.

1. ¿De qué cosas hablan los amigos de Fabián?

Los amigos de Fabián hablan de libros, de ciencias, de deportes.

_____

_____

2. ¿De qué están cansados los amigos de Fabián?

Los amigos de Fabián están cansados de escuchar porque él habla

todo el tiempo de música.

_____

_____

UNIDAD 2 • Escuchar C
Lección 2

86 ¡Avancemos! 1
Cuaderno: Práctica por niveles

Unidad 2, Lección 2
Escuchar C

Leer A

> ![AVANZA!] **Goal:** Read about a survey made to the students.

Nombre	¿Cómo estás y por qué?
Sandra	Estoy ocupada porque tengo que estudiar ciencias. Es una clase muy interesante.
David	Estoy emocionado porque voy a la clase de música. Toco la guitarra todos los lunes.
Sarita	Estoy contenta porque siempre saco una buena nota en inglés.

¿Comprendiste?

Answer the following questions in complete sentences:

1. ¿Saca Sarita una mala nota en inglés?

No, Sarita nunca saca una mala nota en inglés.

2. ¿Está ocupada Sandra? Explica.

Sandra está ocupada porque tiene que estudiar ciencias.

3. ¿Está David deprimido? Explica.

No, David está emocionado.

¿Qué piensas?

Answer the following questions.

¿Cómo estás cuando vas a...

1. la clase de ciencias? *Answers will vary:* **Cuando voy a la clase de ciencias, estoy aburrido.**

2. la clase de español? *Answers will vary:* **Cuando voy a la clase de español, estoy emocionado.**

3. la biblioteca? *Answers will vary:* **Cuando voy a la biblioteca, estoy contento.**

Leer B

 ¡AVANZA! **Goal:** Read a sign with the description of a lost backpack.

¿Dónde está mi mochila?

Dentro de mi mochila hay un cuaderno, una calculadora, lápices, papeles, una pluma y ¡mi examen de matemáticas!

Siempre tengo mi mochila. Voy a la cafetería, al gimnasio y al pasillo que está cerca de la biblioteca. Siempre tengo mi mochila pero ahora ¡no está!

Estoy nervioso: ¡Necesito el examen y está dentro de mi mochila!

—Miguel

¿Comprendiste?

Read Miguel's sign describing the lost backpack. Then, read each sentence below and answer **cierto** (true) or **falso** (false).

C (F) **1.** Dentro de la mochila hay un libro.

C (F) **2.** Miguel nunca tiene su mochila.

C (F) **3.** Miguel siempre va al pasillo cerca de la oficina.

(C) F **4.** Miguel no está tranquilo.

(C) F **5.** Miguel necesita el examen de matemáticas.

¿Qué piensas?

Answer the following question in a complete sentence.

¿Está Miguel nervioso? Explica.

Answers will vary: **Está nervioso porque el examen de**

matemáticas está dentro de la mochila y no tiene la mochila.

_____

_____

_____

Leer C

> **¡AVANZA!** **Goal:** Read an article from the schools newspaper.

¡Vamos a pasar un rato divertido!

¿Están aburridos?

Los chicos del club pasan un rato divertido con amigos.

Todos los viernes en la tarde, unos estudiantes van a la biblioteca y hablan de los libros. Van a la clase al lado de la oficina del director y hablan de ciencias. ¡Es muy interesante!

Muchos estudiantes van al gimnasio y practican deportes. ¡Es muy emocionante! Después, todos van a la cafetería, compran refrescos y escuchan música. ¡Es muy divertido!

¿Comprendiste?

Read the article above and then complete the sentences below.

1. El club es para los chicos que están aburridos.

2. Todos los viernes en la tarde , los chicos pasan un rato divertido.

3. Los chicos hablan de libros en la biblioteca.

4. Hablan de ciencias en la clase al lado de la oficina del director.

5. Los chicos escuchan música en la cafetería.

¿Qué piensas?

Answer the following questions in complete sentences.

1. ¿Vas a un club después de las clases?¿Qué club?

   Answers will vary: **Sí, después de clases voy al club Miramar.**

2. ¿Es divertido hablar de ciencias?¿De libros?

   Answers will vary: **Hablar de ciencias y de libros es divertido, porque es**

   divertido pasar un rato con amigos.

Escribir A

> **¡AVANZA!** **Goal:** Write about yourself and your school.

Step 1

Respond to the following survey by writing how you feel when certain things happen at school. Use the words from the box.

Cuando...	¿Cómo estás?
Sacas una mala nota	*Cuando saco una mala nota, estoy triste.*
Practicas mucho deporte	*Cuando practico mucho deporte, estoy cansado.*
Estás en la cafetería	*Cuando estoy en la cafetería, estoy contento.*

triste
cansado(a)
contento(a)

Step 2

Answer the following question about yourself in a complete sentence:

¿Cuándo estás nervioso?

Answers will vary: **Estoy nervioso cuando tengo un examen de**

matemáticas.

_____

Step 3

Evaluate your writing using the information in the table.

Writing Criteria	Excellent	Good	Needs Work
Content	You have answered the question completely.	You have partially answered the question.	You have not answered the question.
Communication	Most of your response is clear.	Some of your response is clear.	Your response is not very clear.
Accuracy	You make few mistakes in grammar and vocabulary.	You make some mistakes in grammar and vocabulary.	You make many mistakes in grammar and vocabulary.

Escribir B

> **¡AVANZA!** **Goal:** Write about yourself and your school.

Step 1

Respond to the following survey by writing where things are at your school.

¿Dónde está...	Está...
el gimnasio?	*Answers will vary:* **cerca de la oficina del director.**
la biblioteca?	*Answers will vary:* **cerca de la clase de ciencias.**
la cafetería?	*Answers will vary:* **cerca de los baños**

Step 2

Write three complete sentences about the location of some things at your school. Use the words from the survey above.

> *Answers will vary:* **El pasillo está al lado de la clase de ciencias. Los baños**
>
> **están cerca de la cafetería. La oficina del director está cerca del gimnasio.**

Step 3

Evaluate your writing using the information in the table.

Writing Criteria	Excellent	Good	Needs Work
Content	You have written three complete sentences.	You have written two complete sentences.	You have written only one complete sentences.
Communication	Most of your sentences are clear.	Some of your sentences are clear.	Your sentences are not very clear.
Accuracy	You make few mistakes in grammar and vocabulary.	You make some mistakes in grammar and vocabulary.	You make many mistakes in grammar and vocabulary.

Escribir C

> **¡AVANZA!** **Goal:** Write about you and your school.

Step 1

Respond to the following survey by writing how you feel when certain things happen at school.

Cuando...	¿Cómo estás?
pasas un rato con amigos	tranquilo
estás en la clase de inglés	contento
estás en la clase de matemáticas	nervioso
estás en el gimnasio	cansado
estás en la cafetería	emocionado

Step 2

Use four answers from the survey above to describe how you feel at school.

Answers will vary: **Cuando paso un rato con mis amigos estoy tranquilo. Cuando estoy en la clase de matemáticas estoy nervioso. En la clase de inglés estoy contento. En la cafetería estoy emocionado, pero en el gimnasio estoy cansado.**

Step 3

Evaluate your writing using the information in the table below.

Writing Criteria	Excellent	Good	Needs Work
Content	You have included four sentences to describe how you feel.	You have included three sentences to describe how you feel.	You include two or fewer sentences to describe how you feel.
Communication	Most of your response is clear.	Some of your response is clear.	Your message is not very clear.
Accuracy	You make few mistakes in grammar and vocabulary.	You make some mistakes in grammar and vocabulary.	You make many mistakes in grammar and vocabulary.

UNIDAD 2 Lección 2 • Escribir C

Cultura A

┌───┐
│ ¡AVANZA! **Goal:** Review cultural information about Mexico.   │
└───┘

1 **Mexican culture** Read the following statements and answer *true* or *false*.

Ⓣ F **1.** Frida Kahlo was influenced by indigenous culture.

T Ⓕ **2.** The Andrés Barbero Museum of Ethnography is in Mexico.

T Ⓕ **3.** San Andrés is the capital of Mexico.

Ⓣ F **4.** Tortillas and enchiladas are typical Mexican dishes.

2 **In Mexico and the Dominican Republic** Choose the correct word to complete the following sentences.

1. The Piedra del Sol was a (calendar / clock) that the Aztecs created.

2. (Forestry / Tourism) is an important industry in the Dominican Republic.

3. Two of the languages spoken in Mexico are Spanish and (Portuguese / Maya).

4. Mexico's currency is called the (peso / dollar).

5. The National Museum of (Mexico / Anthropology) contains artifacts from indigenous cultures of Mexico.

3 **Art** Write a brief paragraph describing Frida Kahlo. What kind of art did she create?

Answers will vary: **Frida Kahlo was a Mexican painter. She created many**

self-portraits.

_____

_____

_____

_____

_____

_____

Cultura B

> ¡AVANZA! **Goal:** Review cultural information about Mexico.

1 **Mexico** Complete the following sentences with one of the multiple choice phrases.

1. The languages spoken in Mexico are __b__

   a. Spanish, chibcha, and other indigenous languages
   b. Spanish, maya, and other indigenous languages
   c. Spanish, taíno, and other indigenous languages

2. Frida Kahlo was a Mexican artist; she painted many __a__

   a. self-portraits
   b. murals
   c. landscapes

3. Frida Kahlo was influenced by __c__ culture in her style of painting and style of dress.

   a. Caribbean
   b. European
   c. indigenous

2 **Sites in Mexico** Where in Mexico are the following places?

Place to Visit	Where Are They Located?
The Museo Nacional de Antropología	In Mexico City
Jardín Principal	In San Miguel de Allende
The pyramid of Kukulcán	In Chichén Itzá

3 **In the Anthropology Museum** The **Piedra del Sol** is stored in the National Museum of Anthropology. Describe the **Piedra del Sol.** Which culture is it from and what was it used for? What does it look like? Also, describe the museum. What are some of the rooms found there? What other items might you expect to find in the museum?

Answers will vary: **The Piedra del Sol is a calendar that the Aztecs created.**

_____

_____

_____

_____

_____

_____

Cultura C

> ¡AVANZA! **Goal:** Review cultural information about Mexico.

1 **In Mexico** Complete the following sentences with the correct word or phrase.

1. This museum has artifacts from various indigenous cultures in Mexico.

National Museum of Anthropology

2. The currency of Mexico *the peso*

3. A calendar created by the Aztecs **Piedra del Sol**

4. One of the languages, other than Spanish, spoken in Mexico maya

5. The capital of Mexico Mexico City

2 **Art and Artifacts** Answer the following questions about Mexico.

1. How was Frida Kahlo influenced by indigenous culture?

She was influenced in her style of painting and in her style of clothing.

2. What type of painting did Frida Kahlo often create?

She created many self-portraits.

3. How much does the Piedra del Sol weigh?

The Piedra del Sol weighs almost twenty-five tons.

3 **Museums** Think of a museum you have visited or that you know about, and compare it to the National Museum of Anthropology. Write a paragraph that describes what kinds of objects are kept there. Where are they from? Who made them?

Answers will vary.

_____

_____

_____

_____

Comparación cultural: Horarios y clases

Level 1, pp. 132-133

Lectura y escritura

After reading the paragraphs about how Rafael, Andrea, and Juan Carlos spend a typical day at school, write a paragraph about your daily schedule. Use the information on the clocks to write sentences, and then write a paragraph that describes your daily schedule.

Step 1

Complete the two clocks by listing your classes and after-school activities. Use arrows to point to the correct times.

modelo:

clase de ciencias

clase de inglés   a.m.   p.m.

jugar al fútbol

estudiar

a.m.

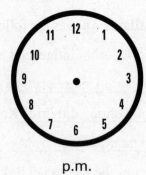

p.m.

Step 2

Now take the details from the two clocks and write a sentence for each of the activities you labeled on the clocks.

_____

_____

_____

_____

_____

_____

_____

Comparación cultural: Horarios y clases

Lectura y escritura (continued)

Step 3

Now write your paragraph using the sentences you wrote as a guide. Include an introductory sentence and use: **tener, tener que, ir,** and **ir a** to write about your daily schedule.

_____

_____

_____

_____

_____

_____

_____

Checklist

Be sure that…

☐ all the details about your daily schedule from your clocks are included in the paragraph;

☐ you use details to describe, as clearly as possible, all your after school activities;

☐ you include new vocabulary words and **tener, tener que, ir** and **ir a**.

Rubric

Evaluate your writing using the rubric below.

Writing criteria	Excellent	Good	Needs Work
Content	Your paragraph includes many details about your daily schedule.	Your paragraph includes some details about your daily schedule.	Your paragraph includes few details about your daily schedule.
Communication	Most of your paragraph is organized and easy to follow.	Parts of your paragraph are organized and easy to follow.	Your paragraph is disorganized and hard to follow.
Accuracy	Your paragraph has few mistakes in grammar and vocabulary.	Your paragraph has some mistakes in grammar and vocabulary.	Your paragraph has many mistakes in grammar and vocabulary.

Comparación cultural: Horarios y clases

Compara con tu mundo

Now write a comparison about your daily schedule and that of one of the three students from page 133. Organize your comparison by listing morning and afternoon activities, and classes.

Step 1

Use the table to organize your comparison by times. Write details for each activity in your daily schedule and that of the student you chose.

MI HORARIO a.m.	EL HORARIO DE _____ a.m.
8:00	8:00
9:00	9:00
10:00	10:00
11:00	11:00
12:00	12:00
MI HORARIO p.m.	**EL HORARIO DE _____ p.m.**
1:00	1:00
2:00	2:00
3:00	3:00
4:00	4:00
5:00	5:00

Step 2

Now use the details from the table to write a comparison. Include an introductory sentence and write about each part of the schedules. Use **tener, tener que, ir, ir a** to describe your daily schedule and that of the student you chose.

_____
_____
_____
_____
_____
_____

Unidad 2
Comparación cultural: Horarios y clases
98
¡Avancemos! 1
Cuaderno: Práctica por niveles

Vocabulario A

¡AVANZA! **Goal:** Talk about foods and beverages.

1 Natalia likes to eat a healthy breakfast. Write an "X" next to each breakfast food from those listed below.

1. __X__ el cereal
2. __X__ los huevos
3. __X__ la banana
4. ____ la hamburguesa
5. __X__ la manzana

6. __X__ el jugo de naranja
7. ____ la pizza
8. ____ el sándwich de jamón y queso
9. ____ los refrescos
10. ____ la sopa

2 Carlos is making lunch. Complete the following sentences with a word or expression from the box.

leche	compartir	tengo hambre	nutritivas

1. A Alfredo le gustan las comidas _____ nutritivas _____ .
2. A nosotros nos gusta beber _____ leche _____ .
3. Es la hora del almuerzo. Yo _____ tengo hambre _____ . Necesito comer.
4. Ella no tiene almuerzo. Tengo que _____ compartir _____ mi sándwich con una amiga.

3 What do you like to eat for dinner? Answer the following questions in complete sentences.

1. ¿Te gusta comer sopa en la cena?

   Answers will vary: **Sí, (No, no) me gusta comer sopa en la cena.**

2. ¿Te gusta beber jugo de naranja?

   Answers will vary: **Sí, (No, no) me gusta beber jugo de naranja.**

3. ¿Qué frutas te gusta comer?

   Answers will vary: **Me gusta comer manzanas.**

Vocabulario B

> ¡AVANZA! **Goal:** Talk about foods and beverages.

1 We all like to eat good, nutritious foods. From the choices below, choose the one that best completes each sentence.

1. Es importante comer comidas (horribles / <u>nutritivas</u>).

2. ¿Quién quiere beber un (<u>jugo</u> / pan)?

3. Todos los días Verónica tiene que (<u>compartir</u> / vender) su sándwich porque es muy grande.

4. Antes de ir a la escuela, Juan prepara cereal para (la cena / <u>el desayuno</u>).

5. El (<u>yogur</u> / refresco) es nutritivo.

2 Gustavo and Carla discuss their eating habits. Complete their conversation.

tengo ganas de	tengo sed	leche	jugo
cereal	nutritivas	horrible	

Gustavo: A mí me gusta comer **1.** _____cereal_____ en el desayuno.

Carla: A mí me gusta comer huevos en el desayuno. También me gusta beber

2. _____leche_____ . Es rica.

Gustavo: A mí no me gusta la leche. **3.** Es _____horrible_____ . Cuando

4. _____tengo sed_____ me gusta más beber **5.** _____jugo_____

de naranja.

Carla: Todos los días como uvas porque son **6.** _____nutritivas_____ .

Gustavo: Ahora **7.** _____tengo ganas de_____ comer una hamburguesa. Siempre tengo

hambre a las doce.

3 ¿Qué te gusta comer? Answer the following questions in complete sentences. *Answers will vary:*

1. ¿Qué te gusta comer en el desayuno?

En el desayuno me gusta comer huevos y pan.

2. ¿Te gusta más comer el desayuno o el almuerzo? ¿Por qué?

Me gusta más comer el almuerzo porque me gustan las hamburguesas.

Vocabulario C

> ¡AVANZA! **Goal:** Talk about foods and beverages.

1 Asking questions is a good way to get to know people. Complete the following questions using words from the box.

1. ¿ _____Cuál_____ te gusta más: una hamburguesa o un sándwich? Me gusta más un sándwich.

2. ¿ _____Por qué_____ bebes jugo de naranja y no bebes un refresco? Porque es más nutritivo.

3. ¿ _____Dónde_____ venden comidas nutritivas? Venden comidas nutritivas en la cafetería.

4. ¿ A _____quiénes_____ les gustan los huevos? A mis amigos les gustan.

dónde
quiénes
cuál
por qué

2 It's important to eat healthy foods. Choose a word from the vocabulary to complete each sentence:

1. En la cafetería de mi escuela _____venden_____ muchas comidas y bebidas.

2. No nos gusta beber _____café_____ con el desayuno; nos gusta más beber leche.

3. Yo bebo jugo de naranja porque _____tengo sed_____ .

4. ¿ _____Cuál_____ es más nutritivo: una banana o pan?

3 Look at the following drawing and write three sentences about it. Where is it? What meal is it? What foods are there?

Answers will vary: **En la cafetería venden comida, hay sopa, manzanas,**

bananas y uvas. Es la una, la hora del almuerzo. A la chica le gusta beber

leche, y comer hamburguesas y papas fritas.

Gramática A *Gustar* with Nouns

> **¡AVANZA!** **Goal:** Ask questions and talk about which foods you like and don't like.

1 Everyone likes something different. Underline the verb that completes each sentence.

1. A Victoria (le gusta/ le gustan) la comida que prepara la mamá.

2. A nosotros (nos gustan / nos gusta) las papas fritas.

3. A Elena y a Sonia no (les gusta / les gustan) la sopa.

4. A ti no (te gusta / te gustan) el café.

5. A mí (me gusta / me gustan) las uvas.

2 What do the following people like? Write the correct form of the verb **gustar** in each sentence.

1. A mí _____me gusta_____ la cena que prepara Sebastián.

2. A Patricia _____le gustan_____ las hamburguesas, las papas fritas y los refrescos.

3. A nosotras _____nos gusta_____ la comida nutritiva.

4. A ustedes _____les gustan_____ las manzanas y las uvas.

5. ¿A ti _____te gustan_____ mucho los huevos?

3 In complete sentences, answer the following questions.

modelo: A mí me gusta (me gustan)...

1. ¿Qué comidas te gustan más?

   Answers will vary: **A mí me gustan más las hamburguesas y las papas fritas.**

2. ¿Qué comidas no te gustan?

   Answers will vary: **No me gustan las uvas.**

Gramática B *Gustar* with Nouns

¡AVANZA! **Goal:** Ask questions and talk about which foods you like and don't like.

1 What do they like? Ask these people what they like using the words from the box.

los huevos	el café	el jugo de naranja
el yogur	la leche	las uvas

modelo: Ernesto: *¿Te gusta el yogur?*

1. Lucía y Augusto: *Answers will vary:* **¿Les gustan los huevos?**

2. Señora Menchero: *Answers will vary:* **¿Le gusta el jugo de naranja?**

3. Gregorio y Luz: *Answers will vary:* **¿Les gustan las uvas?**

2 These students like cafeteria food. Complete the following paragraph with the appropriate form of the verb **gustar**.

A mis amigos **1.** ____les gusta____ mucho la comida de la cafetería. A Esmeralda **2.** ____le gustan____ las papas fritas y los refrescos. A Rodrigo **3.** ____le gusta____ más la fruta. A mí **4.** ____me gustan____ los sándwiches y la leche. Pero a todos nosotros **5.** ____nos gusta____ mucho el yogur. Y a ti, ¿qué **6.** ____te gusta____ ?

3 Answer the following questions about food. Use complete sentences.

1. ¿Qué te gusta en el almuerzo?

Answers will vary: **En el almuerzo me gusta un sándwich de jamón y queso.**

2. ¿Te gustan las comidas nutritivas? ¿Cuáles te gustan más?

Answers will vary: **Sí, me gustan las comidas nutritivas. Me gustan más las uvas.**

Gramática C *Gustar* with Nouns

Level 1, pp. 145-149

¡AVANZA! ▶ **Goal:** Ask questions and talk about which foods you like and don't like.

---

1 We all like to eat different things. Complete each sentence with a form of **gustar**.

1. A Valeria _____*le gustan*_____ las frutas.

2. A Juanjo y a Bruno no _____*les gusta*_____ el café.

3. A Teresa y a mí _____*nos gusta*_____ el yogur en el desayuno.

4. A nosotros _____*nos gustan*_____ las comidas nutritivas.

5. A ti _____*te gustan*_____ los huevos en la cena.

2 What do these people like? Follow the model and write complete sentences.

modelo: Hernán / la fruta **A Hernán le gusta la fruta.**

1. Sandra / los refrescos

A Sandra le gustan los refrescos.

2. Carla y Octavio / los sándwiches

A Carla y a Octavio les gustan los sándwiches.

3. tú / el yogur en la cena

A ti te gusta el yogur en la cena.

4. yo / más la leche

A mí me gusta más la leche.

3 Write two complete sentences about two different friends of yours and what they like to eat for lunch in the school cafeteria. Then write one more sentence about what you like.

Answers will vary: **A mi amiga Carla le gusta comprar una hamburguesa**

en la cafetería en el almuerzo. A mi amigo Roberto le gustan

los sándwiches en el almuerzo. A mí me gusta la pizza.

Gramática A *Present Tense of **-er** and **-ir** Verbs*

> **¡AVANZA!** **Goal:** Use the present tense to tell what people do.

1 Match each subject on the left with its appropriate ending on the right.

1. _d_ Yo...   **a.** aprendemos mucho en las clases.

2. _e_ Luis y Gustavo...   **b.** compartes el almuerzo con amigos.

3. _b_ Tú...   **c.** bebe jugo de naranja.

4. _c_ Carla...   **d.** como huevos en el desayuno.

5. _a_ Natalia y yo...   **e.** leen un libro.

2 Complete each sentence with the correct form of the appropriate verb. Each verb will be used only once.

1. Tú siempre _____ bebes _____ agua después de correr.

2. Yo siempre _____ hago _____ la tarea después de las clases.

3. La cafetería _____ vende _____ unas hamburguesas muy ricas.

4. ¿Usted _____ escribe _____ correos electrónicos a sus amigos?

5. ¿ _____ Compartimos _____ un sándwich, tú y yo? Es muy grande para una persona.

| hacer |
| beber |
| escribir |
| compartir |
| vender |

3 What are these people doing? Use elements from each box to write three complete sentences.

nosotras	aprender	el almuerzo
usted	compartir	una carta
yo	escribir	el español

1. *Answers will vary:* **Nosotras compartimos el almuerzo.**

2. *Answers will vary:* **Usted escribe una carta.**

3. *Answers will vary:* **Yo aprendo el español.**

Gramática B *Present Tense of -er and -ir Verbs*

¡AVANZA! **Goal:** Use the present tense to tell what people do.

---

❶ Everyone does something different. Underline the correct form of the verb.

1. Anastasia (<u>corre</u> / corres) todas las mañanas.

2. Yo (comes / <u>como</u>) un sándwich en la cafetería.

3. Mis amigos (hacemos / <u>hacen</u>) mucha tarea.

4. Penélope y yo (leen / <u>leemos</u>) un libro en la biblioteca.

5. ¿(<u>Bebes</u> / Beben) tú leche en el desayuno?

❷ Complete each sentence with the correct form of one of the following verbs: **beber, compartir, escribir,** or **vender**.

1. Nosotras _____*vendemos*_____ frutas muy ricas.

2. Roberto y Mario son amigos y siempre _____*comparten*_____ el almuerzo.

3. Jacinto y yo _____*escribimos*_____ correos electrónicos todos los días.

4. ¿Por qué el señor López no _____*bebe*_____ café?

❸ Look at the drawings below and write what these people eat and drink for breakfast every day. Follow the model.

la señora Pérez

Manuela y Tomás

modelo: Todos los días, la señora Pérez come huevos, pan y yogur y bebe café en el desayuno.

1. *Answers will vary:* **Todos los días, Manuela y Tomás comen cereal y beben** _____

leche en el desayuno. _____

Gramática C *Present Tense of -er and -ir Verbs*

| ¡AVANZA! | **Goal:** Use the present tense to tell what people do. |

1 Complete each sentence with the correct form of the appropriate verb.

hacer	beber	comer
leer	compartir	

1. Todas las mañanas, la señora Mendoza _____*bebe*_____ un café.

2. Mis amigas Lucía y Andrea _____*comen*_____ en la cafetería.

3. A las ocho de la noche, yo _____*hago*_____ la tarea para la clase de español.

4. ¿Cuál de estos libros _____*lee*_____ usted esta tarde?

5. Eduardo y yo _____*compartimos*_____ todo.

2 Write sentences to describe what these people are doing.

1. Julia / beber un refresco

Julia siempre bebe un refresco. _____

2. María y yo / escribir en el pizarrón

María y yo escribimos en el pizarrón. _____

3. tú / aprender el español

Tú aprendes el español. _____

4. yo / hacer mucha tarea

Yo hago mucha tarea. _____

3 You and your friends always buy lunch at the cafeteria. Write three complete sentences about what food and drink is in the cafeteria and what you and your friends eat and drink. Do you share anything?

Answers will vary: **En la cafetería hay sopa, sándwiches y hamburguesas.**

También venden jugos de frutas y refrescos. Jorge y Natalia beben jugo

de naranja. Todos nosotros comemos sándwiches y compartimos

papas fritas.

Integración: Hablar

Level 1, pp. 153-155
WB CD 02 track 01

There is very popular diner called "El Sándwich Divertido" near Alejandro's workplace, but it is always busy. He's very happy because he can now look at the menu online, and leave a phone message to order what he wants to have for lunch the next day, without waiting in line. Read the menu and listen to the phone message to find out what he likes to eat.

Fuente 1 Leer

Read the online menu for "El Sándwich Divertido."

El Sándwich Divertido

Menú de almuerzo

Comidas

Hamburguesa	$ 4.50
Sándwich de jamón y queso	$ 3.75
Papas fritas	$ 2.25
Sopa	$ 3.00

Bebidas

Refrescos	$ 0.75
Jugo de naranja	$ 0.60
Jugo de manzana	$ 0.70
Agua	$ 0.50

Fuente 2 Escuchar   CD 02 track 02

Then listen to Alejandro's voicemail message for "El Sándwich Divertido." Take notes.

_____

_____

Hablar

Based on the information given, what does Alejandro feel like having for lunch at "El Sándwich Divertido?"

modelo: Alejandro tiene ganas de... Porque no le gustan....También tiene ganas de...

Answers will vary: **Alejandro tiene ganas de comer sopa y un sándwich de jamón y queso porque es atlético. No le gustan las hamburguesas y no le gustan los refrescos. Alejandro tiene ganas de beber jugo.**

Nombre _____ Clase _____ Fecha _____

Integración: Escribir

Level 1, pp. 153-155
WB CD 02 track 03

Ramón plays in a soccer league. He logs onto an educational Web site called "Fútbol para Todos" and finds out that a soccer player must follow a nutritious, healthy diet like any other athlete. Ramón believes he doesn't have the kinds of food at home in order to have a healthy breakfast the next morning. However, his mom leaves a message for him saying it's not so. Read the ad and listen to the voicemail in order to write about what Ramón eats for breakfast.

Fuente 1 Leer

Read the ad on the soccer Web site.

> ▶ Comida que tienes que comer para jugar al fútbol.
>
> **¿Te gusta jugar al fútbol?** Muy bien, tienes que preparar un desayuno bueno. Tienes que comer yogur, cereal y beber mucho jugo de naranja, ¡no café! Necesitas beber jugo de naranja porque es nutritivo. También es bueno comer frutas en el desayuno. Tienes que comer manzanas. El desayuno es una comida muy importante en el día. Tienes que comer comida nutritiva para jugar al fútbol.

Fuente 2 Escuchar   *CD 02 track 04*

Listen to the voicemail message that Ramón's mother left on his answering machine. Take notes.

_____
_____
_____

Escribir

Based on the information provided, what kinds of food and drinks should Ramón have for breakfast? What kinds of food and drinks should he avoid?

modelo: Ramón tiene que comer... No...y no es bueno...

Answers will vary: **Ramón tiene que comer cereal y frutas. No es nutritivo**

comer galletas y no es bueno beber café.

_____
_____
_____
_____

UNIDAD 3 • Lección 1 Integración: Escribir

¡Avancemos! 1
Cuaderno: Práctica por niveles

Unidad 3, Lección 1
Integración: Escribir   **109**

Escuchar A

Level 1, pp. 160-161
WB CD 02 tracks 05-06

> **¡AVANZA!** **Goal:** Listen to find out about what some people eat.

1 Listen to Carla and take notes. Then, read each sentence and answer **cierto** (*true*) or **falso** (*false*).

C (F) **1.** Elena bebe leche.

(C) F **2.** A Carla le gusta el jugo de fruta.

C (F) **3.** Carla y Elena siempre comen hamburguesas.

(C) F **4.** A Elena le gustan más los refrescos.

C (F) **5.** El desayuno de Elena es nutritivo.

2 Listen to Natalia and take notes. Then, complete the sentences below.

1. Natalia come en _____la cafetería_____ hoy.

2. En la cafetería _____venden_____ sopa.

3. Natalia bebe _____jugo de naranja_____ .

4. A Natalia le gustan _____los sándwiches_____ de la cafetería.

5. Amalia no come con Natalia y los otros amigos porque no le gusta la comida _____nutritiva_____ .

Escuchar B

Level 1, pp. 160-161
WB CD 02 tracks 07-08

> ¡AVANZA! **Goal:** Listen to find out about what some people eat.

1 Listen to Andrés and take notes. Then, complete the following sentences.

1. El papá de Andrés siempre prepara _____ el desayuno _____ para la familia.

2. El papá de Andrés come _____ huevos y pan _____ todos los días.

3. A Andrés y al papá les gusta beber _____ jugo de naranja _____ .

4. La mamá de Andrés come _____ yogur con frutas _____ .

5. Andrés y la mamá comparten _____ bananas _____ .

2 Listen to Mrs. Márquez. Then, answer the questions below in complete sentences.

1. ¿A todos les gusta la comida de la señora Márquez?

Sí, a todos les gusta la comida de la señora Márquez.

2. ¿A quiénes les gusta el jugo de naranja?

A Verónica y al papá les gusta el jugo de naranja.

3. ¿Quién come frutas y cereal?

La señora Márquez come frutas y cereal.

4. ¿Qué comparten Andrea y la señora Márquez?

Muchas veces ellas comparten unas frutas.

Escuchar C

> ¡AVANZA! **Goal:** Listen to find out about what some people eat.

1 Listen to Lucía talk about her food. Take notes. Then list the foods she likes and she does not like.

Le gustan		No le gustan	
1. la leche	6.	el café	
2. el yogur	7.	los sándwiches de jamón	
3. los sándwiches de queso	8.	las naranjas	
4. las bananas	9.	las uvas	
5. las manzanas	10.	la sopa	

2 Listen to Santiago and take notes. Then, in complete sentences, answer the questions about what they like.

1. ¿Qué come Ana?

   Answers will vary: **Ana come cereal, huevos y sándwiches de queso.**

2. ¿Qué le gusta a Santiago?

   Answers will vary: **A Santiago le gustan los refrescos, el cereal y todos los**

   sándwiches.

3. ¿Qué comparten los dos amigos?

   Answers will vary: **Ellos comparten un sándwich de queso.**

UNIDAD 3 • Escuchar C
Lección 1

Unidad 3, Lección 1
Escuchar C

112

¡Avancemos! 1
Cuaderno: Práctica por niveles

Leer A

| ¡AVANZA! | **Goal:** Read about what types of food people like. |

The school cafeteria conducted a survey of what students like to eat and drink. Alfonsina and her friends listed the following.

¿Qué te gusta?

Nombre	¿Qué comes?	¿Qué bebes?
Alfonsina	hamburguesas y papas fritas	refrescos
Carla	yogur y frutas	jugos de frutas
Iván	papas fritas	refrescos
Santiago	sándwiches de jamón y papas fritas	leche

¿Comprendiste?

Answer the following questions in complete sentences.

1. ¿Qué bebidas le gustan a Alfonsina?

A Alfonsina le gustan los refrescos.

2. ¿Iván bebe bedidas nutritivas?

No, Iván no bebe bebidas nutritivas.

3. ¿Quién come comida nutritiva?

Carla come comida nutritiva.

4. ¿Qué comida les gusta más a los estudiantes?

A los estudiantes les gustan más las papas fritas.

¿Qué piensas?

1. ¿Es bueno comer papas fritas todos los días?

Answers will vary: **Sí, (No, no) es bueno comer papas fritas todos**

los días.

2. ¿Qué te gusta comer?

Answers will vary: **Me gusta comer comida nutritiva.**

Leer B

> **¡AVANZA!** **Goal:** Read about what types of food people like.

Nora is a school athlete who likes nutritious foods. She wrote this letter to the school newspaper about what she eats.

> Hola. Me llamo Nora. Ahora, contesto la pregunta de muchos chicos: ¿Qué comes tú? A mí me gusta la comida nutritiva. Es buena y rica. Nunca bebo café y nunca bebo refrescos porque no son buenos. Me gustan más la leche, el yogur y los jugos de frutas. Siempre como frutas, huevos, sopa y otras comidas nutritivas. No me gustan las papas fritas y no me gusta la pizza. Sí, son ricas, pero no son nutritivas.
>
> *Nora Ayala*

¿Comprendiste?

Read Nora's letter. Then complete the sentences below:

1. La pregunta de los chicos es: ¿ _____ Qué comes tú _____ ?

2. La comida nutritiva también _____ es rica _____ .

3. A Nora no le gusta beber _____ café y refrescos _____ .

4. A Nora no le gusta comer _____ papas fritas y pizza _____ .

5. Las papas fritas y la pizza son ricas pero no son _____ nutritivas _____ .

¿Qué piensas?

1. ¿Qué comida nutritiva es rica?

   Answers will vary: **El yogur es una comida nutritiva y rica.**

2. ¿Te gustan comidas que no son nutritivas? ¿Cuáles?

   Answers will vary: **Sí, me gustan comidas que no son nutritivas. Me gustan**

   la pizza y los refrescos.

Leer C

| ¡AVANZA! | **Goal:** Read about what types of food people like. |

Carmen wrote the following e-mail message to her friend, Carla.

> Carla:
> Tengo que comer comida más nutritiva (leche, huevos, jugo de naranja). Pero me gustan más otras comidas. Me gustan mucho las papas fritas y los refrescos. Siempre como papas fritas y bebo refrescos en el almuerzo. ¡Las papas fritas son muy ricas! Tú tienes una lista de comidas nutritivas en el cuaderno, ¿no? ¿Compartes la lista?
> -Carmen

¿Comprendiste?

Read Carmen's e-mail message. Then, read each sentence and circle **C** for **cierto** (*true*) or **F** for **falso** (*false*).

Ⓒ F **1.** A Carmen no le gusta la comida nutritiva.

C Ⓕ **2.** Es bueno comer papas fritas.

C Ⓕ **3.** Carmen siempre bebe leche.

C Ⓕ **4.** A Carmen le gusta más el jugo de naranja.

Ⓒ F **5.** Carla tiene en el cuaderno un menú de comidas nutritivas.

¿Qué piensas?

1. En tu opinión, ¿los chicos de hoy comen comida nutritiva?

Answers will vary: **No, los chicos de hoy no comen comida nutritiva porque comen mucha pizza y papas fritas.**

2. ¿Por qué necesita vender frutas la cafetería?

Answers will vary: **La cafetería necesita vender frutas porque son muy nutritivas.**

Escribir A

> ¡AVANZA! **Goal:** Write about what you eat and drink.

Step 1

Your school cafeteria wants to know about your eating habits. Complete the following chart.

¿Qué te gusta comer?	¿Qué te gusta beber?
1. *Answers will vary:* **hamburguesas**	1. *Answers will vary:* **refrescos**
2. **sándwiches**	2. **leche**
3. **queso**	3. **jugo**

Step 2

Write two sentences about whether you like healthy food and why. Use the verbs **hacer** and **comer**.

Answers will vary: **Me gusta la comida nutritiva porque es rica. Hago y**

como un desayuno nutritivo todos los días.

Step 3

Evaluate your writing using the information in the table.

Writing Criteria	Excellent	Good	Needs Work
Content	You include two sentences about whether you like healthy food and why.	You include one sentence aobut whether you like healthy food and why.	You do not include sentences about whether you like healthy food and why.
Communication	Most of your writing is organized and easy to follow.	Some of your writing is organized and easy to follow.	Your writing is disorganized and hard to follow.
Accuracy	Your writing has few mistakes in grammar and vocabulary.	Your writing has some mistakes in grammar and vocabulary.	Your writing has many mistakes in grammar and vocabulary.

Escribir A

UNIDAD 3
Lección 1

Unidad 3, Lección 1
Escribir A

116

¡Avancemos! 1
Cuaderno: Práctica por niveles

Escribir B

¡AVANZA! **Goal:** Write about what you eat and drink.

Step 1

What types of foods do you eat? Write your answers in the chart below.

Desayuno	Almuerzo
1. *Answers will vary:* **cereal**	1. *Answers will vary:* **sándwich**
2. huevos	2. hamburguesa
3. pan	3. yogur
4. frutas	4. sopa

Step 2

Write three complete sentences about foods that you like to eat during the day, and when.

modelo: Me gusta el cereal porque es nutritivo. Como cereal y leche en el desayuno.

Answers will vary: **Me gustan las frutas porque son buenas. Como frutas y cereal en el desayuno. El jamón es muy rico. Como un sándwich de jamón y queso en el almuerzo.**

Step 3

Evaluate your writing using the information in the table.

Writing Criteria	Excellent	Good	Needs Work
Content	You include three sentences about foods you like to eat and when.	You include two sentences about foods you like to eat and when.	You include one or fewer sentences about foods you like to eat and when.
Communication	Most of your paragraph is organized and easy to follow.	Parts of your paragraph are organized and easy to follow.	Your paragraph is disorganized and hard to follow.
Accuracy	You paragraph has few mistakes in grammar and vocabulary.	Your paragraph has some mistakes in grammar and vocabulary.	You paragraph has many mistakes in grammar and vocabulary.

Escribir C

> **¡AVANZA!** **Goal:** Write about what you eat and drink.

Step 1

Answer the following survey about what nutritious foods and beverages also taste good.

Comidas nutritivas y ricas	Bebidas nutritivas y ricas
1. *Answers will vary:* **huevos**	1. *Answers will vary:* **jugo de manzana**
2. **queso**	2. **jugo de naranja**
3. **pan**	3. **leche**
4. **yogur**	4. **agua**

Step 2

Use the survey above to write five complete sentences about a nutritious meal you prepare at your house. State who likes what foods and beverages.

Answers will vary: **Preparo un desayuno nutritivo. A mí me gustan los**

huevos, el queso y la leche. A mi papá le gustan el pan y el jugo de naranja.

A mi mamá le gustan las frutas y el jugo de manzana. A todos nosotros

nos gusta el agua.

Step 3

Evaluate your writing using the information in the table.

Writing Criteria	Excellent	Good	Needs Work
Content	You include five sentences about a nutritious meal you prepare.	You include three to four sentences about a nutritious meal you prepare.	You include two or fewer sentences about a nutritious meal you prepare.
Communication	Most of your paragraph is organized and easy to follow.	Parts of your paragraph are organized and easy to follow.	Your paragraph is disorganized and hard to follow.
Accuracy	You paragraph has few mistakes in grammar and vocabulary.	Your paragraph has some mistakes in grammar and vocabulary.	You paragraph has many mistakes in grammar and vocabulary.

Unidad 3, Lección 1
Escribir C

118

¡Avancemos! 1
Cuaderno: Práctica por niveles

UNIDAD 3
Lección 1

Escribir C

Cultura A

> **¡AVANZA!** **Goal:** Review cultural information about Puerto Rico.

1 **Puerto Rico** Read the following statements about Puerto Rico and circle *true* or *false*.

T (F) **1.** The capital of Puerto Rico is San José.

(T) F **2.** Puerto Rico is an island.

(T) F **3.** The currency of Puerto Rico is the U.S. dollar.

(T) F **4.** *Pinchos* are a typical food from Puerto Rico.

2 **Puerto Rican culture** Complete the following sentences.

1. The **coquí** is a (butterfly / frog) found throughout the Parque Nacional El Yunque.

2. You can find colonial-style houses painted with bright colors in the district known as (Nuevo / Viejo) San Juan.

3. A popular site in the Parque Nacional El Yunque is the (Cascada / Calle) de la Coca.

4. (Tostones / Pupusas) are a common side dish in Puerto Rico.

5. A popular cold treat in Puerto Rico is a(n) (alcapurria / piragua).

3 **The Plaza de Colón** Describe the Plaza de Colón. Where is it located? What can people see and do there? How would you spend an afternoon at this plaza?

Answers will vary.

_____

_____

_____

_____

_____

_____

_____

Nombre _____ Clase _____ Fecha _____

Cultura B

Level 1, pp. 160-161

> **¡AVANZA!** **Goal:** Review cultural information about Puerto Rico.

1 **Puerto Rico and El Salvador** Choose the multiple choice item that best completes each statement.

1. **La piragua** is a name for a Puerto Rican __b__ .

   a. river   **b.** cold dessert   **c.** dance

2. A typical Salvadorean food is the __a__ .

   a. pupusa   **b.** piragua   **c.** pincho

3. The capital of Puerto Rico is __c__ .

   a. San José   **b.** San Jacinto   **c.** San Juan

4. The currency of Puerto Rico is the __b__ .

   a. peso   **b.** dollar   **c.** bolívar

2 **In Puerto Rico** Complete the following sentences.

1. Puerto Ricans like to eat a food known as _____pinchos_____ , which are skewers of chicken or pork.

2. The _____coquí_____ is a tree frog that is found in Puerto Rico.

3. One of the waterfalls in the Parque Nacional El Yunque is called the Cascada de la _____Coca_____ .

4. You can find a statue of Christopher Columbus in _____The Plaza de Colón_____ .

5. _____Old/Viejo San Juan_____ is the colonial quarter of Puerto Rico's capital.

3 **Puerto Rican Cuisine** Create a menu for a Puerto Rican restaurant that serves traditional cooking, or **la cocina criolla**. Include an introduction sentence that describes the influences of la cocina criolla *and brief descriptions of each dish, along with prices.*

Answers will vary. _____

_____

_____

_____

_____

_____

UNIDAD 3 Lección 1 · Cultura B

Unidad 3, Lección 1
Cultura B
120

¡Avancemos! 1
Cuaderno: Práctica por niveles

Cultura C

> ¡AVANZA! **Goal:** Review cultural information about Puerto Rico.

1 **Activities in Puerto Rico** Write where you can do the following in Puerto Rico.

I can....	in/at
See waterfalls	the Parque Nacional El Yunque
Eat *pinchos*	barbecues and/or snack stands
See colonial-style houses	Viejo San Juan

2 **Puerto Rico** Answer the following questions about Puerto Rico.

1. What are the two official languages of Puerto Rico? The two official languages of Puerto Rico are English and Spanish.

2. What famous waterfall is in the Parque Nacional El Yunque? The Cascada de la Coca is in the Parque Nacional El Yunque.

3. Where do Puerto Ricans like to spend time with their families? Puerto Ricans like to visit parks or go to the beach with their families.

4. What is **la cocina criolla?** **La cocina criolla** is traditional Puerto Rican cooking, which is a blend of African, Spanish, and indigenous influences.

3 **Viejo San Juan** Puerto Rico has many beautiful places of interest. The island is known for its parks, colonial homes, waterfalls, and many other attractions. Write a paragraph about two places that you would most like to visit if you had the opportunity to go to Puerto Rico. Describe what you would do in each place and why you would like to visit it.

Answers will vary.

_____

_____

_____

_____

_____

Vocabulario A

> ¡AVANZA! **Goal:** Talk about family.

1 Look at Andrés' family tree. Then, read each sentence and circle **C** for **cierto** *(true)* or **F** for **falso** *(false)*.

C (F) **1.** Cecilia es la prima de Andrés.

(C) F **2.** Julián es el abuelo de Andrés y Luis.

C (F) **3.** Isabel es la tía de Mariela.

(C) F **4.** Javier es el tío de Luis.

(C) F **5.** Elena es la abuela de Cecilia y Mariela.

2 Look at the family tree above. Then, fill in each blank to complete the sentences.

1. Elena es _____la madre_____ de Armando.

2. Luis es _____el hermano_____ de Mariela.

3. Cecilia es _____la hermana_____ de Andrés.

4. Mariela y Luis son _____los primos_____ de Andrés y Cecilia.

3 Answer the following question in a complete sentence. Write all numbers in words. Follow the model.

modelo: Hoy es el doce de enero de dos mil siete.

1. ¿Cuál es la fecha de hoy?

Answers will vary: **Hoy es el once de febrero de dos mil siete.** _____

Vocabulario B

> ¡AVANZA! **Goal:** Talk about family.

1 Betania is talking about her family. Underline the word that best completes each sentence.

1. Mi padre es (el hijo / <u>el hermano</u>) de mi tía.

2. Mi tía es (<u>la madre</u> / la abuelo) de mi primo.

3. Mi prima es (la madrasta / <u>la hija</u>) de mi tía.

4. Mi abuelo es (el hermano / <u>el padre</u>) de mi tío.

2 Complete the following sentences with the family relationships.

1. El hermano de mi padre es mi _____ tío _____.

2. Mis abuelos tienen dos hijas. La tía de mi prima es mi _____ madre _____.

3. El padre de mi madre es mi _____ abuelo _____.

4. La hija del hermano de mi padre es mi _____ prima _____.

3 Answer the following questions in complete sentences. Write any numbers in words.

1. ¿Cuál es la fecha de hoy?

Answers will vary: **Hoy es el trece de febrero de dos mil siete.** _____

2. ¿Tienes un gato o un perro?

Answers will vary: **Sí, tengo dos gatos y un perro.** _____

¡Avancemos! 1
Cuaderno: Práctica por niveles

UNIDAD 3 • Vocabulario B
Lección 2

Unidad 3, Lección 2
Vocabulario B **123**

Vocabulario C

┌───┐
│ ¡AVANZA! **Goal:** Talk about family.   │
└───┘

1 Santiago is talking about his family. Fill in the correct answers.

Me llamo Santiago. Yo soy el hijo de Gloria Soriano. Mi

_____hermana_____ se llama Victoria; ella también es la hija de

Gloria Soriano. El hermano de mi madre se llama Federico López. Él

es mi _____tío_____ . Mi tío tiene tres hijos. Ellos son mis

_____primos_____ .

2 Use the chart below to answer the questions about Jorge's family.

Persona	Cumpleaños	Años
la madre de Jorge	17/10	60
el primo de Jorge	25/2	15

1. ¿Cuándo es el cumpleaños de la madre de Jorge?

El cumpleaños de la madre de Jorge es el diecisiete de octubre.

2. ¿Cuántos años tiene el primo de Jorge?

El primo de Jorge tiene quince años.

3 ¿Cuál es la fecha de nacimiento de estas personas? Write your answers in complete sentences. Write any numbers in words and use the information in parentheses.

1. Cristóbal Colón (August 26, 1451): La fecha de nacimiento de Cristóbal Colón

es el veintiséis de agosto de mil cuatrocientos cincuenta y uno.

2. Simón Bolívar (July 24, 1783): La fecha de nacimiento de Simón Bolívar es el

veinticuatro de julio de mil setecientos ochenta y tres.

UNIDAD 3 • Vocabulario C
Lección 2

124 Unidad 3, Lección 2
Vocabulario C

¡Avancemos! 1
Cuaderno: Práctica por niveles

Gramática A *Possessive adjectives*

> **¡AVANZA!** **Goal:** Use possessive adjectives to talk about family.

1 Alejandro talks about family. Underline the word that best completes each sentence.

1. Tengo tres hermanos. (<u>Mis</u> / Sus) hermanos se llaman Miguel, Luis y Pedro.

2. Los padres de Javier son jóvenes. (Sus / <u>Su</u>) madre tiene 35 años.

3. Mis hermanos y yo hablamos con los abuelos todos los domingos. (Sus / <u>Nuestros</u>) abuelos son muy buenos.

4. Tú vives con (<u>tus</u> / sus) padres.

5. A María y a Néstor les gustan los primos. (<u>Su</u> / Sus) prima mayor se llama Ariana.

2 Change the following possessive adjectives and their nouns from singular to plural.

modelo: mi hermano / **mis** hermano**s**

1. nuestro primo / _____ nuestros primos _____

2. su tío / _____ sus tíos _____

3. mi amiga / _____ mis amigas _____

4. tu hermano mayor / _____ tus hermanos mayores _____

3 Look at the drawings. Then, write complete sentences.

modelo: el hermano de Sandra: Su hermano practica deportes.

1. la prima de Julio: <u>Su prima escribe correos electrónicos.</u>

2. los primos de Felipe: <u>Sus primos corren.</u>

Gramática B *Possessive adjectives*

> **¡AVANZA!** **Goal:** Use possessive adjectives to talk about family.

1 Choose the word that best completes each sentence.

1. Los padres de Inés tienen tres hijos. __b__ hijo mayor estudia arte.
   a. Sus   b. Su   c. Tus

2. Tú tienes una abuela muy joven. __a__ dos abuelas son jóvenes.
   a. Tus   b. Tu   c. Sus

3. Mis hermanos y yo tenemos dos primos. __c__ primos viven en Boston.
   a. Nuestro   b. Nuestras   c. Nuestros

4. Inés tiene una familia muy grande. __c__ familia es de Miami.
   a. Tu   b. Sus   c. Su

2 Use possessive adjectives to write complete sentences about Miguel's family. Follow the model.

modelo: tú / padres / ser / simpáticos: Tus padres son simpáticos.

1. yo / hermanos / ser / altos Mis hermanos son altos.
2. usted / tías / vivir / lejos Sus tías viven lejos.
3. nosotros / abuelo / llamarse / Julián Nuestro abuelo se llama Julián.
4. Andrés y Cecilia / hermana / tener / cinco años Su hermana tiene cinco años.

3 Answer the following questions in complete sentences.

1. ¿Cuál es la fecha de nacimiento de tu padre?
   Answers will vary: **Su fecha de nacimiento es el dos de abril mil novecientos setenta.**

2. ¿Cuántos años tienes?
   Answers will vary: **Tengo quince años.**

4. ¿Cuál es tu fecha de nacimiento?
   Answers will vary: **Mi fecha de nacimiento es el diecisiete de octubre de mil novecientos noventa y cuatro.**

Gramática C *Possessive adjectives*

Level 1, pp. 169-173

> **¡AVANZA!** **Goal:** Use possessive adjectives to talk about family.

❶ Julián describes his family. Complete the paragraph using possessive adjectives.

Las hijas de mi tía son **1.** _____ mis _____ primas. Una

se llama Noemí y **2.** _____ sus _____ hermanas se llaman

Rosario y Débora. **3.** _____ Nuestras _____ madres son hermanas.

4. _____ Nuestro _____ abuelo es joven. Él tiene cincuenta y cinco

años y **5.** _____ su _____ cumpleaños es el veinte de junio.

❷ Describe your own family members or those of a family you know by answering the following questions.

1. ¿Quién es atlético(a)?

Answers will vary: **Mi hermana menor es atlética.**

2. ¿Quién prepara la cena?

Answers will vary: **Mi madre y mi padre preparan la cena.**

3. ¿Quiénes tienen catorce años o más?

Answers will vary: **Mis padres y yo tenemos catorce años o más.**

4. ¿Quién tiene un cumpleaños en junio, julio o agosto?

Answers will vary: **Mi tío tiene un cumpleaños en julio.**

5. ¿Quién es la persona menor en la familia? ¿Cuándo es su cumpleaños?

Answers will vary: **Mi primo es la persona menor. Su cumpleaños es el dos**

de enero.

❸ Write three complete sentences to describe your family or a family you know. Use **mi(s)**, **su(s)** and **nuestro(s)** or **nuestra(s)**.

1. *Answers will vary:* **Nuestros primos son muy divertidos.**

2. *Answers will vary:* **Mi tía se llama Amelia y tiene cuarenta y seis años.**

3. *Answers will vary:* **Su hermano Fernando es muy atlético.**

Gramática A   *Comparatives*

> ┃AVANZA!┃ **Goal:** Make comparisons.

① Draw a line from the word pair on the left to the appropriate comparison on the right.

1. aprender / enseñar — **a.** más grande que
2. una ventana / un lápiz — **b.** menos rico que
3. un café / una pizza — **c.** tan importante como
4. Rafael Tufiño / yo — **d.** más artístico que

② Use the comparatives **más... que, menos... que**, **tan... como** and **tanto como** to complete the following sentences.

1. Luisa es _____ más _____ joven _____ que _____ su abuela.

2. Trabajar es _____ menos _____ divertido _____ que _____ pasar un rato con los amigos.

3. Soy atlético; me gusta jugar al fútbol _____ tanto _____ _____ como _____ correr.

4. Beber leche es _____ tan _____ nutritivo _____ como _____ comer yogur.

③ Answer the following question in a complete sentence.

1. ¿Te gusta la clase de matemáticas tanto como la clase de español? ¿Por qué?

   Answers will vary: **Sí, (No, no) me gusta la clase de matemáticas tanto**

   como la clase de español porque aprender español es tan(más) interesante

   como(que) aprender matemáticas.

Gramática B *Comparatives*

> **¡AVANZA!** **Goal:** Make comparisons.

1 Read each sentence and fill in the blank with the correct answer from the choices given.

1. Roberta tiene trece años y su hermano tiene once años. Su hermano es __c__ que ella.

    a. peor　　　　　　　　**b.** mayor　　　　　　　　**c.** menor

2. Roberta tiene tres hermanos mayores. Ellos tienen __a__ que ella.

    a. más años　　　　　　　**b.** menos años　　　　　　**c.** tantos años

3. Roberta tiene trece años. Enrique tiene veinte años y Sandra también tiene veinte años.

    Sandra es __a__ de Roberta.

    a. la hermana mayor　　　　**b.** la hermana menor　　　　**c.** la madre

2 Use comparatives to complete the following sentences.

1. estudiar / aprender / tan importante como

    Estudiar es tan importante como aprender.

2. la clase de matemáticas / la clase de arte / tan interesante como

    La clase de matemáticas es tan interesante como la clase de arte.

3. preparar la cena / trabajar después de las clases / menos difícil que

    Preparar la cena es menos difícil que trabajar después de las clases.

4. hablar por teléfono / mirar la televisión / tan interesante como

    Hablar por teléfono es tan interesante como mirar la televisión.

3 Use a comparative expression to describe what these people like more. Follow the model.

    modelo:　A mi papá le gusta practicar deportes más que trabajar.

1. ¿Qué le gusta más a tu amigo: el yogur o la leche?

    Answers will vary: A mi amigo le gusta más la leche que el yogur.

2. ¿Qué le gustan más a tu amiga: los gatos o los perros?

    Answers will vary: A mi amiga le gustan los gatos más que los perros.

UNIDAD 3
Lección 2 • Gramática B

Gramática C *Comparatives*

¡AVANZA!	**Goal:** Make comparisons.

1 Your teacher has asked you to compare activities and things in your life. Use a comparative expression with the word in parentheses to complete each sentence. *Answers will vary:*

1. Mirar la televisión es _____**tan divertido como**_____ montar en bicicleta. (divertido)

2. La clase de ciencias es _____**más fácil que**_____ la clase de matemáticas. (fácil)

3. El yogur es _____**menos rico que**_____ un refresco. (rico)

4. Un refresco es _____**menos nutritivo que**_____ el yogur. (nutritivo)

2 Re-write these statements using a different comparative expression.

1. Estudiar es más importante que practicar deportes.

   Answers will vary: **Estudiar es tan importante como practicar deportes.**

2. No preguntar es más inteligente que preguntar.

   Answers will vary: **No preguntar es menos inteligente que preguntar.**

3. El desayuno es menos nutritivo que la cena.

   Answers will vary: **El desayuno es tan nutritivo como la cena.**

4. Los gatos son tan malos como los perros.

   Answers will vary: **Los gatos son peores que los perros.**

3 Use comparative expressions to describe what your friends like more.

1. *Answers will vary:* **A mi amiga Lidia le gustan las frutas más que las**

   hamburguesas.

2. *Answers will vary:* **A mis amigos Carlos y Alex les gusta escuchar música**

   más que estudiar.

3. *Answers will vary:* **A Isabel le gusta practicar deportes más que descansar.**

Integración: Hablar

Level 1, pp. 177-179
WB CD 02 track 11

Juan is very happy. The new school year has begun and he has a Spanish teacher that is related to the recently elected president of the country. The whole school is interested in learning more about the Spanish teacher, so she writes about her family on the school Web site, and the principal talks about her over the loudspeaker on the first day of the school year. Read the Web article and listen to the announcement to find out how she is related to the president.

Fuente 1 Leer

Read the school newspaper article...

FAMILIA DEL PRESIDENTE

¡Hola! Me llamo María Cristina, soy la maestra de español. Me gusta enseñar el español en la escuela. Yo no soy la hija del presidente de nuestro país. Yo soy un año y ocho meses mayor que la hija del presidente. Pero ella y yo somos familia del presidente. El padre de ella es hijo del padre de mi padre. Sí, el presidente es hijo de mi abuelo.

Fuente 2 Escuchar   CD 02 track 12

Listen to the principal's loudspeaker message on the first day of the school year. Take notes.

_____

_____

_____

_____

Hablar

What is the relationship between María Graciela and María Cristina? Explain.

modelo: María Graciela es... María Cristina es..., porque el presidente es...

Answers may vary: **María Graciela es la hija del presidente. María Cristina es la prima de María Graciela, porque el presidente es el tío de María Cristina.**

Integración: Escribir

Today, Mr. Juan Márquez has become the oldest man in the country. Newspapers and radio shows are talking about him. Everyone wants to know more about him; how he spends his time, when he was born, who his family is, and more! Read the newspaper article and listen to the radio show to find out how old he is.

Fuente 1 Leer

Read the newspaper article about Juan Márquez, the oldest man in the country.

¡Feliz cumpleaños señor Márquez!

Su nombre es Juan Márquez. Es mayor que usted, es mayor que yo y mayor que todos en el país. Sí, ¡es de nuestro país! Su familia es muy grande y tiene hermanos, hermanas y primos. Pero todos tienen menos años que él. Hoy todos están emocionados, porque hoy es 23 de enero y es su cumpleaños. Ahora él es el hombre más viejo del país. ¡Feliz cumpleaños señor Márquez!

Fuente 2 Escuchar   CD 02 track 14

Listen to the radio talk show about señor Juan. Take notes.

_____

_____

_____

_____

Escribir

How old is Mr. Márquez? Explain your answer.

modelo: El señor Márquez tiene..., porque su fecha...Y hoy es...

Answers will vary: **El señor Márquez tiene... años porque su fecha de**

nacimiento es el veintitrés de enero de mil novecientos dos. Y hoy es...

_____

_____

_____

_____

_____

UNIDAD 3 • Integración:
Lección 2   Escribir

Unidad 3, Lección 2
132 Integración: Escribir

¡Avancemos! 1
Cuaderno: Práctica por niveles

Escuchar A

> ¡AVANZA! **Goal:** Listen to find out about family relationships.

1 Listen to Enrique and take notes. Then, match the names with the family relationship that each person has to Enrique.

1. Alicia y Jorge   a. primos
2. Norma   b. abuelos
3. Raúl y Julia   c. padres
4. Sofía   d. tía
5. Ernesto y Luisa   e. hermana

2 Listen to Sofía and take notes. Then, complete the sentences below.

1. Sofía es _____menor_____ que su hermano.

2. Sofía y su familia van a Puerto Rico en _____diciembre_____ .

3. A Sofía le gusta estar con _____sus primos_____ más que con sus amigos.

4. El primo _____mayor_____ de Sofía es inteligente.

Escuchar B

Level 1, pp. 184-185
WB CD 02 tracks 17-18

> ¡AVANZA! **Goal:** Listen to find out about family relationships.

1 Listen to Jimena and take notes. Then, indicate which family members Jimena has and doesn't have by putting the following words in the correct column.

abuelos	padre	hermanos	tía	primos
madre	madrastra	abuelas	hermana	primas

Tiene	No tiene…
padre	madre
madrastra	hermanos
hermana	abuelos
abuelas	primos
tía	
primas	

2 Listen to Enrique and take notes. Then, answer the following questions.

1. ¿Cómo es Blanca?

Blanca es más divertida que los amigos de Enrique.

2. ¿Qué le gusta hacer a Blanca?

A Blanca le gusta leer, tocar la guitarra y preparar la comida.

3. ¿Qué hacen los primos con los abuelos?

Los dos preparan la comida, miran la televisión y pasean con los abuelos.

4. ¿Cómo es la comida de su abuela?

La comida de su abuela es tan buena como la comida de su padre.

Escuchar C

> ¡AVANZA! **Goal:** Listen to find out about family relationships.

1 Listen to Mariano and take notes. Then explain how the following people are related to him by filling in the blank with the appropriate word.

1. Javier es su _____ primo _____

2. Teresa es su _____ abuela _____

3. Diana es su _____ tía _____

4. Carmen y Felipe son sus _____ padres _____

5. Tomás es su _____ hermano _____

6. Anita es su _____ hermana _____

2 Listen to Lucía and take notes. Then answer the questions below in complete sentences.

1. ¿Por qué a Lucía le gusta pasar un rato con sus primos?

   Le gusta pasar un rato con sus primos porque son más divertidos que su hermana.

2. ¿Es Lucía mayor que sus primos?

   No, Lucía es menor que sus primos.

3. ¿Es la hermana de Lucía mayor que sus primos?

   Sí, la hermana de Lucía es mayor que sus primos.

4. ¿Qué les gusta hacer a los primos de Lucía?

   Answers will vary: A los primos de Lucía les gusta andar en patineta tanto

   como montar en bicicleta.

5. ¿Cómo es la hermana de Lucía?

   La hermana de Lucía es simpática pero es más seria que Lucía.

Leer A

Level 1, pp. 184-185

> **¡AVANZA!** **Goal:** Read about a family reunion.

The following is an invitation to a family reunion.

Reunión de la familia Serrano
¡Atención a todos los Serrano!

Nuestra reunión anual es el 29 de julio a las 5:00 en el Club campestre. En la reunión hay más personas que antes... ¡porque en abril y mayo hay dos nacimientos! Como siempre, en la reunión hay mucha comida y música. Los abuelos Serrano, Irma y Juan, van a la reunión con sus 9 hijos. Y los 9 hijos llevan a todos sus hijos. ¡Son más de 40 chicos! Este año la reunión es muy especial porque también es el día del cumpleaños de Juan.

Tíos, primos, hermanos, abuelos... ¡todos a la reunión!

¿Comprendiste?

Read the Serrano family invitation. Then, read each sentence and circle **C** for **cierto** (*true*) or **F** for **falso** (*false*).

C (F) **1.** La reunión es el veintiséis de julio.

(C) F **2.** La familia Serrano es más grande que antes.

(C) F **3.** Irma es abuela de más de cuarenta chicos.

C (F) **4.** Juan no tiene hijos.

(C) F **5.** El veintinueve de julio es el cumpleaños de Juan.

¿Qué piensas?

¿Qué te gusta hacer con tus amigos(as)?

Answers will vary: Me gusta pasar un rato con mis amigos después de las clases.

Leer B

> ▶¡AVANZA! **Goal:** Read about family.

Paula wrote a letter to her friend Marisol, explaining why she can't go to her birthday.

Marisol:

No voy a tu cumpleaños porque tengo que estar con mis abuelos. Mis abuelos viven lejos en Puerto Rico, y llegan el día de tu cumpleaños, el primero de septiembre. Todos los años, llegan en diciembre, pero el mes de septiembre les gusta más que diciembre. Mis tíos y mis padres están muy emocionados porque llegan sus padres. También mis primos están contentos. Yo estoy tan contenta como ellos, pero también estoy triste porque no voy a tu cumpleaños. Salimos y bebemos un refresco el día después de tu cumpleaños... ¿Te gusta mi idea?

Tu amiga,

Paula

¿Comprendiste?

Read Paula's letter. Then, complete the following sentences.

1. Paula no va al cumpleaños porque tiene que estar con sus _____abuelos_____ .

2. Los tíos y los padres de Paula están muy emocionados porque llegan

   _____sus_____ padres.

3. Los primos de Paula están _____tan_____ contentos _____como_____ ella.

4. Paula también está _____triste_____ porque no va al cumpleaños.

5. A los abuelos de Paula les gusta el mes de _____diciembre_____ menos que el mes

   de septiembre.

¿Qué piensas?

¿Te gusta pasar un rato con tu familia? ¿Por qué?

Answers will vary: **Me gusta pasar un rato con mi familia porque**

es divertido.

Leer C

> ¡AVANZA! **Goal:** Read about family.

Rubén and Emilio are both going to Puerto Rico. They talk about their families.

> Hola Emilio: Tengo que hablar con mis padres pero no hay problema.
> A mis padres les gusta descansar más que trabajar... ¡ Y en Puerto Rico,
> ellos descansan mucho! Pero, ¿cuándo vamos a Puerto Rico? Yo tengo
> ganas de ir en marzo, cuando hace frío en Nueva York. ¿Te gusta la idea?
> Rubén
>
> ----
> >Hola Rubén: ¿Cómo estás? ¿Cómo está tu familia? Tienes que hablar con
> >ellos sobre cuándo vamos a Puerto Rico. No escribo más ahora porque
> >mi madre y yo tenemos que preparar la cena: ¡una pizza de jamón! Me
> >gusta la pizza de mi madre más que la pizza de la cafetería.
> >Emilio

¿Comprendiste?

Read the e-mails. Then answer the following questions in complete sentences.

1. ¿Qué les gusta hacer a los padres de Rubén? ¿Qué hacen en Puerto Rico?

A los padres de Rubén les gusta descansar más que trabajar. En Puerto Rico

descansan mucho.

2. ¿Por qué no escribe más ahora Emilio?

Emilio no escribe más ahora porque tiene que preparar la cena.

3. ¿Qué le gusta más a Emilio?

A Emilio le gusta la pizza de su madre más que la pizza de la cafetería.

4. ¿Cuándo tiene ganas de ir Rubén a Puerto Rico?

Rubén tiene ganas de ir a Puerto Rico en marzo.

¿Qué piensas?

1. ¿Es divertido ir a otro país con un amigo?

Sí, (No, no) es muy divertido ir a otro país con un amigo.

2. ¿Te gusta ir a otro país con amigos más que con tu familia?

Sí, (No, no) me gusta ir con amigos más que con mi familia.

Escribir A

> ¡AVANZA! **Goal:** Write about family.

Step 1

Complete this chart using information about yourself and someone important in your life. Write out all dates in words.

Nombre	Fecha de nacimiento
Answers will vary: Chris	*Answers will vary:* **el doce de abril de mil novecientos noventa y uno**
Answers will vary: Emily	*Answers will vary:* **el catorce de mayo de dos mil uno**

Step 2

Use the information from the chart above to write two sentences about your birth date and the birth date of someone important in your life.

Answers will vary: **Mi fecha de nacimiento es el doce de abril de mil**

novecientos noventa y uno. El catorce de mayo de dos mil uno es

importante porque es la fecha de nacimiento de mi hermana menor.

Step 3

Evaluate your writing using the information in the table.

Writing Criteria	Excellent	Good	Needs Work
Content	Your have included two sentences about your birth date and the birth date of someone important to you.	Your have included one sentences about your birth date and the birth date of someone important to you.	Your have not included sentences about your birth date and the birth date of someone important to you.
Communication	Most of your response is organized and easy to follow.	Parts of your response are organized and easy to follow.	Your response is disorganized and hard to follow.
Accuracy	Your response has few mistakes in grammar and vocabulary.	Your response has some mistakes in grammar and vocabulary.	Your response has many mistakes in grammar and vocabulary.

Nombre _____ Clase _____ Fecha _____

Escribir B

Level 1, pp. 184-185

 Goal: Write about family.

Step 1

Complete this chart. Write the dates in words.

Tu fecha de nacimiento	Fecha de nacimiento de una persona de tu familia	Fecha de nacimiento de tu amigo(a)
Answers will vary: **el veintisiete de agosto de mil novecientos ochenta y nueve**	*Answers will vary:* **el veintidós de febrero de mil novecientos sesenta y dos**	*Answers will vary:* **el treinta y uno de enero de mil novecientos ochenta y ocho**

Step 2

Write four sentences about the dates above and why they are important to you.

Answers will vary: **Mi fecha de nacimiento es el veintisiete de agosto de mil**

novecientos ochenta y nueve. La fecha de nacimiento de mi madre es el veintidós

de febrero de mil novecientos sesenta y dos. La fecha de nacimiento de mi amiga

es el treinta y uno de enero de mil novecientos ochenta y ocho. Son fechas

importantes porque son los cumpleaños de mi madre y mi mejor amiga.

Step 3

Evaluate your writing using the information in the table.

Writing Criteria	Excellent	Good	Needs Work
Content	Your paragraph describes why three dates are important to you.	Your paragraph describes why two dates are important to you.	Your paragraph describes why one date is important to you.
Communication	Most of your paragraph is organized and easy to follow.	Parts of your paragraph are organized and easy to follow.	Your paragraph is disorganized and hard to follow.
Accuracy	Your paragraph has few mistakes in grammar and vocabulary.	Your paragraph has some mistakes in grammar and vocabulary.	Your paragraph has many mistakes in grammar and vocabulary.

UNIDAD 3 • Escribir B Lección 2

Escribir C

> ¡AVANZA! **Goal:** Write about family.

Step 1

Complete the chart below. Write in the missing months. In the middle column, write the name and birthday of the family member or friend who has a birthday that month. Also write the relationship between that person and you. In the third column, write the year of birth in words.
Answers will vary.

Mes	Cumpleaños	Año de nacimiento
febrero	**18 de febrero: Mi hermana, María**	**mil novecientos noventa y siete**
marzo	**28 de marzo: Mi tío, Luis**	**mil novecientos cincuenta y uno**
abril	**14 de abril: Mi madre, Lucía**	**mil novecientos sesenta y nueve**
mayo	**7 de mayo: Mi abuela, Luisa**	**mil novecientos treinta y cuatro**
junio	**4 de junio: Mi amigo, Pedro**	**mil novecientos noventa**

Step 2

Write about the chart above in six complete sentences. Include family relationships.

Answers will vary: **La fecha de nacimiento de mi abuela es el siete de mayo de mil novecientos treinta y cuatro. Mis abuelos tienen una hija. Su cumpleaños es el catorce de abril. Mi madre se llama Lucía. Mi madre tiene un hermano, mi tío Luis. Su cumpleaños es el veintiocho de marzo.**

Step 3

Evaluate your writing using the information in the table.

Writing Criteria	Excellent	Good	Needs Work
Content	Your paragraph includes many details and new vocabulary.	Your paragraph includes some details and new vocabulary.	Your paragraph includes little information or new vocabulary.
Communication	Most of your paragraph is clear.	Some of your paragraph is clear.	Your paragraph is not clear.
Accuracy	Your paragraph has few mistakes in grammar and vocabulary.	Your paragraph has some mistakes in grammar and vocabulary.	Your paragraph has many mistakes in grammar and vocabulary.

UNIDAD 3 Lección 2 • Escribir C

Cultura A

> **¡AVANZA!** **Goal:** Review cultural information about Puerto Rico.

1 **Puerto Rico** Read the following statements about Puerto Rico and circle *true* or *false*.

T (F) **1.** The capital of Puerto Rico is San José.

(T) F **2.** **Sobremesa** is when families spend time together after a meal.

(T) F **3.** The currency of Puerto Rico is the U.S. dollar.

(T) F **4.** Puerto Rico is a commonwealth of the United States.

T (F) **5.** In Puerto Rico there are only two political parties.

T (F) **6.** Puerto Rican elections generally have a low voter turnout.

2 **Puerto Rico and Peru** Choose the correct word to complete the following sentences.

1. The fifteenth birthday celebration for young women in Puerto Rico is called (**fiesta** / **quinceañero**).

2. The artist who painted many portraits called *Goyita* is (Picasso / Rafael Tufiño).

3. The *Goyita* paintings are portraits of the artist's (mother / grandmother).

4. Peruvian girls often have fourteen or fifteen (dances / maids of honor) at their fifteenth birthday celebration.

3 **Quinceañeras** Describe a **quinceañera.** Compare this celebration with the *Sweet Sixteen* celebration in the United States. How are they similar or different? What are some traditional activities for each?

Answers will vary:

_____

_____

_____

_____

_____

_____

_____

Unidad 3, Lección 2
Cultura A
142

¡Avancemos! 1
Cuaderno: Práctica por niveles

UNIDAD 3 • Cultura A
Lección 2

Cultura B

¡AVANZA! **Goal:** Review cultural information about Puerto Rico.

1 **About Puerto Rico** Choose the multiple choice item that best completes each statement.

1. During the elections in Puerto Rico a __a__ is elected.

   a. governor **b.** president **c.** prime minister

2. The political party that wants Puerto Rico elected as the 51st state is __c__

   a. Independista Puertorriqueño **b.** **Popular Democrático** **c.Nuevo Progresista**

3. Puerto Rico is a(n) __b__

   a. peninsula **b.** island **c.** bay

2 **Celebrations and art** Answer the following questions about Puerto Rico and Peru in complete sentences.

1. Who does artist Rafael Tufiño represent in his series of paintings called *Goyita?*

   He represents his mother.

2. How does Peruvian artist Fernando Sayán Polo's painting *Niña campesina sonriente* reflect his country? It shows a girl from the Andean region of Peru who is wearing traditional

   clothing.

3. What is a **quinceañera?** The **quinceañera** is a fifteenth birthday celebration for Latin

   American girls.

4. What are three **quinceañera** traditions? Answers will vary: Some traditions include:

   a toast, dancing a waltz, a banquet, and having maids of honor.

3 It is very important to Puerto Ricans to vote and participate in the elections. Briefly compare elections and political parties in Puerto Rico and in the United States, and explain why it is important to vote.

   Answers will vary.

   _____
   _____
   _____
   _____
   _____

UNIDAD 3 Lección 2 • Cultura B

Cultura C

> **¡AVANZA!** **Goal:** Review cultural information about Puerto Rico.

1 **Political parties** In the chart below, briefly describe what each political party supports.

Name of political party	In favor of...
Popular Democrático	the current political status
Independentista Puertorriqueño	independence for Puerto Rico
Nuevo Progresista	making Puerto Rico the 51st state of the United States

2 **Puerto Rico** Answer the following questions about Puerto Rico.

1. What are young women called when they have their fifteenth birthday?

They are called **quinceañeras.**

2. Instead of having a fifteenth birthday celebration, which birthday do many Puerto Rican girls celebrate with a large party?

Many Puerto Rican girls have a large sixteenth birthday celebration instead.

3. Who painted the *Goyita* portraits and who is represented in the paintings?

Rafael Tufiño painted the *Goyita* portratits of his mother.

3 **Plan a quinceañero** Write an invitation for a **quinceañero.** In your invitation, describe what will take place at the party. What kind of food will be served and what kind of music will be played? What kinds of traditional activities will be part of the celebration? Also include important details, such as when and where it will take place.

Answers will vary. _____

_____

_____

_____

_____

_____

_____

_____

Comparación cultural: ¿Qué comemos?

Lectura y escritura

After reading the paragraphs about how María Luisa, Silvia, and José enjoy a Sunday meal, write a paragraph about a typical Sunday meal. Use the information on your mind map to write sentences, and then write a paragraph that describes your typical Sunday meal.

Step 1

Complete the mind map describing as many details as possible about your Sunday meals.

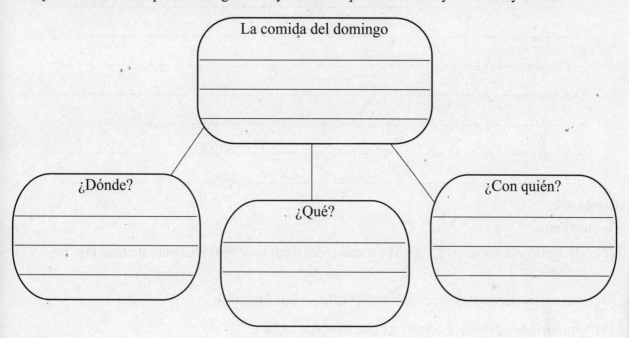

La comida del domingo

¿Dónde?

¿Qué?

¿Con quién?

Step 2

Now take the details from the mind map and write a sentence for each topic on the mind map.

_____
_____
_____
_____
_____
_____
_____
_____
_____

¡Avancemos! 1
Cuaderno: Práctica por niveles

UNIDAD 3 • Comparación
Lección 2 cultural

Unidad 3
Comparación cultural: ¿Qué comemos? **145**

Comparación cultural: ¿Qué comemos?

Level 1, pp. 186-187

Lectura y escritura (continued)

Step 3

Now write your paragraph using the sentences you wrote as a guide. Include an introduction sentence and use possessive adjectives such as **mi, mis, su, sus** to write about your typical Sunday meal.

_____

_____

_____

_____

_____

_____

_____

Checklist

Be sure that…

☐ all the details about your typical Sunday meal from your mind map are included in the paragraph;

☐ you use details to describe each aspect of your Sunday meal;

☐ you include possessive adjectives and new vocabulary.

Rubric

Evaluate your writing using the rubric below.

Writing criteria	Excellent	Good	Needs Work
Content	Your paragraph includes many details about your typical Sunday meal.	Your paragraph includes some details about your typical Sunday meal.	Your paragraph includes few details about your typical Sunday meal.
Communication	Most of your paragraph is organized and easy to follow.	Parts of your paragraph are organized and easy to follow.	Your paragraph is disorganized and hard to follow.
Accuracy	Your paragraph has few mistakes in grammar and vocabulary.	Your paragraph has some mistakes in grammar and vocabulary.	Your paragraph has many mistakes in grammar and vocabulary.

Unidad 3
Comparación cultural: ¿Qué comemos?

146

¡Avancemos! 1
Cuaderno: Práctica por niveles

UNIDAD 3 • Comparación cultural
Lección 2

Comparación cultural: ¿Qué comemos?

Level 1, pp. 186-187

Compara con tu mundo

Now write a comparison about your typical Sunday meal and that of one of the students on page 187. Organize your comparison by topics. First, compare the place where you have your Sunday meal, then the food you eat, and lastly with whom you eat.

Step 1

Use the table to organize your comparison by topics. Write details for each topic about your typical Sunday meal and that of the student you chose.

Categorías	Mi almuerzo/cena	El almuerzo/cena de _____
¿Dónde?		
¿Qué?		
¿Con quién?		

Step 2

Now use the details from the table to write a comparison. Include an introduction sentence and write about each category. Use possessive adjectives such as **mi, mis, su, sus** to describe your typical Sunday meal and that of the student you chose.

_____
_____
_____
_____
_____
_____
_____
_____
_____

UNIDAD 3 • Comparación
Lección 2 cultural

Vocabulario A

> ¡AVANZA! **Goal:** Talk about clothes.

---

1 You need to get dressed. Place an "x" next to those items that go on the upper part of your body.

_X_ la chaqueta	____ los zapatos
____ los pantalones	____ los jeans
_X_ la blusa	_X_ la camiseta
_X_ el sombrero	_X_ la camisa
____ los calcetines	____ los pantalones cortos

2 There are many things in the store in a variety of colors. Choose the correct word in parentheses to complete the following sentences.

1. A mí me gustan las camisas (rojas / azul) como una manzana.

2. El vestido es tan (negro / blanco) como la leche.

3. Esa camisa es del color de una banana. Es (amarilla / negro).

4. Muchas veces los jeans son (azules / anaranjados).

5. En Estados Unidos el dólar es (verde / marrón).

3 Answer the following question in a complete sentence.

1. ¿Qué estación te gusta más?

   Answers will vary: **Me gusta más el otoño.**

2. ¿Qué ropa te gusta comprar en el verano?

   Answers will vary: **Me gusta comprar un vestido.**

3. ¿Qué ropa te gusta comprar en el otoño?

   Answers will vary: **Me gusta comprar un gorro.**

Unidad 4, Lección 1
Vocabulario A

148

¡Avancemos! 1
Cuaderno: Práctica por niveles

UNIDAD 4 • Vocabulario A
Lección 1

Vocabulario B

> ¡AVANZA! **Goal:** Talk about clothes.

---

1 **¿Tienes frío o tienes calor?** In the left column, write three cold weather clothing items. In the right column, write three warm weather clothing items. Use the words from the box.

Frío	Calor
la chaqueta	los pantalones cortos
los calcetines	la blusa
el gorro	el vestido

> los pantalones cortos
> la chaqueta
> la blusa
> los calcetines
> el vestido
> el gorro

2 Norma and Laura tend to be opposites. Complete the sentences below.

1. A Norma le gusta la primavera pero a Laura le gusta _____el otoño_____ .

2. A Laura le gusta una camisa blanca pero a Norma le gusta más una

   camisa _____negra_____ .

3. Cuando Norma tiene calor Laura _____tiene frío_____ .

4. A Laura le gusta la ropa vieja pero a Norma le gusta la ropa _____nueva_____ .

3 Answer the following questions about your life in complete sentences.

1. ¿Te gusta ir de compras?

   Answers will vary: **Sí (No, no) me gusta ir de compras.**

2. ¿Cuál es la tienda que más te gusta?

   Answers will vary: **La tienda que más me gusta es La Favorita.**

3. ¿Qué ropa te gusta comprar?

   Answers will vary: **Me gusta comprar camisas.**

4. ¿Cuánto cuestan los pantalones?

   Answers will vary: **Los pantalones cuestan treinta dólares.**

¡Avancemos! 1
Cuaderno: Práctica por niveles

Unidad 4, Lección 1
Vocabulario B **149**

UNIDAD 4 • Vocabulario B
Lección 1

Vocabulario C

> **¡AVANZA!** **Goal:** Talk about clothes.

1 Fill in the blank with the appropriate color word.

1. La banana es _____ amarilla _____ .

2. Los jeans son _____ azules _____ .

3. Mi tío es muy viejo. Tiene el cabello _____ blanco _____ .

4. A mí me gustan las manzanas _____ rojas / verdes _____ .

5. Cuando está muy oscuro, todo es de color _____ negro _____ .

2 **¿Vamos de compras?** Write the answer to the following questions.

1. ¿Adónde te gusta ir de compras?

   Answers will vary: **Me gusta ir de compras al centro comercial.**

2. ¿Con qué tipo de dinero tienes que pagar en Estados Unidos?

   En Estados Unidos tienes que pagar con el dólar.

3. ¿Con qué tipo de dinero tienes que pagar en Europa?

   En Europa tienes que pagar con el euro.

4. ¿Por qué llevamos gorros y chaquetas en invierno?

   En invierno llevamos gorros y chaquetas porque tenemos frío.

3 Write three sentences describing what clothes you like to wear from head to toe in spring. Make sure to include the colors of the items you describe and where you buy them.

Answers will vary: **En primavera, a mí me gusta llevar ropa nueva. Me gustan las camisetas anaranjadas y los pantalones azules. No me gusta llevar sombrero. Me gusta ir de compras al centro comercial.**

UNIDAD 4 • Vocabulario C
Lección 1

150 Unidad 4, Lección 1
Vocabulario C

¡Avancemos! 1
Cuaderno: Práctica por niveles

Gramática A   *Stem-Changing Verbs: e→ie*

¡AVANZA! **Goal:** Use stem-changing verbs to talk about shopping.

---

1 Underline the verb in parentheses that completes each sentence.

1. Jimena tiene suerte. Siempre compra la ropa que (prefieres / <u>prefiere</u>).

2. Yo no (<u>entiendo</u> / entiendes) qué quieres.

3. Santiago (pierden / <u>pierde</u>) su sombrero.

4. En el otoño Luis y Rosana (compramos / <u>compran</u>) la ropa de invierno.

5. La tienda de ropa (<u>cierra</u> / cierran) a las 8:00 p.m.

2 Complete the sentences using the verbs in parentheses.

1. Nosotros no _____*queremos*_____ pantalones negros. (querer)

2. Paula _____*piensa*_____ en qué cosas puede comprar para el cumpleaños de Juan. (pensar)

3. Alejandro y Noemí _____*entienden*_____ bien las clases de matemáticas. (entender)

4. Irma, ¿ _____*quieres*_____ (tú) ir a comprar una blusa roja? (querer)

5. Todas las mañanas, Jaime _____*empieza*_____ su día contento. (empezar)

3 In a complete sentence, explain what you want to buy for a friend's birthday at your favorite clothing store.

modelo: Yo quiero comprar unos pantalones amarillos y una camiseta azul para el cumpleaños de Marisol.

<u>*Answers will vary:* **Yo quiero comprar unos pantalones azules en la**</u>

<u>**tienda de ropa para mi amiga Luisa.**</u>

_____

_____

Gramática B *Stem-Changing Verbs: e→ie*

> **¡AVANZA!** **Goal:** Use stem-changing verbs to talk about shopping.

❶ Lucía and her friends go shopping. Choose the verb that completes each sentence.

1. Lucía, ¿ __a__ ir a comprar unos pantalones para tu cumpleaños?

    a. quieres   **b.** quiere   **c.** quiero   **d.** queremos

2. Sergio y Eduardo __d__ que no necesitan un gorro en invierno.

    a. piensas   **b.** piensa   **c.** pienso   **d.** piensan

3. Ana y yo __c__ las preguntas de la señora.

    a. entiendo   **b.** entiendes   **c.** entendemos   **d.** entiende

4. Cuando voy de compras con él, Juan siempre __b__ el dinero.

    a. pierden   **b.** pierde   **c.** pierdes   **d.** perdemos

5. Javier y tú __d__ temprano la tienda.

    a. cierro   **b.** cierras   **c.** cierra   **d.** cerráis

❷ **¿Qué hacen?** Write complete sentences using the elements below.

1. entender el español / nosotras

    Nosotras entendemos el español.

2. no querer sombreros amarillos / Ramón y Antonio

    Ramón y Antonio no quieren sombreros amarillos.

3. preferir la primavera / vosotras

    Vosotras preferís la primavera.

4. ¿hacer / tú / qué / querer?

    ¿Qué quieres hacer (tú)?

❸ Write two sentences describing what you wear in winter and why.

    Answers will vary: **En invierno, tengo mucho frío y necesito**

    ropa para el frío. Llevo gorro y chaqueta todos los días.

    _____

    _____

UNIDAD 4 • Gramática B
Lección 1

152 Unidad 4, Lección 1
Gramática B

¡Avancemos! 1
Cuaderno: Práctica por niveles

Gramática C *Stem-Changing Verbs: e→ie*

> **¡AVANZA!** **Goal:** Use stem-changing verbs to talk about shopping.

1 María and her friend Lucas like to shop. Complete the text below with the correct verb form.

Mi amigo Lucas y yo siempre **1.** _____queremos_____ ir de compras.

Él compra ropa de invierno en verano. El señor de la tienda nunca

2. _____entiende_____ por qué necesita una chaqueta en julio.

Muchas veces la tienda **3.** _____cierra_____ y nosotros no

compramos nada.

querer
cerrar
entender

2 Complete the following sentences by conjugating the correct verb from the pair in parentheses.

1. Laura y Ana nunca _____pierden_____ sus sombreros. (empezar / perder)

2. Camila y Julia _____prefieren_____ las camisas rojas. (cerrar / preferir)

3. En España, el invierno _____empieza_____ en diciembre. (entender / empezar)

4. Nosotros no _____entendemos_____ a las personas que llevan pantalones cortos en

invierno. (entender / tener)

5. Pablo _____cierra_____ su chaqueta cuando tiene frío. (pensar / cerrar)

3 Write three complete sentences about why you go to the mall. What do you want to buy when you go there? Use the following verbs: **querer**, **preferir** and **pensar**.

Answers will vary: **Voy al centro comercial de El Paso cuando quiero**

comprar pantalones. Pienso que los pantalones del centro comercial

de El Paso son más bonitos que los pantalones de la tienda cerca de

la escuela. Prefiero ir a El Paso a comprar ropa.

Gramática A *Direct Object Pronouns*

> ¡AVANZA! **Goal:** Use direct object pronouns to talk about clothes.

1 Everyone likes new clothes. Write the direct object pronoun for each sentence.

1. Me gusta esa blusa. Quiero comprar la_____ .

2. Jorge tiene unos zapatos muy bonitos. Él _____ los _____ compra en la tienda.

3. Mi hermana prefiere un sombrero grande. No quiere perder lo_____ .

4. ¿Prefieres los pantalones negros? _____ Los _____ compro para tu cumpleaños.

2 We all love shopping! Re-write the following sentences, replacing the direct object with the direct object pronouns.

1. Quiero la blusa verde.

La quiero.

2. Prefieren los zapatos marrones.

Los prefieren.

3. Las personas del centro comercial entienden a mis amigos y a mí.

Las personas del centro comercial nos entienden.

4. Queremos comprar la chaqueta.

Answers will vary: **Queremos comprarla./La queremos comprar.**

3 Write what the following people want or prefer. Replace the words in parentheses with a direct object pronoun.

modelo: (Una camisa azul) / yo / querer: **Yo la quiero.**

1. (Dos chaquetas negras) / las chicas / preferir:

Las chicas las prefieren:

2. (Tres pantalones cortos) / Manuel / querer:

Manuel los quiere.

3. (El sombrero grande) / nosotros / querer:

Nosotros lo queremos.

UNIDAD 4
Lección 1
• Gramática A

Unidad 4, Lección 1
Gramática A

154

¡Avancemos! 1
Cuaderno: Práctica por niveles

Gramática B *Direct Object Pronouns*

> ¡AVANZA! **Goal:** Use direct object pronouns to talk about clothes.

1 Underline the correct direct object pronoun for each sentence.

1. Tengo una blusa azul. ¿(La / Lo) necesitas?

2. Tengo un sombrero blanco. ¿Vosotros (lo / te) queréis?

3. Tenemos que hablar. ¿Prefieres llamar(te / me) por teléfono?

4. Necesito una camiseta verde. La tienda (nos / la) vende.

5. Mi prima y yo tenemos muchos vestidos. Siempre (los / nos) compartimos.

2 Write a complete sentence using the elements below and replacing the words in parentheses with a direct object pronoun.

modelo: Mabel / hablar (yo) Mabel me habla.

1. Jorge y Ernesto / quieren cerrar (su tienda) temprano

  Answers may vary: **Jorge y Ernesto (la quieren cerrar)**

  (quieren cerrarla) temprano.

2. Sonia y yo / nunca perder (el dinero) en la tienda

  Sonia y yo nunca lo perdemos en la tienda.

3. yo / no entender (tú)

  Yo no te entiendo.

4. tú / hablar del invierno en España (nosotros)

  Tú nos hablas del invierno en España.

3 Write complete sentences using a direct object pronoun.

modelo: ¿Necesitas una camisa para la fiesta? Sí, (No, no) la necesito para la fiesta.

1. ¿Necesitas unos calcetines para el invierno?

  Sí, (No, no) los necesito para el invierno.

2. ¿Necesitas las camisetas anaranjadas para la escuela?

  Sí, (No, no) las necesito para la escuela.

3. ¿Necesitas el vestido para la escuela?

  Sí, (No, no) lo necesito para la escuela.

Gramática C *Direct Object Pronouns*

Level 1, pp. 204–206

> **¡AVANZA!** **Goal:** Use direct object pronouns to talk about clothes.

❶ Mariela and Sebastián are shopping. Write the correct direct object pronoun.

Mariela:	Hola, Sebastián. ¡Qué camisa más linda!, ¿ _La_ compras?
Sebastián:	Hola, Mariela. Sí, _la_ compro y también los pantalones. ¿Te gustan?
Mariela:	Sí, me gustan. _Los._ venden por cuarenta euros.
Sebastián:	Yo prefiero el vestido negro.
Mariela:	¿Un vestido negro? Ya _lo_ tengo, pero quiero los pantalones.
Sebastián:	Pero tienes que comprar _los_ ahora. La tienda cierra en diez minutos. ¿Me entiendes?
Mariela:	Sí, _te_ entiendo. ¡Vamos!

❷ **Vamos de compras**. Write the correct direct object pronoun.

1. Necesito ropa nueva. _____La_____ compro hoy.

2. ¿Dónde están mis zapatos? Siempre _____los_____ pierdo.

3. Tú no debes comprar el sombrero. Prefiero comprar_____lo_____ yo.

4. Las chaquetas son bonitas. _____Las_____ venden en el centro comercial.

5. Siempre _____te_____ entiendo pero tú nunca me entiendes.

❸ We all have new clothes. Write sentences using the elements below. Replace the direct objects with the correct direct object pronoun.

1. Aníbal / preferir (unas camisas de color rojo)

Aníbal las prefiere.

2. Julieta y Emma / comprar (unos vestidos)

Julieta y Ema los compran.

3. Yo / entender (la clase de ciencias)

Yo la entiendo.

4. Tú / tener que llamar (a nosotros) mañana

Answers will vary: **Tú tienes que llamarnos mañana. / Tú nos tienes que llamar**

mañana.

Integración: Hablar

Level 1, pp. 207–209
WB CD 2 track 21

Winter isn't over yet but many stores already have great sales on winter clothes. Carmen sees an ad in the newspaper and is somewhat interested. But then she listens to a radio commercial for the same store and decides to go right away to get a special offer.

Fuente 1 Leer

Read the newspaper ad from "Señor Invierno".

Señor Invierno

¡Es invierno! ¿Tienes toda la ropa que necesitas para no tener frío?

Tienes que ver cuántas cosas tenemos para la estación más fría del año.

¡Señor Invierno tiene de todo!

Chaquetas negras o marrones: $ 65
Calcetines de invierno, todos los colores: $ 5
Gorros muy divertidos, muchos colores: $ 12
Jeans azules o negros: $ 35

Estamos en el centro comercial «Las Estaciones».

Fuente 2 Escuchar   *CD 02 track 22*

Listen to the radio ad that Carmen listened to. Take notes.

_____

_____

_____

_____

Hablar

It is eight o'clock and Carmen is rushing to the store to take advantage of a special offer. What does she have to buy at "Señor Invierno" to get a free black blouse?

modelo: En la tienda de ropa, Carmen tiene que...

Answers will vary: **En la tienda de ropa, Carmen tiene que comprar una**

chaqueta negra, unos jeans azules y unos calcetines blancos.

Integración: Escribir

Level 1, pp. 207–209
WB CD 2 track 23

Ramón sends an e-mail to the school principal to let him know what kind of clothing students prefer to wear during the summer. The principal is happy to know about students' concerns, so he decides to address them the next day in the morning through the school's loudspeakers.

Fuente 1 Leer

Read Ramón's e-mail to the school principal.

De: Ramón   A: Director de la Escuela Latina

Tema: Señor Director, ¡tenemos calor!

¡Hola, Señor Director!

Soy Ramón, un estudiante de la Escuela Latina. Es julio. Hace calor y los estudiantes quieren llevar ropa de verano. Señor Director, todos tenemos que llevar los pantalones, el gorro, la camisa y la chaqueta de la escuela. Pero, ¡por favor!, hace mucho calor. Queremos llevar camisetas y pantalones cortos, porque es verano y tenemos calor.

¡Muchas gracias!

Ramón

Fuente 2 Escuchar   *CD 02 track 24*

Listen to the principal talking to students. Take notes.

_____

_____

_____

_____

Escribir

What items do students have to wear now for the summer at Escuela Latina? Explain why.

modelo: Los estudiantes tienen que...Pero no tienen que...

Answers will vary: **Los estudiantes tienen que llevar los pantalones y la**

camisa de la Escuela Latina. Pero no tienen que llevar la chaqueta y el gorro.

_____

_____

_____

Escuchar A

> **¡AVANZA!** **Goal:** Listen to people talk about clothes.

1 Listen to the conversation between Fernanda and her mother, Carmen. Take notes. Then underline the word that completes each sentence below.

1. Los sombreros cuestan (<u>quince euros</u> / quince dólares).

2. Cuando empieza el verano, los chicos necesitan sombreros (grandes / <u>nuevos</u>).

3. El sombrero de Fernanda es (<u>blanco</u> / negro).

4. Carmen quiere un sombrero (<u>rojo</u> / blanco).

5. Fernanda prefiere comprar un sombrero (rojo / <u>amarillo</u>).

6. La tienda cierra (<u>tarde</u> / los martes).

2 Now listen to Bárbara. Then, complete the following sentences with the words in the box.

comprarla	ropa	chaquetas	la cierran

1. Bárbara tiene que llegar en cinco minutos a la tienda, porque ____la cierran____ temprano.

2. Bárbara necesita _____ropa_____ nueva de invierno.

3. Bárbara quiere comprar _____chaquetas_____ , gorros y zapatos.

4. Bárbara quiere ropa de invierno. Ella prefiere _____comprarla_____ en otoño.

Escuchar B

> **¡AVANZA!** **Goal:** Listen to people talk about clothes.

1 Listen to Agustina. Then, draw a line from the people on the left to what they do.

1. Alejandra, Beatriz y Agustina

2. Alejandra

3. Las amigas de Beatriz

4. Agustina

5. Beatriz

a. compra la ropa de invierno en otoño.

b. no entienden a Beatriz.

c. compra la ropa de invierno en invierno.

d. quieren comprar todo en la tienda.

e. va siempre al centro comercial.

2 Listen to Carina. Then, complete the sentences below:

1. _____El hermano_____ de la amiga de Carina quiere ir de compras.

2. Su amiga _____piensa_____ que su hermano es un buen amigo.

3. Carina no quiere ir de compras en _____invierno_____ porque tiene frío.

4. Carina prefiere _____ir de compras_____ con ellos mañana.

Unidad 4, Lección 1
Escuchar B

160

¡Avancemos! 1
Cuaderno: Práctica por niveles

UNIDAD 4 • Escuchar B
Lección 1

Escuchar C

¡AVANZA! **Goal:** Listen to people talk about clothes.

1 Listen to Emilio. Then, read each sentence and fill in the blanks with the correct season.

1. La familia de Emilio prefiere el _____ verano _____ .

2. En _____ invierno _____ hacen menos cosas.

3. En _____ verano _____ , montan en bicicleta y pasean.

4. La ropa de _____ invierno _____ es fea.

5. Los colores de _____ verano _____ no son feos.

2 Listen to Alicia and take notes. Then answer the following questions with complete sentences:

1. ¿Qué hace Alicia?

Alicia vende ropa en una tienda del centro comercial.

2. ¿Por qué trabajan mucho?

Porque cierran la tienda tarde y muchas personas van de compras.

3. ¿Qué venden cuando empieza una estación?

Cuando empieza una estación, venden mucha ropa.

4. ¿Por qué venden muchos sombreros ahora?

Venden muchos sombreros porque es verano.

5. ¿Cómo prefieren los sombreros los chicos?

Los chicos prefieren los sombreros pequeños y negros.

¡Avancemos! 1
Cuaderno: Práctica por niveles

Unidad 4, Lección 1
Escuchar C   **161**

UNIDAD 4
Lección 1 • Escuchar C

Leer A

> ¡AVANZA! **Goal:** Read about the seasons.

Hola, soy Julieta. Tengo quince años y vivo en España. Llevo una chaqueta y un gorro porque tengo mucho frío. Ahora es invierno y en invierno nunca tengo calor. A mí me gusta más el verano. Hago más actividades en verano y la ropa de verano es muy bonita. Prefiero llevar vestidos de verano y pantalones cortos.

¿Quieres escribirme? ¡Quiero ser tu amiga!

Besos,

Julieta

¿Comprendiste?

Read Julieta's letter. Then, read each sentence and answer **cierto** *(true)* or **falso** *(false)*.

Ⓒ F   **1.** Julieta prefiere el verano.

C Ⓕ   **2.** Julieta tiene un gorro porque le gusta.

Ⓒ F   **3.** En invierno, Julieta no tiene calor.

C Ⓕ   **4.** Las chaquetas son para el verano.

Ⓒ F   **5.** La ropa de verano es más bonita.

¿Qué piensas?

¿Prefieres la ropa de invierno, o la ropa de verano? ¿Por qué?

Answers will vary: **Yo prefiero la ropa de verano porque es más**

bonita.

_____

_____

Unidad 4, Lección 1
Leer A

162

¡Avancemos! 1
Cuaderno: Práctica por niveles

Leer A · UNIDAD 4 Lección 1

Leer B

> **¡AVANZA!** **Goal:** Read about the seasons.

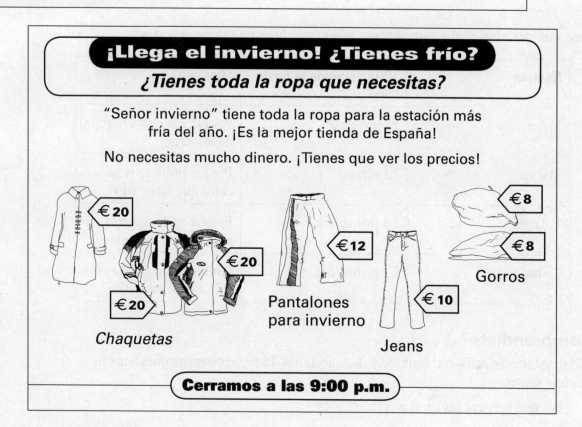

¡Llega el invierno! ¿Tienes frío?
¿Tienes toda la ropa que necesitas?

"Señor invierno" tiene toda la ropa para la estación más fría del año. ¡Es la mejor tienda de España!

No necesitas mucho dinero. ¡Tienes que ver los precios!

€ 20

€ 20

€ 20

Chaquetas

€12

Pantalones para invierno

€ 10

Jeans

€ 8

€ 8

Gorros

Cerramos a las 9:00 p.m.

¿Comprendiste?

Read the store's ad. Then, answer the following questions in complete sentences:

1. ¿Qué ropa venden en la tienda?

   Venden ropa de invierno.

2. ¿Cuánto cuestan las chaquetas?

   Las chaquetas cuestan veinte euros.

3. ¿Por qué la tienda no tiene pantalones cortos?

   Porque vende ropa de invierno y los pantalones cortos son de verano.

¿Qué piensas?

¿Prefieres ir de compras con un amigo? ¿Por qué?

   Answers will vary: **Sí, prefiero ir de compras con un amigo, porque un**

   amigo te dice lo que piensa de la ropa que compras.

¡Avancemos! 1
Cuaderno: Práctica por niveles

UNIDAD 4
Lección 1
•
Leer B

Unidad 4, Lección 1
Leer B **163**

Leer C

¡AVANZA! **Goal:** Read about the seasons.

These students answered a survey about what their favorite season is and why.

Nombre	¿Qué estación te gusta más?	¿Por qué?
Javier	El invierno	Porque me gusta la ropa de invierno.
Martín	El verano	Porque prefiero tener calor que tener frío.
Yolanda	La primavera	Porque no tengo frío y no hace mucho calor.
Laura	La primavera	Porque me gusta llevar mi vestido amarillo.

¿Comprendiste?

Read the students' answers. Complete the questions. Then, answer the questions in complete sentences.

1. ¿Por qué prefiere Javier el invierno?

   Porque le gusta la ropa de invierno.

2. ¿A Martín le gusta tener frío?

   No, Martín prefiere tener calor.

3. ¿Qué piensan Laura y Yolanda?

   Piensan que la primavera es mejor.

4. ¿Cuándo lleva Laura su vestido amarillo?

   Lo lleva en primavera.

¿Qué piensas?

¿Qué estación te gusta más? ¿Por qué?

   Answers will vary: **Pienso que la primavera es mejor porque hace sol y**

   me gusta pasear con mis amigos.

Escribir A

> **¡AVANZA!**　**Goal:** Write about clothes.

Step 1

Look at the drawings. Then make a list of which items you prefer to wear in the winter.

1. 　2. 　3. 　4.

Answers will vary: **la camisa grande, los pantalones negros.**

_____

_____

Step 2

Use the list above to write two sentences about the kinds of clothes you like to wear during the summer and during the winter.

Answers will vary: **Para invierno me gusta llevar ropa marrón y para verano**

me gusta más ropa amarilla. Para invierno me gustan los pantalones

y chaquetas.

Step 3

Evaluate your writing using the information in the table below.

Writing Criteria	Excellent	Good	Needs Work
Content	You included two sentences to tell about the kinds of clothes you like to wear.	You included two sentences to tell about the kinds of clothes you like to wear.	You included one sentence to tell about the kinds of clothes you like to wear.
Communication	Most of your response is clear.	Some of your response is clear.	Your message is not very clear.
Accuracy	You make few mistakes in grammar and vocabulary.	You make some mistakes in grammar and vocabulary.	You make many mistakes in grammar and vocabulary.

Escribir B

> **¡AVANZA!** **Goal:** Write about clothes.

Step 1

Write a list of which clothes above you and your friends prefer wearing.

En invierno, yo

Answers will vary: **prefiero gorros, pantalones, calcetines y una chaqueta.**

En verano, mis amigos

Answers will vary: **prefieren zapatos, camisetas, vestidos, pantalones cortos y sombreros.**

Step 2

In four complete sentences, say what season it is and describe what you are wearing today.

Answers will vary: **Hoy es un día de otoño. Llevo unos jeans azules, y una camiseta roja. Llevo una chaqueta marrón. También llevo unos zapatos negros.**

Step 3

Evaluate your writing using the information in the table below.

Writing Criteria	Excellent	Good	Needs Work
Content	You have included four sentences about the clothes you are wearing.	You have included two to three sentences about the clothes you are wearing.	You have included one or fewer sentences about the clothes you are wearing.
Communication	Most of your sentences are clear.	Some of your sentences are clear.	Your sentences are not very clear.
Accuracy	Your sentences have few mistakes in grammar and vocabulary.	Your sentences have some mistakes in grammar and vocabulary.	Your sentences have many mistakes in grammar and vocabulary.

Unidad 4, Lección 1
Escribir B
166

¡Avancemos! 1
Cuaderno: Práctica por niveles

UNIDAD 4 • Escribir B
Lección 1

Escribir C

> **¡AVANZA!** **Goal:** Write about clothes.

Step 1

¿Qué ropa quieres comprar? Make a list of four items of clothing you want to buy.

Answers will vary: **una blusa anaranjada, unos zapatos rojos, unos**

pantalones blancos y un vestido negro.

Step 2

Write complete sentences about the four items above and about how much you think each item you want to buy costs.

Answers will vary: **Quiero comprar una blusa anaranjada. Cuesta**

diez dólares. Los zapatos rojos cuestan treinta dólares. Los pantalones

blancos cuestan veinticinco dólares. El vestido negro cuesta veinte

dólares.

Step 3

Evaluate your writing using the information in the table below.

Writing Criteria	Excellent	Good	Needs Work
Content	You have included five sentences to talk about the clothes you want to buy.	You have included three to four sentences to talk about the clothes you want to buy.	You have You have included two sentences to talk about the clothes you want to buy.
Communication	Most of your response is clear.	Some of your response is clear.	Your message is not very clear.
Accuracy	Your response has few mistakes in grammar and vocabulary.	Your response has some mistakes in grammar and vocabulary.	Your response has many mistakes in grammar and vocabulary.

UNIDAD 4
Lección 1

Escribir C

Cultura A

> **¡AVANZA!** **Goal:** Review cultural information about Spain.

1 **Spanish culture** Read the following sentences about Spain and answer *true* or *false*.

Ⓣ F **1.** Spain is a country in Europe.

T Ⓕ **2.** The capital of Spain is Morelos.

T Ⓕ **3.** Most people in Spain shop at large shopping malls.

Ⓣ F **4.** **Paella** is a typical dish of Spain.

Ⓣ F **5.** Miguel Cervantes de Saavedra was a famous Spanish writer.

2 **About Spain** Complete the following sentences with one of the multiple-choice words or phrases.

1. The currency used in Spain is the ___a___

  a. euro   **b.** dollar   **c.** peso

2. In Spain, many young people dress for **sevillanas** during the **Feria de** ___b___

  a. **Junio**   **b.** **Abril**   **c.** **Mayo**

3. Surrealist art is often inspired by ___b___

  a. history   **b.** dreams   **c.** nature

3 **Compare climates** Fill out the chart to compare the months of February and July in Chile, Spain, and in your state. Then, briefly describe the climate in these places and explain how they are similar and different.

	February	July
Spain	winter, cooler	summer, hot
Chile	summer, warmer	winter, cooler
My state	Answers will vary.	Answers will vary.

Answers will vary. _____

_____

_____

_____

Unidad 4, Lección 1
Cultura A
168

¡Avancemos! 1
Cuaderno: Práctica por niveles

UNIDAD 4
Lección 1 • Cultura A

Cultura B

> ¡AVANZA! **Goal:** Review cultural information about Spain.

1 **In Spain** Complete the following sentences about Spanish culture.

1. The climate in Spain in July is often _____hot_____ .

2. The capital of Spain is _____Madrid_____ .

3. One of the favorite sports of Spaniards is _____soccer_____ .

4. A famous Spanish artist who painted Don Quijote and Sancho Panza was
   ____Pablo Picasso____ .

5. Aside from tortilla española and paella, ____gazpacho____ is another typical
   Spanish food.

6. The traditional costume of Seville is called **el traje de** ____sevillana____ .

2 **Artists and writers** Draw lines to match the following artists or writers with their works.

Don Quijote novel ——————— Salvador Dalí

«Invierno tardío» poem ——————— Miguel Cervantes de Saavedra

La Persistencia de la Memoria painting ——————— Antonio Colinas

3 **Surrealism** Describe what surrealist art is like using the painting *La persistencia de la memoria* on page 203 of your book as an example. Do you like this style of art? Why or why not?

Answers will vary. _____

_____

_____

_____

_____

_____

_____

Cultura C

> ¡AVANZA! **Goal:** Review cultural information about Spain.

1 **Spain** Complete the following sentences about Spain.

1. Don Quijote and Sancho Panza are characters in a novel by _____Cervantes_____ .

2. The official languages of Spain are _____Spanish_____ , _____Catalan_____ , _____Galician_____ and _____Basque_____ .

3. *La persistencia de memoria* is a famous painting by _____Salvador Dalí_____ .

4. The capital of Spain is _____Madrid_____ .

5. Paella is a typical _____dish/food_____ of Spain.

6. Girls from Seville wear **el traje de sevillana** during the _____Feria de Abril_____ celebration.

2 **Spanish culture** Answer the following questions with complete sentences.

1. What is the climate like in Spain in the month of July? ___In the month of July, in Spain,___ it is summer and hot.

2. In the games against Barcelona FC, which chant do the Real Madrid fans sing?

   In the games against FC, the Real Madrid fans sing their team's chant,

   ¡Hala Madrid!

3. What are some characteristics of surrealist art?

   Surrealist art may be inspired by dreams or represent images from the

   artist's imagination.

3 **Spanish poetry** Describe the imagery in Antonio Colinas' poem *Invierno tardío* on page 211. What is the message of this poem?

   Answers will vary.

   _____

   _____

   _____

UNIDAD 4
Lección 1
Cultura C

170 Unidad 4, Lección 1
Cultura C

¡Avancemos! 1
Cuaderno: Práctica por niveles

Vocabulario A

> **¡AVANZA!** **Goal:** Describe food, places and events in town.

1 You're going out with friends. Place the related words from the box in the columns.

el cine	**el restaurante**
1. la película	4. el camarero
2. las entradas	5. la comida
3. la ventanilla	6. el pollo

> la película
> el camarero
> la ventanilla
> las entradas
> el plato principal

2 This is what people are eating in a restaurant. Write the name of the food you see.

1.

2.

3.

4.

5.

6.

1. el pescado
2. la ensalada
3. el bistec

4. el arroz y el pollo
5. las verduras
6. el brócoli

3 Answer the following question in a complete sentence.

Cuando vas al cine, ¿vas a pie, en coche o en autobús?

Answers will vary: **Cuando voy al cine voy en coche.**

_____

¡Avancemos! 1
Cuaderno: Práctica por niveles

UNIDAD 4 • Vocabulario A
Lección 2

Unidad 4, Lección 2
Vocabulario A **171**

Vocabulario B

> **¡AVANZA!** **Goal:** Describe food, places and events in town.

1 Underline the word that does not belong in each series.

1. pollo / bistec / pescado / <u>ensalada</u>
2. cuenta / camarero / propina / <u>parque</u>
3. teatro / cine / <u>frijoles</u> / concierto
4. tomate / brócoli / patatas / <u>autobús</u>
5. <u>pastel</u> / cine / entradas / ventanilla

2 Alejandro and Manuel are friends but they like doing different things. Complete the sentences with the correct word.

1. A Alejandro no le gusta ir al teatro; prefiere ir al _____cine_____ a ver películas.
2. El brócoli es verdura y el bistec es _____carne_____ .
3. Alejandro no va al centro en coche. Siempre va a _____pie_____ , pero Manuel siempre va en _____coche_____ o en autobús.
4. Manuel siempre _____pide_____ la comida cuando van a un restaurante a almorzar.
5. Alejandro piensa que ir al restaurante _____cuesta_____ mucho dinero.

3 Write two complete sentences stating the means of transportation your friends use to get to school.

1. *Answers will vary:* **Ariel llega a la escuela a pie.**

_____

_____

2. *Answers will vary:* **Verónica llega a la escuela en coche.**

_____

_____

Unidad 4, Lección 2
Vocabulario B
172
¡Avancemos! 1
Cuaderno: Práctica por niveles
UNIDAD 4 • Vocabulario B
Lección 2

Vocabulario C

Level 1, pp. 218–222
WB CD 2 tracks 35–36

> ¡AVANZA! **Goal:** Describe food, places and events in town.

1 Úrsula and Andrés go out every weekend. Circle the word that completes the following sentences.

1. A Úrsula le gusta ver una película en el (**cine**/ parque / café).

2. A Andrés le gusta ir a un (autobús / coche /**concierto**) para escuchar música rock.

3. Úrsula y Andrés compran (pollo /**entradas**/ frijoles) para el cine.

4. Úrsula y Andrés van a comer a un (teatro / ventanilla /**restaurante**).

2 Answer the questions with complete sentences, using the words from the vocabulary.

1. ¿Adónde vas a comer cuando tienes hambre?

Voy a comer al restaurante.

2. ¿Qué necesitas del camarero para poder pagar?

Necesito la cuenta.

3. ¿Qué tienes que leer para pedir la comida?

Tengo que leer el menú.

4. ¿Qué postre preparan para un cumpleaños?

Preparan pastel de postre.

5. ¿Qué recibe el camarero cuando hace un buen trabajo?

Cuando el camarero hace un buen trabajo, recibe una propina.

3 Write four sentences about what you do when you go to a restaurant. Remember to mention how you go, what you do and what you order.

Answers will vary: **Voy en coche con mis padres al restaurante Miramar.**

Siempre pido carne con patatas como plato principal. De postre me gusta

comer pastel. Los camareros sirven muy bien en el restaurante.

_____

_____

UNIDAD 4
Lección 2 • Vocabulario C

Gramática A *Stem-Changing Verbs: o → ue*

> **¡AVANZA!** **Goal:** Use stem-changing verbs to talk about places.

1 Lorena and her friends go to lunch at a restaurant. Choose the correct verb from those in parentheses.

1. Lorena no (puedo / puede) comer carne.

2. Lorena y Armando (almuerzan / almorzamos) temprano.

3. Este plato (cuesta / cuestan) doce euros.

4. Lorena y yo siempre (volvéis / volvemos) al restaurante.

5. Yo (encuentran / encuentro) el bistec más rico en el restaurante.

2 Complete the following sentences using the verbs in parentheses.

1. Verónica _____almuerza_____ brócoli y pescado. (almorzar)

2. Las patatas _____cuestan_____ cuatro euros. (costar)

3. ¿Vosotras _____volvéis_____ al teatro el fin de semana? (volver)

4. Yo _____duermo_____ después del almuerzo porque estoy muy cansado. (dormir)

3 Answer the following question in a complete sentence.

1. ¿A qué hora duermes por la noche?

Answers will vary: **Yo duermo a las 9:00 p.m.**

2. ¿Dónde almuerzas con tus amigos?

Answers will vary: **Yo almuerzo con mis amigos en el centro comercial.**

3. ¿Cuándo vas al teatro?

Answers will vary: **Yo voy al teatro los sábados.**

UNIDAD 4
Lección 2

Gramática A

174

Unidad 4, Lección 2
Gramática A

¡Avancemos! 1
Cuaderno: Práctica por niveles

Gramática B *Stem-Changing Verbs: o → ue*

> **¡AVANZA!** **Goal:** Use stem-changing verbs to talk about places.

1 Julián and his friends have fun around town. Choose the correct verb to complete each sentence.

1. Julián __b__ muy contento del concierto.

   a. vuelves **b.** vuelve **c.** vuelvo **d.** volvemos

2. Claudia y Tomás __c__ en el restaurante de la calle Madrid.

   a. almorzamos **b.** almorzáis **c.** almuerzan **d.** almuerza

3. Pedro, Lucas y yo __d__ ir al café a las 3:00 p.m.

   a. puede **b.** pueden **c.** puedes **d.** podemos

4. Las entradas del cine __d__ cinco euros.

   a. cuesta **b.** cuestas **c.** cuesto **d.** cuestan

5. ¿Tú __a__ a Laura en el parque?

   a. encuentras **b.** encuentran **c.** encuentra **d.** encontráis

2 Use the information from the table to write three sentences about what these people do.

Luis	volver	a la 1:30 p.m.
Raúl y Graciela	almorzar	la calle del cine
Cecilia y yo	encontrar	el restaurante

1. *Answers will vary:* **Luis vuelve a la 1:30 p.m.**

2. *Answers will vary:* **Raúl y Graciela almuerzan en el restaurante.**

3. *Answers will vary:* **Graciela y yo encontramos la calle del cine.**

3 Write a complete sentence to describe what you can have for lunch at your favorite restaurant.

Answers will vary: **Yo puedo almorzar pollo, carne, ensalada, postre y verduras.**

Gramática C *Stem-Changing Verbs: o → ue*

¡AVANZA! **Goal:** Use stem-changing verbs to talk about places.

1 Armando always has lunch at the restaurant on calle Infanta. Complete the sentences below using the verbs in parentheses:

1. Armando _____*almuerza*_____ carne o pollo. (almorzar)

2. Armando y Noemí _____*pueden*_____ ir a pie al restaurante. (poder)

3. Armando y yo _____*volvemos*_____ a casa en autobús. (volver)

4. Nosotros _____*encontramos*_____ un restaurante para almorzar. (encontrar)

5. El almuerzo _____*cuesta*_____ quince euros. (costar)

2 Your friends go to many places. Write sentences about your friends using the verbs provided.

1. (almuerzan)

   Answers will vary: **Juan y María almuerzan en el centro comercial.**

2. (dormís)

   Answers will vary: **Vosotros dormís temprano.**

3. (encuentro)

   Answers will vary: **Yo encuentro a Ana en el restaurante.**

4. (podemos)

   Answers will vary: **Ana y yo podemos ir al teatro a pie.**

5. (vuelves)

   Answers will vary: **Tú vuelves a casa muy tarde.**

3 Write three sentences about your weekend. Use the verbs **poder**, **dormir** and **almorzar**.

   Answers will vary: **Los sábados puedo dormir por el día. Duermo de 3:00 a**

   4:00 de la tarde. Almuerzo con mis amigos en el parque o en el centro

   comercial.

UNIDAD 4
Lección 2
• Gramática C

176 **Unidad 4, Lección 2**
Gramática C

¡Avancemos! 1
Cuaderno: Práctica por niveles

Gramática A *Stem-Changing Verbs: e → i*

> ⏵¡AVANZA! **Goal:** Use stem-changing verbs to talk about what you do.

1 **¡Vamos a almorzar!** Underline the correct verb to complete the dialogue between Jimena and Lucas.

1. Jimena: ¿Tú (pide / <u>pides</u>) el menú?

2. Lucas: Lo tengo aquí. Yo (piden / <u>pido</u>) bistec como siempre.

3. Jimena: ¿El camarero (<u>sirve</u> / sirven) nuestra mesa?

4. Lucas: No, los camareros (<u>sirven</u> / servimos) la otra mesa.

5. Jimena: ¿Nosotros ya (pedís / <u>pedimos</u>) la comida?

2 Everybody loves going to the restaurant on **calle Córdoba**! Complete the sentences with the correct form of the verbs given.

1. Cecilia _____ pide _____ unas patatas. (pedir)

2. Javier y yo _____ pedimos _____ pollo. (pedir)

3. ¿Qué _____ pides _____ tú? (pedir)

4. El camarero _____ sirve _____ muchos platos durante el día. (servir)

5. Los camareros del restaurante _____ sirven _____ muy bien la comida. (servir)

3 Answer the following questions about yourself in a complete sentence:

1. ¿Qué pides muchas veces como plato principal?

   Answers will vary: **Yo pido un bistec con patatas.** _____

2. ¿Qué piden tus amigos como plato principal?

   Answers will vary: **Ellos piden pollo con arroz.** _____

3. ¿Dónde almuerzas?

   Answers will vary: **Yo almuerzo en la cafetería.** _____

¡Avancemos! 1
Cuaderno: Práctica por niveles

Unidad 4, Lección 2
Gramática A **177**

UNIDAD 4
Lección 2

UNIDAD 4 • Gramática A

Gramática B *Stem-Changing Verbs: e → i*

¡AVANZA! **Goal:** Use stem-changing verbs to talk about what you do.

1 Today is Juan's birthday. Choose the verb that completes each sentence.

1. Juan __d__ pollo y arroz.

a. pido **b.** pides **c.** piden **d.** pide

2. ¿Tú __a__ bistec y verduras?

a. pides **b.** piden **c.** pedimos **d.** pido

3. Los camareros __c__ nuestra comida.

a. sirvo **b.** sirve **c.** sirven **d.** servimos

2 Juan and Norma go out to eat. Tell what they order by using the words in parentheses and then tell what the waiter serves them by using the words in the box.

tomate	pastel	brócoli	bistec

modelo: Norma (carne): Norma pide carne y el camarero sirve un bistec.

1. Juan (verduras) Juan pide verduras y el camarero sirve brócoli.

2. Norma y Juan (ensalada) Norma y Juan piden ensalada y el camarero

sirve tomate.

3. Norma (postre) Norma pide postre y el camarero sirve pastel.

3 Answer the following questions in a complete sentence.

1. ¿Qué pides siempre para almorzar?

Answers will vary: **Yo siempre pido pollo con arroz para almorzar.**

2. ¿Qué pides cuando no hay carne?

Answers will vary: **Yo pido patatas.**

3. ¿Qué piden tus padres para almorzar?

Answers will vary: **Mis padres piden pescado con verduras.**

Gramática C *Stem-Changing Verbs: e → i*

Level 1, pp. 228–230

> **¡AVANZA!** **Goal:** Use stem-changing verbs to talk about what you do.

1 One group of friends always goes out to eat on the weekend. Complete the dialog using the verbs **pedir** and **servir**.

Roberto: Yo pido un bistec con patatas. ¿Qué _____pides_____ tú?

Natalia: Yo _____pido_____ pollo con verduras.

Roberto: El camarero _____sirve_____ un pollo muy rico.

Natalia: ¡Roberto! Hoy ellos no _____sirven_____ bistec. ¿Pides otra cosa?

Roberto: Bueno, nosotros _____pedimos_____ pollo.

2 Some friends are at a restaurant for lunch. However, the waiter mixes up their orders. Write what each person orders and what the waiter serves in complete sentences.

modelo: bistec (Raúl) / pollo: Raúl pide bistec pero el camarero sirve pollo.

1. pescado (Irma y Raúl) / ensalada:

Irma y Raúl piden pescado pero el camarero sirve ensalada.

2. brócoli (Irma y yo) / tomate:

Irma y yo pedimos brócoli pero el camarero sirve tomate.

3. arroz (Raúl y tú) / patatas:

Raúl y tú pedís arroz pero el camarero sirve patatas.

4. pescado (Yo)/ verduras:

Yo pido pescado pero el camarero sirve verduras.

3 You are having friends over for lunch. Write three sentences about what you serve each person.

1. *Answers will vary:* **Sirvo un bistec a Manuel.**

2. *Answers will vary:* **Sirvo verduras a Sonia.**

3. *Answers will vary:* **Sirvo ensalada a Olga.**

Integración: Hablar

Level 1, pp. 231–233
WB CD 2 track 31

Gabriela, who lives in Madrid, loves to go to the movies. She is looking for movie ads in the city's online newspaper. An ad for the movie *¿Dónde está mi hijo?* catches her eye, but she wants to know more about it, so she listens to the movie review on a radio show. Unfortunately, they end up giving away the entire plot.

Fuente 1 Leer

Read the movie ad in an online newspaper.

> ## La película: *¿Dónde está mi hijo?*
>
> Usted tiene que ver *¿Dónde está mi hijo?*, una película muy triste. A las once de la mañana, una madre va de compras con su hijo al centro comercial. A las doce, van a un restaurante para almorzar. Ella va al baño y cuando vuelve, no encuentra a su hijo!

Fuente 2 Escuchar   *CD 02 track 32*

Listen to a review of the movie on a radio program. Take notes.

_____

_____

_____

Hablar

What is the sequence of events in the movie *¿Dónde está mi hijo?* Remember to include information from both the newspaper ad and the review in the radio show.

modelo: En la película, una madre va...Pero quince años...

Answers will vary: **En la película, una madre va al baño en un restaurante.**

Cuando vuelve no encuentra a su hijo. Pero quince años después mira al

camarero de un restaurante y entiende que es su hijo.

Integración: Escribir

Level 1, pp. 231–233
WB CD track 33

Restaurante de la Abuela has an ad in a newspaper. They claim that their food tastes like traditional homemade Spanish food. Ramiro reads the ad and decides to leave a message for his friend Liliana. He wants to meet her for lunch at the restaurant. Ramiro knows what Liliana likes to eat, so he lets her know his suggestions.

Fuente 1 Leer

Read the ad for "Restaurante de la Abuela"...

Restaurante de la Abuela

RESTAURANTE PARA TODA LA FAMILIA

¿Puedes pensar en el mejor lugar para comer? La comida del Restaurante de la Abuela es como la comida que comes en casa.

Aquí encuentras el menú más rico de toda la ciudad: platos principales de carne, pollo y pescado; verduras, como brócoli y patatas; arroz español; ensaladas de tomate muy ricas. Cuando vienes una vez, ¡vuelves siempre!

Estamos en la Calle Valladolid, número trescientos.

Fuente 2 Escuchar   *CD 02 track 34*

Listen to Ramiro's voicemail to Liliana. Take notes.

_____

_____

_____

_____

Escribir

Explain what Liliana can eat at the restaurant.

modelo: Liliana no come..., pero en el Restaurante de la Abuela...

Answers will vary: **Liliana no come carne, pero en el Restaurante de la**

Abuela puede comer verduras como brócoli y patatas. También puede

comer arroz español o una ensalada de tomate.

_____

_____

_____

¡Avancemos! 1
Cuaderno: Práctica por niveles

UNIDAD 4 • Integración:
Lección 2   Escribir

Unidad 4, Lección 2
Integración: Escribir   **181**

Escuchar A

Level 1, pp. 238–239
WB CD 2 tracks 35–36

> ¡AVANZA! **Goal:** Listen to people talking about doing things around town.

1 Listen to Norberto. Then, read each statement and answer **cierto** (true) or **falso** (false).

Ⓒ F **1.** Norberto compra las entradas.

C Ⓕ **2.** Las entradas cuestan diez euros.

C Ⓕ **3.** Mariela compra su entrada.

Ⓒ F **4.** Norberto llega dos horas antes al cine.

C Ⓕ **5.** Norberto va a estar en la puerta del cine a las dos.

2 Listen to Mariela. Then answer the following questions:

1. ¿A qué hora tiene que estar Mariela en el cine? a las tres _____

_____

2. ¿Por qué Mariela no va a pie al cine? Porque es tarde y no llega a tiempo. _____

_____

3. ¿Cuándo llega el autobús? en quince minutos _____

_____

UNIDAD 4 • Escuchar A
Lección 2

182
Escuchar A

Unidad 4, Lección 2
Escuchar A

¡Avancemos! 1
Cuaderno: Práctica por niveles

Escuchar B

Level 1, pp. 238–239
WB CD 2 tracks 37–38

> **¡AVANZA!** **Goal:** Listen to people talking about doing things around town.

1 Listen to Carmen and take notes. Then, draw a line from each person to his or her order.

1. Julio
2. Andrés
3. Norma
4. Carmen
5. Todos

a. pescado y verduras
b. ensalada
c. bistec y patatas
d. postre
e. pollo y arroz

2 Listen to the waiter and take notes. Then answer the following questions in complete sentences.

1. ¿Qué día van más personas al restaurante?

   Los viernes van más personas al restaurante.

   _____

2. ¿Por qué vuelven las personas?

   Porque les gusta la comida.

   _____

3. ¿Qué encuentra el camarero en la mesa con la cuenta?

   El camarero encuentra propina en la mesa con la cuenta.

   _____

¡Avancemos! 1
Cuaderno: Práctica por niveles

Unidad 4, Lección 2
Escuchar B   **183**

UNIDAD 4
Lección 2   •   Escuchar B

Escuchar C

Level 1, pp. 238–239
WB CD 2 tracks 39–40

> **¡AVANZA!** **Goal:** Listen to people talking about doing things around town.

❶ Listen to Francisco and take notes. Then, complete the sentences below:

1. Francisco y sus amigos tienen hoy ___un concierto___ de música.

2. Van al ___teatro___ para el concierto.

3. El concierto empieza a ___las cinco___ .

4. ___La entrada___ cuesta dos euros.

5. No piden mucho ___dinero___ por las entradas.

❷ Listen to Olga and Nicolás. Then answer the questions below in complete sentences:

1. ¿Nicolás puede ir al teatro a las dos?

Sí, Nicolás puede ir al teatro a las dos.

2. ¿Qué hay en el teatro? ¿A qué hora?

Hay un concierto de música rock a las cinco.

3. ¿Por qué Olga quiere ir al centro con Nicolás a las dos?

Porque quiere almorzar en el centro.

4. ¿Por qué Nicolás vuelve temprano?

Porque necesita dormir ocho horas.

5. ¿Cuánto cuesta la entrada del concierto?

La entrada cuesta dos euros.

Leer A

┌───┐

¡AVANZA! **Goal:** Read about food and places.

└───┘

Manuel and Antonia go to the movies every Thursday. They see the following sign on the door.

Cine Gran Ilusión

Hoy presentamos la película "¡Adiós a mi gran amor!"

La entrada cuesta cinco euros y puedes comprarla en la ventanilla de 10:00 a.m. a 1:00 p.m.

Horario de película

> 2:00 p.m.
>
> 4:00 p.m.
>
> 6:00 p.m.
>
> 8:00 p.m.

El restaurante Estrellas, dentro del cine, es muy bueno.

¿Comprendiste?

Read the movie theater's sign and then complete the following sentences:

1. Manuel y Antonia pagan _____ *diez euros* _____ por sus entradas de cine.

2. Manuel y Antonia pueden comer en _____ *el restaurante* _____ del cine.

3. Manuel y Antonia compran las entradas en _____ *la ventanilla* _____ .

4. "¡Adiós a mi gran amor!" es el nombre de _____ *la película* _____ .

¿Qué piensas?

¿A qué hora puedes ir al cine de tu ciudad?

Answers will vary: **Puedo ir al cine a las 5:00 p.m., a las 6:00 p.m. y a** _____

las 7:00 p.m. _____

_____

_____

Leer B

Level 1, pp. 238–239

> **¡AVANZA!** **Goal:** Read about food and places.

Julia wants to eat lunch. She reads the following menu.

M e n ú

Plato principal

Bistec con patatas............quince euros

Pollo con arroz..................once euros

Pescado con brócoli.........diez euros

Plato del día

Verduras.....................................nueve euros

Carne con ensalada de tomate.....doce euros

¿Comprendiste?

Read the menu. Then, answer the following questions in complete sentences:

1. Julia lleva diez euros, ¿qué platos puede pedir?

   Ella puede pedir pescado con brócoli o verduras.

2. ¿Por qué?

   Porque son los dos platos que cuestan diez euros o menos.

3. ¿Qué platos de carne sirven en el restaurante?

   Sirven bistec con patatas, pollo con arroz, y carne con ensalada de tomate.

4. ¿Qué sirven de postre?

   No sirven postre.

¿Qué piensas?

¿Qué te gusta pedir en tu restaurante favorito? ¿Por qué?

Answers will vary: **Me gusta pedir bistec con patatas porque la carne**

con patatas es mi plato favorito.

Leer C

 Goal: Read about food and places.

María writes a letter to a friend in another city. Read María's letter and answer the questions.

> *Hola Norma:*
>
> *Quiero invitarte a mi casa. Mis amigos y yo salimos mucho. Todos los sábados, vamos a un concierto de música rock y los domingos vamos al cine. Todos los jueves almorzamos en un restaurante pequeño pero muy bueno. Los viernes vamos al teatro. Los lunes vamos al parque por las tardes. De allí, vamos a un café en el centro comercial y hablamos.*
>
> *¿Puedes venir?*
>
> *Besos,*
>
> *María.*

¿Comprendiste?

Read Maria's letter. Then, write the things that Maria and her friends do on the following days:

1. lunes: Van al parque por las tardes y a un café en el centro comercial.

2. jueves: Almuerzan en un restaurante.

3. viernes: Van al teatro.

4. sábados: Van a un concierto de música rock.

5. domingos: Van al cine.

¿Qué piensas?

1. ¿Haces las actividades que hacen María y sus amigos?

   Answers will vary: **Sí, yo también voy a conciertos de rock y al centro**

   comercial con mis amigos.

2. ¿Te gusta almorzar con tus amigos? ¿Qué comen? ¿Dónde?

   Answers will vary: **Sí, me gusta almorzar con mis amigos los sábados.**

   Comemos pizza en el centro comercial.

Escribir A

 Goal: Write about foods and places.

Step 1

Make a list of four things you and your friends like doing. You can use words from the box.

cine	teatro	restaurante	concierto	parque

Answers will vary: **ir al parque los sábados por la mañana** _____

Answers will vary: **comer arroz en un restaurante** _____

Answers will vary: **ir a un concierto de rock** _____

Answers will vary: **ir al cine a ver una película** _____

Step 2

Write two complete sentences to say where you and your friends like to go and what you do there. Use your list.

1. *Answers will vary:* **Nos gusta ir a un restaurante para comer comida rica.**

2. *Answers will vary:* **Nos gusta ir a un concierto para escuchar música rock.**

Step 3

Evaluate your writing using the information in the table below.

Writing Criteria	Excellent	Good	Needs Work
Content	Your sentences include many details and new vocabulary.	Your sentences include some details and new vocabulary.	Your sentences include little information or new vocabulary.
Communication	Most of your sentences are clear.	Some of your sentences are clear.	Your sentences are not very clear.
Accuracy	Your sentences have few mistakes in grammar and vocabulary.	Your sentences have some mistakes in grammar and vocabulary.	Your sentences have many mistakes in grammar and vocabulary.

UNIDAD 4
Lección 2

Escribir A

Unidad 4, Lección 2
Escribir A

188

¡Avancemos! 1
Cuaderno: Práctica por niveles

Escribir B

> ¡AVANZA! **Goal:** Write about foods and places.

Step 1

Rearrange the letters of the following words and you will find a new word using the circled letters.

1. recaroma: c a (m) a r e r o
2. tecbis: b i s t (e) c
3. laendasa: e (n) s a l a d a
4. teresrantau: r e s t a (u) r a n t e

Hidden word: _____ menú _____

Step 2

Use the words from **Step 1** to write three complete sentences about what you and your family do at a restaurant.

1. *Answers will vary:* **Mi mamá pide bistec y ensalada como plato principal.**

   _____

2. *Answers will vary:* **El camarero del restaurante sirve la**

   comida muy bien. _____

3. *Answers will vary:* **Yo siempre leo todo el menú y pido carne.**

   _____

Step 3

Evaluate your writing using the information in the table below.

Writing Criteria	Excellent	Good	Needs Work
Content	Your sentences include many details and new vocabulary.	Your sentences include some details and new vocabulary.	Your sentences include little information or new vocabulary.
Communication	Most of your sentences are clear.	Some of your sentences are clear.	Your sentences are not very clear.
Accuracy	Your sentences have few mistakes in grammar and vocabulary.	Your sentences have some mistakes in grammar and vocabulary.	Your sentences have many mistakes in grammar and vocabulary.

¡Avancemos! 1
Cuaderno: Práctica por niveles

Unidad 4, Lección 2
Escribir B **189**

UNIDAD 4
Lección 2
•
Escribir B

Escribir C

> **¡AVANZA!** **Goal:** Write about foods and places.

Step 1

¿Qué te gusta pedir en un restaurante? Write four complete sentences about two things you like ordering at a restaurant and two things you don't like ordering.

1. *Answers will vary:* **Me gusta pedir pollo con arroz.**

2. *Answers will vary:* **Me gusta pedir pescado con verduras.**

3. *Answers will vary:* **No me gusta pedir bistec.**

4. *Answers will vary:* **No me gusta pedir brócoli.**

Step 2

Write an e-mail to your friend, describing what you always order at your favorite restaurant.

Answers will vary:

Hola Jaime:

Siempre voy a un restaurante de la calle Sevilla.

Muchas veces pido pollo con arroz, allí lo sirven muy rico. Otras veces

pido pescado con verduras, que también me gustan mucho. No me

gusta el bistec con brócoli.

¿Quieres venir un día?

Adiós,

Juan

Step 3

Evaluate your writing using the information in the table below.

Writing Criteria	Excellent	Good	Needs Work
Content	Your email includes many details and new vocabulary.	Your email includes some details and new vocabulary.	Your email includes little information or new vocabulary.
Communication	Most of your email is clear.	Some of your email is clear.	Your email is not very clear.
Accuracy	Your email has few mistakes in grammar and vocabulary.	Your email has some mistakes in grammar and vocabulary.	Your email has many mistakes in grammar and vocabulary.

Cultura A

> **¡AVANZA!** **Goal:** Review cultural information about Spain.

1 **Spain and Guatemala** Complete the following sentences with one of the multiple choice words or phrases.

1. El Rastro is a famous __c__ in Madrid.

    a. restaurant   **b.** park   **c.** flea market

2. At the market in Chichicastenango, Guatemala, you can buy handicrafts from the __a__ culture.

    a. Maya-Quiché   **b.** Taino   **c.** Aztec

3. Three typical Spanish foods are __b__

    a. chile con carne,   **b. gazpacho, paella,**   **c. pasteles, arroz con**
    burritos, and fajitas   **and tortilla**   **gandules, and pernil**

2 **Sites in Spain and Chile** There are many interesting places in Spain and Chile. Match the places with the corresponding description.

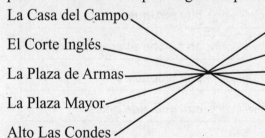

La Casa del Campo   mall in Santiago, Chile

El Corte Inglés   plaza in Madrid with a stamp market on Sundays

La Plaza de Armas   plaza in Santiago with concerts on Sundays

La Plaza Mayor   Spanish department store

Alto Las Condes   park in Madrid with a zoo and swimming pool

3 *Las meninas* Both Diego Velázquez and Salvador Dalí created paintings titled *Las meninas*. Describe and compare both paintings on page 230, and tell how they are similar and different.

Answers will vary.

_____

_____

_____

_____

_____

¡Avancemos! 1
Cuaderno: Práctica por niveles

Unidad 4, Lección 2
Cultura A   **191**

UNIDAD 4
Lección 2 • Cultura A

Cultura B

Level 1, pp. 238–239

> ¡AVANZA! **Goal:** Review cultural information about Spain.

1 **Spain** Read the following sentences about Spain and circle *true* or *false*.

(T) F **1.** The princesses of the Spanish royal family are called **infantas.**

(T) F **2.** One of the oldest flea markets in Madrid is El Rastro.

T (F) **3.** The official painter of King Felipe IV of Spain was Salvador Dalí.

T (F) **4.** In Spain, the only language spoken is Spanish.

(T) F **5.** El Corte Inglés is a Spanish department store.

2 **Things to do in Spain and Chile** In Madrid, Spain, and Santiago, Chile, there are many places to visit. Tell what you can do in the following places.

Places	Things to do
La Casa del Campo	*Answers will vary:* **go to the zoo,**
El Rastro	*Answers will vary:* **buy antiques**
La Plaza Mayor	*Answers will vary:* **go to the stamp market**
Plaza de Armas	*Answers will vary:* **see a concert**
El Cerro San Cristóbal	*Answers will vary:* **eat and ride bikes**

3 **Visiting Madrid** In Madrid, there are many places to take a walk or visit on the weekend. Would you like to visit some? Write a short paragraph about which places in Madrid you would like to visit and why.

Answers will vary.

_____

_____

_____

_____

_____

_____

_____

Cultura C

¡AVANZA! **Goal:** Review cultural information about Spain.

1 **Spain** Choose the correct word to complete the following sentences.

1. (Diego Velázquez /Pablo Picasso) was the official painter of King Felipe IV of Spain.

2. (Pinchos / gazpacho) is/are a typical food in Spain.

3. In the Plaza (Mayor / Menor) of Madrid there is a stamp market on Sundays.

4. The (princesses / queens) of the Spanish royal family are called **infantas**.

2 **Spanish culture** Answer these questions using complete sentences.

1. Who are some of the people in the painting *Las Meninas* by the Spanish painter Diego Velázquez?

Some of the people in the painting *Las Meninas* are the

princess, her attendants and the painter himself.

2. What can people buy when they visit El Rastro in Madrid?

At El Rastro, people can buy antiques, secondhand

clothing, compact discs, books, and pieces of art.

3. Which languages are spoken in Spain?

The languages spoken in Spain are Spanish, Catalan, Galician

and Basque.

3 **At the market** Describe both El Rastro and the Chichicastenango markets. What would you buy in each place? Which market would you prefer to visit and why?

Answers will vary. El Rastro is a flea market in Madrid. It has hundreds of

stalls where people can buy antiques, secondhand clothing, and many

other items. The Chichicastenango market is in Guatemala. You can buy

many Mayan handicrafts there, as well as fruits, vegetables, and flowers.

I would prefer to visit El Rastro because I like shopping for antiques.

I would buy books and CDs there.

Comparación cultural: ¿Adónde vamos el sábado?

Lectura y escritura

After reading the paragraphs about what Anita, Rodrigo, and Armando do for fun on Saturdays, write a paragraph about what you like to do on Saturdays. Use the information on your activity chart to write sentences, and then write a paragraph that describes what you do for fun on Saturdays.

Step 1

Complete the activity chart describing as many details as possible about the activities you do for fun on Saturdays.

Categoría	Detalles
lugares	
ropa	
actividades	

Step 2

Now take the details from the activity chart and write a sentence for each topic on the chart.

_____

_____

_____

_____

_____

_____

_____

_____

_____

UNIDAD 4 • Comparación cultural
Lección 2

194

Unidad 4
Comparación cultural: ¿Adónde vamos el sábado?

¡Avancemos! 1
Cuaderno: Práctica por niveles

Comparación cultural: ¿Adónde vamos el sábado?
Lectura y escritura (continued)
Step 3

Now write your paragraph using the sentences you wrote as a guide. Include an introduction sentence and use the verbs **ir a** + **infinitive** and **querer** + **infinitive** to write about what you do for fun on Saturdays.

_____

_____

_____

_____

_____

_____

_____

Checklist

Be sure that…

☐ all the details about your Saturday activities from your chart are included in the paragraph;

☐ you use details to describe what you do for fun on Saturdays.

☐ you include new vocabulary words and the verbs **ir a** + **infinitive** and **querer** + **infinitive.**

Rubric

Evaluate your writing using the rubric below.

Writing criteria	Excellent	Good	Needs Work
Content	Your paragraph includes many details about what you do for fun on Saturdays.	Your paragraph includes some details about what you do for fun on Saturdays.	Your paragraph includes few details about what you do for fun on Saturdays.
Communication	Most of your paragraph is organized and easy to follow.	Parts of your paragraph are organized and easy to follow.	Your paragraph is disorganized and hard to follow.
Accuracy	Your paragraph has few mistakes in grammar and vocabulary.	Your paragraph has some mistakes in grammar and vocabulary.	Your paragraph has many mistakes in grammar and vocabulary.

UNIDAD 4 • Comparación
Lección 2 cultural

Level 1, pp. 240–241

Comparación cultural: ¿Adónde vamos el sábado?

Compara con tu mundo

Now write a comparison about what you do for fun on Saturdays and that of one of the three students from page 241. Organize your comparison by topics. First, compare the places you go, then the clothes you wear, and lastly your favorite activities.

Step 1

Use the table to organize your comparison by topics. Write details for each topic about what you do for fun on Saturdays and that of the student you chose.

Categoría	Mi descripción	La descripción de _____
lugares		
ropa		
actividades		

Step 2

Now use the details from the table to write a comparison. Include an introduction sentence and write about each topic. Use the verbs **ir a** + **infinitive, querer** + **infinitive** to describe the sequence of your Saturday activities and those of the student you chose.

_____

_____

_____

_____

_____

_____

_____

_____

UNIDAD 4 • Comparación cultural
Lección 2

Unidad 4
Comparación cultural: ¿Adónde vamos el sábado?

196

¡Avancemos! 1
Cuaderno: Práctica por niveles

Vocabulario A

Level 1, pp. 248-252

 Goal: Describe a house and household items.

1 Lucas' house is very big. Draw a line from the places in the house to the activities done in each.

1. el cuarto   mirar la televisión

2. la escalera   preparar la comida

3. la sala   comer con la familia

4. el comedor   dormir

5. la cocina   subir y bajar

2 There's always a lot to do at home. Complete the following sentences with a word from the box.

discos compactos	lector DVD	videojuegos
sillón	cortinas	

1. En la sala, mi hermano y yo jugamos _____videojuegos_____ .

2. A mi familia le gusta la música; por eso tenemos muchos _____discos compactos_____ .

3. En mi cuarto veo películas con mi _____lector DVD_____ .

4. Delante de las ventanas, mi mamá usa _____cortinas_____ blancas.

5. Mi padre descansa en un _____sillón_____ en la sala.

3 Answer the following questions in complete sentences.

1. ¿Tienes un tocadiscos compactos en tu cuarto?

   Answers will vary: **Sí, tengo un tocadiscos compactos en mi cuarto.**

   _____

2. ¿Tienes un lector DVD en la sala de tu casa?

   Answers will vary: **Sí, tengo un lector DVD en la sala de mi casa.**

   _____

Vocabulario B

> **¡AVANZA!** **Goal:** Describe a house and household items.

1 Luis invites his friends to his house. Circle the word that completes each sentence.

1. Luis tiene un (radio / patio) en su cuarto.

2. El padre de Luis usa (el sillón / las cortinas) para descansar.

3. La hermana de Luis compró un (jardín / espejo).

4. La madre de Luis tiene unas (alfombras / cortinas) en el suelo.

5. Luis y sus amigos escuchan unos (discos compactos / muebles).

6. La casa de Luis tiene dos (pisos / suelos).

2 Pedro is doing some things in his house. Complete the following sentences:

modelo: Pedro baja del primer piso a la planta baja del apartamento.

1. Pedro prepara el desayuno en _____ la cocina _____ .

2. Pedro duerme en una cama en _____ el cuarto _____ .

3. Pedro come con su familia en _____ el comedor _____ .

4. Pedro sube _____ la escalera _____ .

5. Pedro tiene ropa en _____ el armario _____ de su cuarto.

6. Pedro juega al fútbol en _____ el jardín _____ .

3 In three complete sentences describe the furniture you have in your living room.

Answers will vary:

En la sala de mi casa hay un sillón, un televisor, una alfombra y cortinas.

También hay un espejo grande y una escalera. En la sala hay una alfombra

roja.

Vocabulario C

> ¡AVANZA! **Goal:** Describe a house and household items.

1 Look at the words in the vocabulary box and write them in the appropriate column. Items in the word bank may be used more than once.

las cortinas	el televisor	la cama
el armario	el comedor	el sofá
el espejo	la cómoda	la lámpara

el comedor	el cuarto	la sala
la lámpara	el armario	las cortinas
las cortinas	el televisor	el sofá
	la cama	el televisor
	la lámpara	la lámpara
	la cómoda	
	el espejo	

2 Ana has a big house. In complete sentences, describe what she does in each of the places below.

modelo: Escalera: **Ana sube la escalera para ir a su cuarto.**

1. comedor: _Answers will vary:_ **Ana almuerza en el comedor.** _____

2. sala: _Answers will vary:_ **Ana mira la televisión en la sala.** _____

3. cocina: _Answers will vary:_ **Ana prepara la comida en la cocina.** _____

4. cuarto: _Answers will vary:_ **Ana escucha música en su cuarto.** _____

5. jardín: _Answers will vary:_ **Ana lee un libro en el jardín.** _____

3 In two complete sentences, describe what you do in your room.

1. _Answers will vary:_ **En mi cuarto, juego videojuegos.** _____

2. _Answers will vary:_ **En mi cuarto, escucho discos compactos.** _____

Gramática A *Ser and estar*

Level 1, pp. 253-257

> ¡AVANZA! **Goal:** Describe people and locations using ser or estar.

1 Julieta's friends all have different personal traits. Complete the sentences below using the verb in parenthesis.

1. María _____ es _____ inteligente. (ser)

2. Julio y Marcos _____ están _____ en Ecuador. (estar)

3. Norma y yo _____ estamos _____ cansadas. (estar)

4. Tú _____ eres _____ un estudiante de español. (ser)

5. Hoy _____ es _____ el tres de agosto. (ser)

2 There's a lot to say about the students below. Complete the following sentences using the words from the word box.

están	estás	soy	son
somos	estoy	están	está

1. Yo _____ soy _____ de Ecuador.

2. Rafael _____ está _____ contento.

3. Nosotros _____ somos _____ estudiantes.

4. María y tú _____ están _____ bien.

5. Ellos _____ son _____ mis maestros.

6. Señora y Señor Perdomo, ¿ustedes _____ están _____ en casa hoy?

7. ¡Hola, María Fernanda! ¿Cómo _____ estás _____ tú?

8. ¡Hola, Mario! Yo _____ estoy _____ bien.

3 Describe yourself and your friends by answering the following questions with a complete sentence.

1. ¿Cómo estás?

   Answers will vary: **¡Yo estoy muy bien!** _____

2. ¿Cómo son tus amigos o tus amigas?

   Answers will vary: **Mis amigos son altos, bajos, inteligentes y trabajadores.** _____

Gramática B *Ser and estar*

> **¡AVANZA!** **Goal:** Describe people and locations using **ser** or **estar**.

1 Write four complete sentences about the following students' characteristics. Use the information in the table.

Laura	ser	inteligente(s)
Silvia y Andrés	estar	ocupado(a)(s)
Camila y yo	ser	de Ecuador
Ramiro	estar	cansad(o)(a)

1. *Answers will vary:* **Laura es de Ecuador.**
2. *Answers will vary:* **Silvia y Andrés son inteligentes.**
3. *Answers will vary:* **Camila y yo somos de Ecuador.**
4. *Answers will vary:* **Ramiro está cansado.**

2 Nicolás is introducing his friends. Complete the sentences with either **ser** or **estar**.

1. Javier _____ es _____ maestro.
2. Armando y Luisa _____ están _____ en la escuela.
3. Miguel y yo _____ estamos _____ enojados.
4. Tú _____ eres _____ un buen amigo.
5. Norberto y tú _____ están _____ emocionados.

3 Using two complete sentences, describe two of your friends and say where he or she is from.

Answers will vary: **Mi amigo Jorge es divertido, bueno y estudioso. Él es de**

Perú y está en mi clase.

_____

_____

_____

Gramática C *Ser and estar*

> **¡AVANZA!** **Goal:** Describe people and locations using **ser** or **estar**.

1 Carina and her friends each have their own characteristics. Get to know them by completing the following sentences with the correct verb form of **ser** or **estar**.

1. Ernesto y Matías _____ son _____ buenas personas.

2. Isabel _____ está _____ bien.

3. Miriam y yo _____ somos _____ maestras.

4. ¿Tú _____ estás _____ contento?

5. Marta _____ es _____ mi amiga.

6. El _____ está _____ feliz.

7. Ellos _____ son _____ de México.

8. Ustedes _____ están _____ cansados.

2 Using the cues below, write complete sentences to say where the following people are or what they are like.

1. Elisa / su cuarto.

   Elisa está en su cuarto.

2. María y Diego / inteligentes.

   María y Diego son muy inteligentes.

3. Pedro y yo / buenos amigos.

   Pedro y yo somos buenos amigos.

4. Gabriela y tú / cansados de caminar.

   Gabriela y tú están cansados de caminar.

3 Write three complete sentences about what you are like, where you are from, and how you are feeling.

Answers will vary: **Soy un buen estudiante y soy muy**

tranquilo. Soy de Los Ángeles. Estoy cansado pero estoy contento.

_____

_____

Gramática A *Ordinal Numbers*

> **¡AVANZA!** **Goal:** Use ordinal numbers to talk about the floors of a building and to indicate the order of things.

1 Match the ordinal numbers in the left column to the appropriate numerals in the right column.

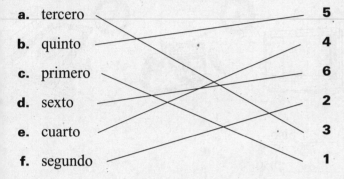

a. tercero   5

b. quinto   4

c. primero   6

d. sexto   2

e. cuarto   3

f. segundo   1

2 The following friends are standing in line, one behind the other, to go into the movies. They are in the following order: Julia, Aníbal, Santiago, Pedro, and Lucía. Complete the sentences below, stating where each is in line:

1. Lucía es la _____ quinta _____ persona.

2. Aníbal es la _____ segunda _____ persona.

3. Pedro es la _____ cuarta _____ persona.

4. Santiago es la _____ tercera _____ persona.

5. Julia es la _____ primera _____ persona.

3 Answer the following question in a complete sentence.

1. ¿Qué es la primera cosa que haces cuando llegas a la escuela?

   Answers will vary: **La primera cosa que hago cuando llego a la escuela es hablar**

   con mis amigos.

2. ¿Qué es la segunda cosa que haces en la mañana?

   Answers will vary: **La segunda cosa que hago en la mañana es levantarme.**

   _____

3. ¿Qué es la primera cosa que haces cuando llegas de la escuela?

   Answers will vary: **La primera cosa que hago cuando llego de la escuela es**

   jugar con mi perro.

Gramática B *Ordinal Numbers*

> **¡AVANZA!** **Goal:** Use ordinal numbers to talk about the floors of a building and to indicate the order of things.

1 Look at the numbers next to each drawing that indicate the floor on which you can find each item. Use ordinal number to complete the sentences.

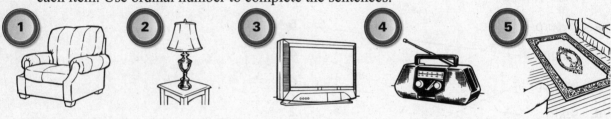

1. Hay sillones en _____ el primer _____ piso.

2. Hay alfombras en _____ el quinto _____ piso.

3. Hay radios en _____ el cuarto _____ piso.

4. Hay lámparas en _____ el segundo _____ piso.

5. Hay televisores en _____ el tercer _____ piso.

2 Pablo, Marcos, Letty, Mirna, and Julio are waiting in line at the bookstore. They are standing in line in the same order they have been mentioned.

1. Mirna es _____ la cuarta _____ en la fila.

2. Marcos es _____ el segundo _____ en la fila.

3. Pablo es _____ el primero _____ en la fila.

4. Julio es _____ el quinto _____ en la fila.

5. Letty es _____ la tercera _____ en la fila.

3 Answer the following questions in complete sentences.

1. ¿Qué es la primera cosa que ves cuando vuelves a tu casa?

   Answers will vary: **Lo primero que veo es una alfombra.**

   _____

2. ¿Cuál es tu tercera clase los lunes?

   Answers will vary: **Mi tercera clase los lunes es ciencias.**

   _____

Gramática C   *Ordinal Numbers*

¡AVANZA! **Goal:** Use ordinal numbers to talk about the floors of a building and to indicate the order of things.

1 The following runners are in a race. Look at their time and tell in which place each runner got to the finish line. Sigue el modelo.

modelo:	Katy Méndez	2:00	**cuarto lugar**
1.	Juana López	3:10	décimo
2.	Manuel Antonio	1:57	primero
3.	Pablo Santos	2:05	sexto
4.	José Colón	3:01	noveno
5.	Julio Ortíz	1:58	segundo
6.	María Gonzalez	2:45	octavo
7.	Roberto Martínez	2:38	séptimo
8.	Rosa Castillo	1:59	tercero
9.	Melvin Bravo	2:01	quinto

2 There are five people in line, in the following order: María, Diana, Carlos, Paola, y Verónica. Complete the text with ordinal numbers.

Hay cuatro personas detrás de la **1.** _____primera_____

persona. Diana está detrás de María y delante de Carlos. Diana es la

2. _____segunda_____ persona en la fila. Verónica está

detrás de Carlos y Paola. Verónica es la

3. _____quinta_____ persona en la fila. Carlos está entre

Diana y Paola. Carlos es la **4.** _____tercera_____ persona

en la fila. Paola está delante de Verónica. Verónica es la

5. _____cuarta_____ · persona de la fila.

3 Write a complete sentence stating what your first, second, and third classes are on Fridays.

Answers will vary: **El viernes la primera clase es historia, la segunda**

clase es ciencias y la tercera clase es español.

Integración: Hablar

Level 1, pp. 261-263
WB CD 03 track 01

Débora has a new apartment and needs to buy things for it. Also, she has to buy clothes for the housewarming party. She hears a radio commercial for a nearby mall where they have everything she wants to buy. So, she decides to go shopping there.

Fuente 1 Leer

Read the information in the mall directory.

> ### CENTRO COMERCIAL ALTAVISTA
>
> PRIMER PISO: ROPA DE MUJERES
>
> SEGUNDO PISO: ROPA DE HOMBRES
>
> TERCER PISO: ROPA DE NIÑOS
>
> CUARTO PISO: MUEBLES
>
> QUINTO PISO: COSAS PARA LA SALA
>
> SEXTO PISO: CINES Y COSAS DIVERTIDAS

Fuente 2 Escuchar   *CD 03 track 02*

Listen to the radio ad that Débora listened to before going to the mall. Take notes.

_____

_____

_____

Hablar

What items can Débora buy for her new place and for the party? Explain where she can find these items.

modelo: Débora puede comprar... en el... piso. Después, puede comprar...en...

Answers will vary: **Débora puede comprar camas, sillones y cómodas en el cuarto piso. Después, puede comprar un radio, un televisor, un tocadiscos compactos, una lámpara y un lector de DVD en el quinto piso. Puede comprar un vestido en el primer piso.**

Integración: Escribir

Vilma is very happy because her parents bought a new house. She really likes the house, so she writes and e-mail to her best friend, Patricia, about the distribution of rooms, colors, and size of her new place. Then Vilma goes to a big department store with her family to buy things for the new place.

Fuente 1 Leer

Read Vilma's e-mail to Patricia...

> ¡Hola Patricia!
>
> ¡Tengo una casa nueva! Es la casa ideal. Tiene una cocina muy grande y tres cuartos. También hay un comedor donde comemos la cena cada noche. Está al lado de la cocina y detrás de la sala. Delante de la casa hay un jardín muy bonito y detrás de la casa hay un patio más grande que el jardín. Esta casa es más grande que la otra y necesitamos más muebles.
>
> Besos,
>
> Vilma

Fuente 2 Escuchar   CD 03 track 04

Listen to Manuel, the clerk at the deparment store, calling the stockroom on the second floor. Take notes.

_____
_____
_____
_____

Escribir

Vilma's family bought a lot of things to furnish their new house. How can they distribute them inside the house?

Modelo: Los sillones están en...y la...

Answers will vary: **Los sillones pueden estar en la sala. La cama grande**

es para el cuarto de los padres de Vilma y las camas pequeñas son

para los otros cuartos. La cómoda y el armario también están en

los cuartos.

_____
_____

Escuchar A

Level 1, pp. 268-269
WB CD 03 tracks 05-06

> **¡AVANZA!** **Goal:** Listen to hear about household items.

1 Listen to Cristian. Then, look at the list and draw a line through the articles that his parents do not buy.

~~cómoda~~

cortinas

~~televisor~~

sillón

~~espejo~~

alfombra

lector DVD

~~radio~~

2 Listen to Olga Uribe talk about her home. Then choose the correct answer to each question.

1. ¿Por qué necesitan Olga y su esposo una casa más grande? __a__

   a. Porque sus hijos vuelven de otra ciudad.

   b. Porque no les gusta la casa que tienen.

2. ¿Qué quieren comprar para sus hijos? __b__

   a. Quieren comprar un sillón, un tocadiscos compactos y un lector DVD.

   b. Quieren comprar camas nuevas, cortinas, radios y alfombras.

3. ¿Dónde están los hijos de Olga? __b__

   a. Están en su cuarto.

   b. Están en otra ciudad.

Escuchar B

Level 1, pp. 268-269
WB CD 03 tracks 07-08

 Goal: Listen to hear about household items.

1 Listen to Carmen and take notes. Then, place an "X" next to the things she has in her room.

1. ____ escalera

2. __X__ cortinas

3. ____ espejo

4. __X__ cama

5. ____ cómoda

6. __X__ discos compactos

7. ____ radio

8. ____ armario

9. __X__ lector DVD

10. ____ sillón

2 Listen to Lorena and Norberto. Then, answer the questions in complete sentences.

1. ¿Qué discos de su músico preferido tiene Lorena?

    Tiene el segundo y el tercero. _____

    _____

2. ¿Qué quiere Lorena?

    Lorena quiere el primer disco de su músico preferido. _____

3. ¿Quién tiene el disco que no tiene Lorena?

    Norberto tiene el disco que no tiene Lorena. _____

    _____

Escuchar C

Level 1, pp. 268-269
WB CD 03 track 09-10

┌───┐
│ ¡AVANZA! **Goal:** Listen about household items.   │
└───┘

1 Listen to the conversation between Claudia and Ana. Take notes. Then complete the table below with what each one does. (Notice that Ana speaks first.)

ser un buen amigo	comprar un radio	comprar discos compactos
comprar un espejo	comprar un apartamento	comprar una alfombra
ir al centro comercial	almorzar con su hermano	

¿Quién?	¿Qué hace?
Claudia	Comprar un radio
Ana	Almorzar con su hermano Comprar una alfombra
El hermano de Ana	Comprar un apartamento
Ana y Claudia	Ir al centro comercial

2 Listen to Martín and take notes. Then complete the sentences.

1. Primero, Martín tiene que ver un apartamento. _____

2. Segundo, Martín tiene que almorzar con sus amigos. _____

3. Tercero, Martín tiene que ir a comprar discos compactos con Juan. _____

4. Cuarto, Martín tiene que comprar unas cortinas. _____

Leer A

> **¡AVANZA!** **Goal:** Read about households.

Juan has a new apartment. There are four different families that live in the building.
The girl on the first floor gives him a list of the families that live there.

La Familia Ordóñez vive en la planta baja.
La Familia Gutiérrez vive en el piso uno.
La Familia Pérez vive en el piso dos.
Juan vive en el piso tres.
La Familia Martínez vive en el piso cuatro.
La Familia Gómez vive en el piso cinco.

¿Comprendiste?

Read the list of families. Then, complete the sentences below using ordinal numbers.

1. La familia Pérez vive en el _____ segundo _____ piso.

2. La familia Gómez está en el _____ quinto _____ piso.

3. La familia Gutiérrez está en el _____ primer _____ piso.

4. Juan vive en el _____ tercer _____ piso.

5. La familia Martínez vive en el _____ cuarto _____ piso.

¿Qué piensas?

¿Piensas que es mejor vivir en el primer piso o en el quinto piso? ¿Por qué?

Answers will vary: **Pienso que es mejor vivir en el primer piso porque no**

necesitas subir la escalera.

_____

_____

_____

_____

_____

Leer B

Level 1, pp. 268-269

 Goal: Read about households.

Señora Díaz has a new house and goes to the mall to buy furniture and appliances. She writes a note about what she buys and at what time. The problem is that she does not write the items in order.

> La señora Díaz compró los discos compactos a las 9:45 a.m. Pero, quince minutos antes, compró un espejo. Dos horas después de comprar los discos compactos, compró las cortinas. A las 10:15 a.m. compró un lector DVD, y luego a las 12:10 p.m. compró una cómoda. A las 4:00 p.m. compró un sillón.

¿Comprendiste?

Read Señora Díaz' notes. Complete the chart with the ordinal number indicating the order in which she bought the following items.

Cosas	Orden
discos compactos	segundo
sillón	sexto
cómoda	quinto
cortinas	cuarto
espejo	primero
lector DVD	tercero

¿Qué piensas?

¿Adónde vas de compras? ¿Cuántos pisos hay allí?

Answers will vary: **Voy de compras al centro comercial. Hay siete pisos allí.**

_____

_____

_____

_____

_____

_____

Leer C

> ¡AVANZA! **Goal:** Read about households.

Roberto writes a letter to his sister to tell her about his new apartment and the people who live in the building.

Julia:

Tengo muchos amigos aquí. Encima de mi apartamento vive Inés, una maestra de ciencias. Encima de Inés, y debajo de Walter, vive Hugo, un estudiante de otra ciudad. Encima del apartamento de Walter está el apartamento de Lorena. Son cinco pisos. Debajo de mi apartamento, en la planta baja, está el apartamento de Ernesto. Allí escuchamos música todos los viernes.

Besos,

Roberto

¿Comprendiste?

Read Roberto's letter. Then complete the table below with the name of the person who lives on each floor.

Piso	Nombre
planta baja	Ernesto
primer piso	Roberto
segundo piso	Inés
tercer piso	Hugo
cuarto piso	Walter
quinto piso	Lorena

¿Qué piensas?

¿Piensas que es divertido vivir en un apartamento con muchos pisos? ¿Por qué?

Answers will vary: **Sí, pienso que es divertido porque muchos chicos viven allí con sus familias.**

_____

_____

_____

Escribir A

> **¡AVANZA!** **Goal:** Write about your house and household items.

Step 1

Make a list of six places in your house. *Order will vary:*

1. sala
2. comedor
3. cocina
4. cuarto
5. patio
6. jardín

Step 2

Classify your list in the table. Choose three places from your list, and write the items you would put in them. *Order will vary:*

el cuarto	el comedor	la sala
1. alfombra	1. cortinas	1. sofá
2. cortinas	2. mesa	2. muebles
3. cama	3. sillas	3. cortinas

Step 3

Write three sentences to state each of the three rooms you chose and what they contain. Use the information from the chart. *Answers will vary:*

Yo tengo una alfombra grande en mi cuarto. Tengo una mesa y cuatro

sillas en el comedor. Tengo un sofá en la sala.

Step 4

Evaluate your writing using the information in the table.

Writing Criteria	Excellent	Good	Needs Work
Content	You described three rooms.	You described two rooms.	You described one room.
Communication	Most of your response is clear.	Some of your response is clear.	Your message is not very clear.
Accuracy	You make few mistakes in grammar and vocabulary.	You make some mistakes in grammar and vocabulary.	You make many mistakes in grammar and vocabulary.

Escribir B

> **¡AVANZA!** **Goal:** Write about your house and household items.

Step 1

Complete the following table with an alphabetical list of furniture and household items in your house: *Answer will vary:*

Muebles	Otras cosas para la casa
Primero: Armario	Primero: Lector DVD
Segundo: Cama	Segundo: Radio
Tercero: Cómoda	Tercero: Televisor
Cuarto: Sillón	Cuarto: Tocadiscos compactos

Step 2

Write a paragraph using the four items from the chart. Use **ser** and **estar**.

Answer will vary: Yo tengo una cama y un armario en mi cuarto. También

tengo un tocadiscos compactos. El tocadiscos compactos está en

la cómoda. Mi papá siempre está en el sillón; le gusta escuchar música.

Step 3

Evaluate your writing using the information in the table.

Writing Criteria	Excellent	Good	Needs Work
Content	You have used the four items from the chart.	You have used some items from the chart.	You have not used any items from the chart.
Communication	Most of your response is clear.	Some of your response is clear.	Your message is not very clear.
Accuracy	You make few mistakes in grammar and vocabulary.	You make some mistakes in grammar and vocabulary.	You make many mistakes in grammar and vocabulary.

Escribir C

Level 1, pp. 268-269

 Goal: Write about your house and household items.

Write a list of the favorite items you have at home in the order that you like them.

Step 1

Complete the table with facts about your favorite things using complete sentences. Use **ser** and **estar**. *Answers will vary:*

Objeto	Ser	Estar
El televisor	El televisor es negro.	El televisor está en la sala.
El radio	El radio es nuevo.	El radio está en mi cuarto.
El tocadiscos compactos	El tocadiscos compactos es de mi papá.	El tocadiscos compactos está en el comedor.

Step 2

Write a paragraph using the information from the chart. Write about your favorite objects and in the order that you like them.

Answers will vary: Mi primer objeto favorito es el radio, que es nuevo

y está en mi cuarto. Mi segundo objeto favorito es el televisor negro que

está en la sala. Mi tercer objeto favorito es el tocadiscos compactos de mi

papá. Está en el comedor.

Step 3

Evaluate your writing using the information in the table.

Writing Criteria	Excellent	Good	Needs Work
Content	You have used all items from the chart.	You have used some items from the chart.	You have not used items from the chart.
Communication	Most of your response is clear.	Some of your response is clear.	Your message is not very clear.
Accuracy	You make few mistakes in grammar and vocabulary.	You make some mistakes in grammar and vocabulary.	You make many mistakes in grammar and vocabulary.

Cultura A

┌───┐
│ ¡AVANZA! **Goal:** Review cultural information about Ecuador. │
└───┘

1 **Ecuadorian culture** Complete the following sentences with one of the multiple choice words or phrases.

1. The capital of Ecuador is __b__

   a. Guayaquil   **b.** Quito   **c.** Otavalo

2. Quechua is one of the __c__ of Ecuador.

   a. typical foods   **b.** volcanoes   **c.** languages

3. Camilo Egas was the Ecuadoran artist who painted __c__

   a. *Las coristas*   **b.** *Las porristas*   **c.** *Las floristas*

2 **Ecuador and Argentina** Choose the correct word to complete the following sentences.

1. Otavalo is a (town / mountain) north of Quito.

2. Cotopaxi, the active volcano, is the (shortest / tallest) in the world.

3. Ushuaia, Argentina is the (southernmost / smallest) city in the world.

4. The Andean mountain chain is in (Central / South) America.

5. Since 2000, the Ecuadorian currency has been the (dollar / peso).

3 **Geography of Ecuador** Explain what is unique about Ecuador's geographical location. What is the Mitad del Mundo monument? Would you like to visit it? Why or why not?

Answers will vary: **Ecuador's geographical location is unique because it**

is located on the equator. The Mitad del Mundo monument is located

on the equator. At the monument you can stand with one foot in

each hemisphere.

_____

_____

_____

Level 1, pp. 268-269

> **¡AVANZA!** **Goal:** Review cultural information about Ecuador.

1 **Ecuador** Read the following sentences about Ecuador and answer *true* or *false*.

T (F) **1.** The Copa Mundial is a baseball tournament.

(T) F **2.** **Canguil** is a typical Ecuadorian dish.

T (F) **3.** The town of Otavalo is south of Quito.

(T) F **4.** In Quito and Guayaquil, the major league soccer teams play on the weekends.

(T) F **5.** The two main languages of Ecuador are Spanish and Quechua.

2 **In Ecuador** Read the following sentences about Ecuador and write the correct words from the box.

Quito	quechua	Egas
Andes	Otavalo	

1. Capital of Ecuador: _____Quito_____

2. Last name of the painter of *Las floristas:* _____Egas_____

3. A language other than Spanish spoken in Ecuador: _____Quechua_____

4. Mountain range in South America: _____Andes_____

5. Market town in Ecuador, north of Quito: _____Otavalo_____

3 **Ecuadorian art** You work at an art museum that is having an exhibit featuring Ecuadorian art. Describe the paintings on p. 245 and p. 255. Tell who painted each and how the painting reflects Ecuadorian culture. Also, give your impressions of each painting.

Answers will vary. _____

_____

_____

_____

_____

Cultura C

> ¡AVANZA! **Goal:** Review cultural information about Ecuador.

1 **Ecuadorian culture** Complete the following sentences about Ecuador by filling in the correct word.

1. Julio Jaramillo was a famous Ecuadorian ___singer___ .

2. ___Quito___ is the capital of Ecuador.

3. In Ecuador, they speak Spanish and many indigenous languages such as ___Quechua___ .

4. Cotopaxi is a ___volcano___ found in Ecuador.

5. Ecuador is located in ___South___ America.

2 **Ecuadorian culture** Answer these questions about Ecuador with complete sentences.

1. What has been the currency of Ecuador since 2000? ___Since 2000, the Ecuadorian___ ___currency has been the United States dollar.___

2. Who was Camilo Egas and what kind of work did he create? ___Camilo Egas was___ ___an artist from Ecuador who painted Las floristas.___

3. Which is the tallest active volcano in the world? ___The tallest active volcano___ ___in the world is Cotopaxi.___

3 **Trip to Ecuador** In Ecuador, there are many beautiful places to visit. If you won a trip for two days to Ecuador, which places would you visit? Write a paragraph about which parts of Ecuador you would like to visit and why.

___Answers will vary.___

_____

_____

_____

Vocabulario A

UNIDAD 5 • Vocabulario A
Lección 2

¡AVANZA!	**Goal:** Talk about chores and responsibilities.

1 We've got to do chores! Place an "x" next to those activities that are household chores.

1. ____ cantar   6. ____ decorar
2. _X_ barrer   7. _X_ planchar
3. ____ bailar   8. _X_ barrer
4. _X_ limpiar   9. ____ comer
5. _X_ lavar   10. ____ celebrar

2 Miriam's dad talks to her about what she has to do around the house today. Complete their conversation using the words from the box.

lavar	la basura	la mesa	las camas	pasar

Padre: ¡Miriam!, tenemos que hacer ____las camas____ del cuarto de Luis.

Miriam: Sí, papá, también tenemos que ____pasar____ la aspiradora.

Padre: Además, tenemos que ____lavar____ los platos.

Miriam: Yo prefiero poner ____la mesa____ .

Padre: Yo saco ____la basura____ .

3 Answer the following questions in a complete sentence.

1. ¿Qué cosas haces para limpiar tu cuarto?

   Answers will vary: **Yo hago la cama y paso la aspiradora.** _____

2. ¿Te gusta bailar en las fiestas?

   Answers will vary: **Sí, me gusta mucho bailar en las fiestas.** _____

3. ¿Con quién celebras tu cumpleaños?

   Answers will vary: **Celebro mi cumpleaños con mis amigos.** _____

Vocabulario B

Level 1, pp. 272-276

> ¡AVANZA! **Goal:** Talk about chores and responsibilities.

1 Inés wants to clean the house. Underline the word that best completes each sentence.

1. Ellas tienen que hacer muchos (secretos / <u>quehaceres</u>) en casa.

2. Inés tiene que pasar (<u>la aspiradora</u> / la ropa).

3. Inés y su mamá tienen que hacer (la basura / <u>la cama</u>).

4. El hermano de Inés tiene que cortar (<u>el césped</u> / el suelo).

5. La mamá de Inés tiene que cocinar (<u>la comida</u> / la mesa).

6. Inés tiene que lavar (los regalos / <u>los platos</u>).

2 Luisa's mom asks her to do some chores around the house. Complete the sentences with the appropriate verb.

1. Tienes que _____*darle de comer*_____ al gato.

2. Debes _____*barrer el suelo*_____ en la cocina; el suelo está sucio.

3. Tienes que _____*planchar la ropa*_____ de tu hermano y la ropa de tu hermana también.

4. Hay que _____*sacar la basura*_____ antes de las 6:00 p.m.

5. Debes _____*poner la mesa*_____ del comedor para la cena.

3 Write three complete sentences to describe what you do to clean up around the house and when you do it.

1. *Answers will vary:* **Yo saco la basura todas las noches.**

2. *Answers will vary:* **Yo hago mi cama todos los días.**

3. *Answers will vary:* **Yo corto el césped dos veces al mes.**

Vocabulario C

> **¡AVANZA!** **Goal:** Talk about chores and responsibilities.

1 A clean house is nicer! Draw a line from the verbs to the nouns to complete the list of chores.

1. hacer
2. barrer
3. pasar
4. lavar
5. cortar
6. planchar
7. poner
8. sacar

a. el césped
b. la basura
c. el suelo
d. la ropa
e. la cama
f. la aspiradora
g. la mesa
h. los platos

2 There's a party at Norma's house today. There's still a lot to do to get ready. Complete the following text.

Hoy damos una fiesta en casa para **1.** _____ celebrar _____

el cumpleaños de mi hermana. No debes decir nada porque

es una **2.** _____ sorpresa _____ . Tengo que

3. _____ envolver _____ el regalo pero necesito buscar papel

de regalo. Tenemos globos y otras **4.** _____ decoraciones _____ .

Los **5.** _____ invitados _____ van a llegar a las cinco y todavía

necesito hacer los quehaceres. ¡Todo está perfecto!

3 Write a description of the chores you do at home. Include at least three chores.

Answers will vary: **Yo barro, pongo la mesa y a veces lavo los platos.**

También paso la aspiradora y cocino los sábados.

_____

_____

_____

Nombre _____ Clase _____ Fecha _____

Gramática A *Irregular Verbs*

Level 1, pp. 277-281

 Goal: Use **dar, decir, poner, salir, traer,** and **venir** to talk about preparations for a party.

1 There's a party at Carla's house today. Circle the verb that completes each sentence.

1. Hoy, su familia (dan / (da)) una fiesta por el cumpleaños de Luis.

2. Sus amigos le ((traen) / traigo) muchos regalos.

3. Por la noche, todos (sales / (salimos)) a cenar.

4. También Carla (venís / (viene)) a la fiesta.

5. Yo (pone / (pongo)) una bonita decoración en el jardín.

6. Nosotros (digo / (decimos)): «¡Feliz cumpleaños, Luis!»

2 Use the elements below to write a complete sentence describing a surprise party.

1. Yo / dar una fiesta. *Yo doy una fiesta.*

2. Jaime y yo / traer regalos. *Jaime y yo traemos regalos.*

3. Marcos / decir a qué hora es la fiesta. *Marcos dice a qué hora es la fiesta.*

4. Carmen y Marcos / poner la mesa. *Carmen y Marcos ponen la mesa.*

5. Ella / pasar la aspiradora. *Ella pasa la aspiradora.*

3 Answer the following question in a complete sentence.

1. ¿Das fiestas en casa?

   Answers will vary: **Sí, doy muchas fiestas en casa.**

   _____

2. ¿Quién viene a tus fiestas?

   Answers will vary: **Mis amigos vienen a mis fiestas.**

   _____

3. ¿Qué traes a la fiesta de cumpleaños de tu amigo(a)?

   Answers will vary: **Traigo un disco compacto de regalo.**

   _____

UNIDAD 5 Lección 2 • Gramática A

¡Avancemos! 1
Cuaderno: Práctica por niveles

Unidad 5, Lección 2
Gramática A   **223**

Gramática B *Irregular Verbs*

> ¡AVANZA! **Goal:** Use **dar**, **decir**, **poner**, **salir**, **traer**, and **venir** to talk about preparations for a party.

1 Lucas's party is tomorrow. Complete the text below, by choosing and correctly conjugating the correct verb in the box.

traer	dar	salir	decir	venir

Lucas y su familia **1.** _____dan_____ una fiesta esta tarde. Yo

2. _____vengo_____ de muy lejos para esta fiesta. Mi hermana y yo

3. _____traemos_____ muchos regalos para Lucas y su familia. Ellos

4. _____dicen_____ que nosotros somos parte de la familia. Mi

hermana y yo **5.** _____salimos_____ en el autobús de esta tarde.

2 Irma always wants to do what Manuel and Sofía do. Complete the dialogue with the correct form of **venir, traer, dar,** or **poner.**

Manuel: Sofía y yo **1.** _____damos_____ fiestas los viernes.

Irma: Yo también **2.** _____doy_____ fiestas los viernes.

Sofía: Manuel y yo **3.** _____ponemos_____ globos en la sala.

Irma: Yo también **4.** _____pongo_____ globos en la sala.

Manuel: Nosotros **5.** _____traemos_____ los discos compactos de rock.

Irma: Yo también **6.** _____traigo_____ los discos compactos de rock.

Sofía: **7.** Nosotros _____decimos_____ que vamos a bailar.

Irma: **8.** Yo también _____digo_____ que vamos a bailar.

3 Write three sentences using the verbs **traer, poner,** and **salir** to describe what you do when you go to a party.

Answers will vary: **Yo traigo regalos a la fiesta. También pongo la mesa para**

ayudar. A las once salgo con mis amigos.

_____

Gramática C *Irregular Verbs*

> **¡AVANZA!** **Goal:** Use **dar, decir, poner, salir, traer,** and **venir** to talk about preparations for a party.

1 Ángel and Ana are invited to a party at my house. Complete each sentences with the appropriate form of the verb.

1. Ángel _____viene_____ a las 3:00 p.m. (venir)

2. Yo nunca _____digo_____ un secreto. (decir)

3. Ángel y Ana _____traen_____ un postre muy rico. (traer)

4. Ana me ayuda y _____pone_____ la mesa. (poner)

5. ¿Tú también _____vienes_____ a mi fiesta? (venir)

2 Today is Juan's birthday. Use the correct form of the verb in parentheses to complete the sentences.

1. Para la fiesta, yo (poner) _____pongo la mesa_____ .

2. Mi amiga Lucía y yo (dar) _____damos regalos a Juan_____ .

3. Jaime y tú (salir) _____salen a bailar en la noche_____ .

4. Andrea y Nicolás (traer) _____traen el postre_____ .

5. También otros amigos de Juan (venir) _____vienen_____ a la fiesta.

3 Write a four sentence paragraph describing what you do when you go to a birthday party. Use at least four of the following verbs: **dar, poner, venir, traer, salir, decir.**

Answers will vary: **Cuando voy a una fiesta de cumpleaños siempre doy**

regalos. También traigo globos. Siempre los pongo en la sala. También me

gusta ayudar con la decoración. Siempre digo «¡Feliz cumpleaños!»

_____

_____

Gramática A   Affirmative **tú** Commands and
Acabar de + infinitive

> **¡AVANZA!** **Goal:** Tell people what to do and say what people just did.

1 You're being asked to do some chores. Underline the sentences that are commands.

1. Ayudas en la cocina.

2. Lava los platos.

3. Pasa la aspiradora.

4. Cortas el césped.

5. Haz la cama.

6. Pon la mesa.

7. Planchan la ropa.

8. Limpiamos la sala.

9. Di el secreto.

10. Cocino todos los días.

2 All these kids do what their mothers ask. Write the mother's command. Follow the model.

modelo: Ana (barrer el suelo).
    Madre: Ana, ¡barre el suelo!

1. Luis (preparar el desayuno).

Madre: Luis, ¡ _____prepara_____ el desayuno!

2. Claudia (servir la cena).

Madre: Claudia, ¡ _____sirve_____ la cena!

3. Laura (barrer el patio).

Madre: Laura, ¡ _____barre_____ el patio!

4. Ernesto (sacar la basura).

Madre: Ernesto, ¡ _____saca_____ la basura!

3 Answer the following questions in a complete sentences:

1. ¿Qué acabas de hacer?

Answers will vary: **Yo acabo de ir a la cafetería.**

2. ¿Con quién acabas de hablar?

Answers will vary: **Yo acabo de hablar con mi amiga Diana.**

3. ¿Adónde acabas de ir?

Answers will vary: **Yo acabo de ir al restaurante.**

Gramática B   *Affirmative **tú** Commands and* *Acabar de + infinitive*

 Goal: Tell people what to do and say what people just did.

1 Your friend is having a party at home today and asks for your help. Complete the sentences by choosing the correct affirmative **tú** command.

1. __c__ los regalos con papel de regalo.

   a. Envuelven   **b.** Envuelves   **c.** Envuelve   **d.** Envuelvo

2. __b__ a buscar a Norma que viene en autobús.

   a. Sales   **b.** Sal   **c.** Sale   **d.** Salen

3. __a__ esos globos en el patio.

   a. Pon   **b.** Pone   **c.** Ponen   **d.** Pones

4. __d__ la primera persona en llegar.

   a. Soy   **b.** Son   **c.** Es   **d.** Sé

2 You and a few friends have just finished cleaning up after a party. Write a sentence with the elements below. Follow the model.

modelo: ¡Saca la basura! (Carmela y yo)
   Carmela y yo acabamos de sacar la basura.

1. ¡Limpia la cocina! (Andrés y Luis)

   Andrés y Luis acaban de limpiar la cocina.

2. ¡Barre el suelo de la cocina! (yo)

   Yo acabo de barrer el suelo de la cocina.

3. ¡Pasa la aspiradora! (Luis)

   Luis acaba de pasar la aspiradora.

4. ¡Lava los platos! (tú)

   Tú acabas de lavar los platos.

3 Your friend is helping you clean your house. Write two sentences telling him or her what to do using two affirmative **tú** commands.

   Answers will vary: **Luis, por favor barre la cocina. Luis, por favor saca**

   la basura.

_____

Gramática C
Affirmative *tú* Commands and *Acabar de* + infinitive

¡AVANZA!	**Goal:** Tell people what to do and say what people just did.

1 Your friend is telling you what to do to help get ready for his party. Complete the sentences with the correct affirmative **tú** command.

1. _____Pon_____ los globos en la sala. (poner)

2. _____Ven_____ a la cocina para cocinar. (venir)

3. _____Barre_____ el suelo en el comedor. (barrer.)

4. _____Lava_____ los platos sucios. (lavar)

5. _____Ve_____ a la tienda a comprar decoraciones. (ir)

6. _____Abre_____ la puerta por favor. (abrir)

2 You ask a friend to help you with your party. Complete the dialog with your requests. Use direct object pronouns.

modelo: **Tu amigo(a):** Tenemos que buscar más globos.
Tú: Búscalos.

1. **Tu amigo(a):** Tenemos que servir el pastel.

   Tú: _____Sírvelo_____

2. **Tu amigo(a):** Tenemos que poner más globos.

   Tú: _____Ponlos_____

3. **Tu amigo(a):** Tenemos que preparar el jugo.

   Tú: _____Prepáralo_____

3 Write a three-sentence message to your friend explaining what chores you've just done. Then use affirmative **tú** commands to tell him or her what to do to help you get ready for your party.

Answers will vary: Hola Juan, acabo de sacar la basura. Ahora, tengo que

pasar la aspiradora y lavar los platos. Por favor pon la mesa y prepara

la comida.

_____

Integración: Hablar

Level 1, pp. 285-287
WB CD 03 track 11

UNIDAD 5
Lección 2 •
Integración:
Hablar

It's Mónica's birthday and her friends Rebeca and Cristina have plans to celebrate. Cristina is in charge of sending invitations, while Rebeca prepares her house for everybody to come.

Fuente 1 Leer

Read the invitation for the surprise party.

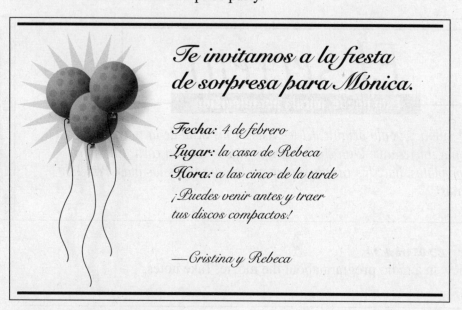

Te invitamos a la fiesta de sorpresa para Mónica.

Fecha: 4 de febrero
Lugar: la casa de Rebeca
Hora: a las cinco de la tarde
¡*Puedes venir antes y traer tus discos compactos!*

—*Cristina y Rebeca*

Fuente 2 Escuchar   *CD 03 track 12*

Listen to the message left by Rebeca on Cristina's voicemail. Take notes.

_____

_____

_____

_____

Hablar

Cristina is planning to arrive early to the surprise party.

modelo: La fiesta es......Si Rebeca llega a las..., tiene que...

Answers will vary: **La fiesta es el sábado a las cinco de la tarde. Si Rebeca llega**

temprano, tiene que ayudar a mover la mesa de la sala al patio,

porque van a bailar.

Integración: Escribir

Level 1, pp. 285-287
CD 03 track 13

The movie *El secreto* advertised and reviewed. Many things happen during the movie, and the sequence of events is supposed to be very entertaining.

Fuente 1 Leer

Read the movie review in a magazine.

El secreto
Esta noche, mírala por televisión.

Busca tu mejor sillón y ponlo delante del televisor. A las ocho de la noche empieza El secreto, película interesante. Una chica trabaja mucho en una casa. Ella barre el suelo, lava los platos, hace las camas y prepara la cena todos los días. Pero hay más, ¡mucho más!.

Fuente 2 Escuchar *CD 03 track 14*

Listen to a review in a radio program about the movie. Take notes.

_____

_____

_____

_____

Escribir

What is the sequence of events in the movie *El secreto*?

modelo: La chica trabaja... Después, ella...

Answers will vary: **La chica trabaja mucho, lava los platos y hace las**

camas. Necesita ayuda. Encuentra un cuarto secreto donde hay

mucho dinero.

_____

_____

_____

_____

_____

Escuchar A

> **¡AVANZA!** **Goal:** Listen to what these people have to do.

1 Listen to Jimena and Mabel. Then, read each statement and answer **Cierto** (*True*) or **Falso** (*False*).

C (F) **1.** Jimena todavía prepara la comida.

(C) F **2.** Mabel todavía limpia la sala.

C (F) **3.** Mabel barre y también pasa la aspiradora.

(C) F **4.** Eduardo tiene que poner la mesa.

C (F) **5.** Eduardo no está en casa.

2 Listen to Norma. Then, answer the following questions in complete sentences.

1. ¿Qué van a hacer los hermanos de Norma?

Van a preparar una fiesta sorpresa.

_____

2. ¿Qué hacen los hermanos de Norma en su casa?

Los hermanos de Norma limpian la casa.

_____

3. ¿Qué celebran hoy?

Celebran el cumpleaños de Norma.

_____

Escuchar B

¡AVANZA! **Goal:** Listen to what these people have to do.

1 Listen to Mariana and take notes. Then, draw a line from the actions in the right column to the person who does it on the left. One person can do more than one thing.

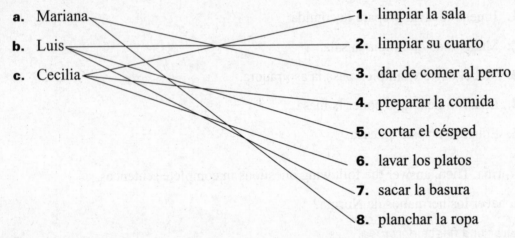

a. Mariana

b. Luis

c. Cecilia

1. limpiar la sala

2. limpiar su cuarto

3. dar de comer al perro

4. preparar la comida

5. cortar el césped

6. lavar los platos

7. sacar la basura

8. planchar la ropa

2 Listen to Luis and Cecilia. Then, answer the following questions in complete sentences.

1. ¿Qué le dice Cecilia a Luis?

   Cecilia le dice: "Tráeme la aspiradora."

2. ¿Por qué Cecilia no quiere ir a buscarla?

   Porque no quiere subir la escalera.

3. ¿Por qué no la trae Luis?

   Porque hace su cama y barre su cuarto.

4. ¿Quién va a ayudar a Luis con su cuarto?

   Cecilia va a ayudarle.

Escuchar C

¡AVANZA! **Goal:** Listen to what these people have to do.

1 Listen to Teresa and her father and take notes. Then, complete the following sentences.

1. Teresa acaba de lavar los platos y sacar la basura.

2. El padre acaba de cortar el césped.

3. Ahora, Teresa va a ayudar a su mama.

4. Ahora, el hermano de Teresa debe poner la mesa.

5. El hermano de Teresa está en su cuarto.

2 Listen to Osvaldo and take notes. Then, in complete sentences, describe what he says about the following things.

1. Los quehaceres de la casa:

A Osvaldo no le gusta hacer los quehaceres de la casa. Los quehaceres de la

casa son para chicas.

2. Cosas que hacen sus amigos:

Los amigos de Osvaldo lavan los platos, ponen la mesa, sacan la basura,

limpian sus cuartos y hacen sus camas. Dicen que Osvaldo tiene

que ayudar.

Level 1, pp. 292-293

 Goal: Read about household chores.

Irma's mom is leaving the city. She leaves a note to tell Irma what she has to do at home.

> Irma:
>
> ¿Puedes ayudar con los quehaceres de la casa?
>
> Hay que preparar el desayuno. Luego, por favor lava los platos. Antes de ir a la escuela, haz la cama, y limpia tu cuarto. Barre la cocina dos veces, en la mañana y en la noche. El domingo hay que cortar el césped del jardín. Luego ¡puedes descansar!
>
> Gracias,
>
> Mamá

¿Comprendiste?

Read the note from Irma's mom. Write the things that Irma has to do in the kitchen. Then write what she must do in her room. Finally, what does she need to do outside?

1. Tiene que preparar el desayuno, lavar los platos y barrer la cocina.

2. Tiene que hacer la cama y limpiar su cuarto.

3. Tiene que cortar el césped del jardín.

¿Qué piensas?

¿Piensas que es bueno ayudar con los quehaceres de la casa? ¿Por qué?

Answers will vary: **Sí, pienso que es muy bueno ayudar con los**

quehaceres de la casa porque puedo ayudar a mis padres.

Leer B

¡AVANZA!	**Goal:** Read about household chores.

Guillermo's father buys a magazine about homes. The following is a letter in that magazine.

> ¡Hola! Tú eres una persona muy ocupada y quieres tu casa siempre limpia.
>
> Aquí hay unas ideas para tenerla así. Primero tu familia debe ayudar. Debes compartir los quehaceres. Tus hijos deben limpiar su cuarto. Ellos necesitan hacer sus camas y limpiar sus cuartos. Pasa la aspiradora en las alfombras una vez por semana. Saca la basura todos los días. Los zapatos necesitan estar limpios antes de entrar a la casa.

¿Comprendiste?

Read the advice from the magazine. Then, complete the sentences.

1. La familia debe compartir los quehaceres.

2. Los hijos limpian su cuarto y hacen sus camas.

3. Para las alfombras, la familia debe pasar la aspiradora una vez por semana.

4. Antes de entrar a la casa, los zapatos deben estar limpios.

¿Qué piensas?

¿Piensas que es importante para una familia compartir los quehaceres? ¿Por qué?

Answers will vary: Pienso que es importante para la familia compartir los quehaceres porque todos necesitan ayudar.

Leer C

> **¡AVANZA!** **Goal:** Read about household chores.

Graciela is having a big party at her house. All of her friends receive the following e-mail.

¡Hola!

El sábado voy a dar una fiesta en mi casa. Es mi cumpleaños y quiero estar con todos mis amigos.

Ven a mi fiesta el sábado a las cinco. Trae tus discos compactos para compartir la música que te gusta con todos.

Hoy pongo unas decoraciones muy bonitas en el patio. Mi papá acaba de cortar el césped y toda la familia ayuda a preparar la fiesta.

¡Ah! Trae mi regalo y envuélvelo con un bonito papel de regalo. (ja ja ja)

Besos,

Graciela

¿Comprendiste?

Read Graciela's e-mail and then answer the following questions.

1. ¿Por qué invita Graciela a sus amigos a su cumpleaños?

Porque quiere estar con sus amigos.

2. ¿Por qué quiere Graciela los discos compactos de todos?

Para compartir la música que les gusta.

3. ¿A qué hora es la fiesta?

La fiesta es a las cinco.

4. ¿Cómo quiere Graciela sus regalos?

Graciela quiere sus regalos en un bonito papel de regalo.

¿Qué piensas?

¿Piensas que es importante invitar a tus amigos a tu cumpleaños? ¿Por qué?

Answers will vary: **Sí, pienso que es importante invitar a mis amigos a mi cumpleaños. Es importante porque me gusta estar con los chicos y las chicas.**

Escribir A

 Goal: Write about chores and responsibilities.

Step 1

Make a list of the six chores you do most at home. *Answers will vary:*

1. sacar la basura

2. hacer mi cama

3. lavar los platos

4. darle de comer al gato

5. cortar el césped

6. poner la mesa

Classify your list in the chart.

Me Gusta	No Me Gusta
1. darle de comer al gato	**1.** sacar la basura
2. cortar el césped	**2.** lavar los platos
3. hacer mi cama	**3.** poner la mesa

Step 2

Write two sentences stating which chores you enjoy doing and three different chores you don't enjoy doing.

Answers will vary: **Me gusta darle de comer al gato, cortar el césped y**

hacer mi cama. No me gusta sacar la basura, lavar los platos y

poner la mesa.

_____

Step 4

Evaluate your writing using the information in the table.

Writing Criteria	Excellent	Good	Needs Work
Content	You have stated which chores you enjoy doing and which you don't.	You have stated some chores you enjoy doing and some you don't.	You have stated few chores you enjoy and don't enjoy doing.
Communication	Most of your response is clear.	Some of your response is clear.	Your message is not very clear.
Accuracy	You make few mistakes in grammar and vocabulary.	You make some mistakes in grammar and vocabulary.	You make many mistakes in grammar and vocabulary.

Escribir B

¡AVANZA! **Goal:** Write about chores and responsibilities.

Step 1

Make a chart with five chores. *Answers will vary.*

Quehaceres
1. cocinar
2. planchar
3. barrer
4. lavar
5. limpiar

Step 2

In a paragraph, say which chores you enjoy the least and which you enjoy the most. Use three ordinal numbers.

Answers will vary: **No me gustan los quehaceres. El primer quehacer que no**

me gusta es barrer. El segundo quehacer que no me gusta es cocinar. El

tercero que no me gusta es planchar, pero me gusta lavar y limpiar.

Step 3

Evaluate your writing using the information in the table.

Writing Criteria	Excellent	Good	Needs Work
Content	You included five chores and three ordinal numbers.	You included some chores and ordinal numbers.	You included few chores and ordinal numbers.
Communication	Most of your response is clear.	Some of your response is clear.	Your message is not very clear.
Accuracy	You make few mistakes in grammar and vocabulary.	You make some mistakes in grammar and vocabulary.	You make many mistakes in grammar and vocabulary.

Escribir C

 Goal: Write about chores and responsibilities.

Step 1

Write a list of six chores your friend has to do to clean his or her house. Use ordinal numbers.

1. *Answers will vary:* **Primero, limpiar la cocina.**

2. *Answers will vary:* **Segundo, lavar los platos.**

3. *Answers will vary:* **Tercero, barrer el suelo.**

4. *Answers will vary:* **Cuarto, pasar la aspiradora en la alfombra.**

5. *Answers will vary:* **Quinto, hacer la cama.**

6. *Answers will vary:* **Sexto, sacar la basura.**

Step 2

Write a paragraph telling your friend what chores to do. Use command forms of the verbs and the ordinal numbers.

Answers will vary: **Marcos, debes ayudar con los quehaceres. Primero, limpia**

la cocina. Segundo, lava los platos. Tercero, corta el césped. Cuarto, pasa

la aspiradora en la alfombra. Quinto, haz tu cama. Sexto, saca la basura.

Step 3

Evaluate your writing using the information in the table.

Writing Criteria	Excellent	Good	Needs Work
Content	You have included six chores and the correct command form.	You have included four to five chores and the correct command form four or five times.	You have included three or fewer chores and the correct command form less than three times.
Communication	Most of your response is clear.	Some of your response is clear.	Your message is not very clear.
Accuracy	You make few mistakes in grammar and vocabulary.	You make some mistakes in grammar and vocabulary.	You make many mistakes in grammar and vocabulary.

Cultura A

Level 1, pp. 292-293

¡AVANZA! **Goal:** Review cultural information about Ecuador.

---

1 **Ecuador and Panama** Complete the following sentences with one of the multiple-choice words or phrases.

1. The languages spoken in Ecuador are ___c___

  a. Spanish, Mayan and other indigenous languages

  b. Spanish, Nahuatl and other indigenous languages

  c. Spanish, Quechua and other indigenous languages

2. Ecuadorians celebrate the Festival of San Juan in the month of ___b___

  a. May   **b.** June   **c.** July

3. El tamborito is a traditional ___a___ from Panama.

  a. dance   **b.** handicraft   **c.** food

2 **Activities and places** In Ecuador there are many interesting things to see and do. Draw lines to match each word from the left column with its explanation on the right.

Otavalo   popular dance of Ecuador

Serenatas Quiteñas   tallest active volcano in the world

Sanjuanito   city known for its textiles

Fiestas de Quito   musical tributes to the city

El Cotopaxi   is celebrated every 6th of December

3 **Fiestas de Quito** The Fiestas de Quito are very joyful and there are many activities. Write about the kinds of activities that are a part of the Fiestas de Quito. What would be your favorite activity and why?

Answers will vary: **Some of the activities in the Fiestas de Quito include**

parades, dances, concerts, and beauty pageants. My favorite activity would

be the dances because I love to dance and listen to music.

_____

_____

_____

Nombre _____ Clase _____ Fecha _____

Cultura B

Level 1, pp. 292-293

UNIDAD 5
Lección 2
•
Cultura B

 Goal: Review cultural information about Ecuador.

1 **Ecuador** Read the following sentences about Ecuador and answer *true* or *false*.

Ⓣ F **1.** The languages spoken in Ecuador are Spanish, Quechua, and other indigenous languages.

Ⓣ F **2.** The city of Quito was founded on December 6.

Ⓣ F **3.** Ecuador is located in South America.

T Ⓕ **4.** The Otavalos of Ecuador are famous for their food.

T Ⓕ **5.** The **Sanjuanito** is an Ecuadorian dance with a sad rhythm.

2 **Ecuadorian culture** Complete the following sentences with the words from the box.

Otavalos	Reina	San Juan	**fritada**

1. The festival of ____San Juan____ is celebrated in the month of June.

2. The ____fritada____ is a popular food in Ecuador.

3. The textile designs of the ____Otavalos____ may have geometric figures.

4. The ____Reina____ de Quito pageant is celebrated during the Fiestas de Quito.

3 **Serenatas** Music is very important in all Spanish-speaking countries. During the Fiestas de Quito, many people sing **serenatas quiteñas**. Write a full sentence to explain what the **serenatas** are. Then write a short **serenata** (one verse) of your own.

Answers will vary: **The 'serenatas quiteñas' are a musical tribute that the**

citizens of Quito sing for their city during the Fiestas de Quito.

_____

_____

_____

_____

_____

Cultura C

¡AVANZA! **Goal:** Review cultural information about Ecuador.

1 **Ecuador** Choose the correct word to complete the following sentences.

1. Aside from Spanish, (Quechua / Maya) is spoken in Ecuador.

2. The (Tamborito / Sanjuanito) is an Ecuadorian dance with a joyful rhythm.

3. The Otavalos of Ecuador are famous for their (food / textiles).

4. The celebration of the Fiestas de Quito last for (one week / one month).

2 **Geography and events** Answer these questions about Ecuador in complete sentences.

1. What is the tallest active volcano in the world and where is it? The tallest active
volcano in the world is Cotopaxi and it is in Ecuador.

2. What is the name of the vast mountain chain in South America? The vast
mountain chain of South America is called **Los Andes**.

3. What popular activities are held every year during the Fiestas de Quito? During the
Fiestas de Quito, there are dances, a pageant, parades, wooden car races,
and **serenatas quiteñas** every year.

3 **Otavalo** Describe the textiles created by the Otavalos. Where do they sell them? Compare the Otavalan textiles with other textiles or handicrafts you have seen in the United States that represent various cultures. Look at the photograph on page 284 of your book to help with your comparison.

The Otavalan textiles are very colorful. They have designs such as

landscapes, animals, people, and geometric designs. They sell the textiles at

a Saturday market, but also sell items internationally.

_____

_____

_____

_____

_____

_____

Comparación cultural: ¡Así celebramos!

Lectura y escritura

After reading the paragraphs about how María Elena, Carla and Daniel enjoy parties and celebrations, write a paragraph about a party or celebration of your own. Use the information on your chart to write sentences, and then write a paragraph that describes your party or celebration.

Step 1

Complete the chart describing as many details as possible about your celebration.

tipo de fiesta y lugar

invitados	comida	actividades

Step 2

Now take the details from the chart and write a sentence for each topic on the chart.

_____

_____

_____

_____

_____

_____

_____

_____

Comparación cultural: ¡Así celebramos!

Lectura y escritura (continued)

Step 3

Now write your paragraph using the sentences you wrote as a guide. Include an introductory sentence and use the verbs **celebrar, venir, traer,** and **poner** to write about your celebration.

_____

_____

_____

_____

_____

_____

Checklist

Be sure that…

☐ all the details about your celebration from your chart are included in the paragraph;

☐ you use details to describe your celebration, the place where you celebrate, as well as the guests, food, and activities;

☐ you include new vocabulary words and the verbs **celebrar, venir, traer,** and **poner.**

Rubric

Evaluate your writing using the rubric below.

Writing criteria	Excellent	Good	Needs Work
Content	Your description includes many details about your celebration.	Your description includes some details about your celebration.	Your description includes few details about your celebration.
Communication	Most of your description is organized and easy to follow.	Parts of your description are organized and easy to follow.	Your description is disorganized and hard to follow.
Accuracy	Your description has few mistakes in grammar and vocabulary.	Your description has some mistakes in grammar and vocabulary.	Your description has many mistakes in grammar and vocabulary.

Comparación cultural: ¡Así celebramos!

Compara con tu mundo

Now write a comparison about your celebration and that of one of the students from page 295. Organize your comparison by topics. First, compare the type of celebration, then the place where you celebrate and the guests, and lastly the food and activities.

Step 1

Use the table to organize your comparisons by topics. Write details for each topic about your celebration and that of the student you chose.

Categoría	Mi Fiesta	La Fiesta de _____
tipo de fiesta		
lugar		
invitados		
invitados		
comida		
actividades		

Step 2

Now use the details from the table to write a comparison. Include an introduction sentence and write about each topic. Use the verbs **celebrar, venir, traer, poner** to describe your celebration and that of the student you chose.

_____

_____

_____

_____

_____

_____

_____

Vocabulario A

> **¡AVANZA!** **Goal:** Talk about sports.

1 María loves playing baseball and tennis. In each column, place an x next to all the words associated with each sport.

El béisbol	El tenis
__X__ el guante	__X__ la raqueta
__X__ el bate	_____ la piscina
__X__ los aficionados	__X__ la cancha
__X__ el casco	__X__ la pelota

2 These students are very sports-minded. Look at the drawings below. Then, complete the sentences with the sport they are playing.

1.  2.  3.  4.  5.

1. A Norma le gusta _____patinar en línea_____ .

2. Pablo juega al _____fútbol americano_____ en el estadio.

3. Lucas y Lucía juegan al _____voleibol_____ en la cancha.

4. Alejandra juega al _____básquetbol_____ en la cancha.

5. Todos los días, Arturo practica _____la natación_____ en la piscina.

3 Write complete sentences to tell you what you need to play the following sports.

Modelo: el tenis: **Necesito una raqueta y una pelota.**

1. el fútbol americano: *Answers will vary:* **Necesito una pelota y un casco.**

2. patinar en línea: *Answers will vary:* **Necesito unos patines en línea.**

3. el básquetbol: *Answers will vary:* **Necesito una pelota y una cancha.**

Vocabulario B

¡AVANZA!	**Goal:** Talk about sports.

1 What do you need for each sport? Draw a line from the word in the left column to its related word on the right.

1. el tenis   **a.** la piscina

2. la natación   **b.** el campo

3. el béisbol   **c.** los patines en línea

4. el fútbol americano   **d.** la raqueta

5. patinar en línea   **e.** el bate

2 Watching or playing sports can be really fun! Complete the following sentences with an expression from the word bank.

las reglas	los campeones	los partidos	un poco peligroso

1. A Juan le gusta ir a los estadios para ver _____los partidos_____ de fútbol americano.

2. Los jugadores que ganan son _____los campeones_____ .

3. Patinar en línea es _____un poco peligroso_____ si no llevas un casco.

4. Leemos el libro sobre el béisbol para comprender _____las reglas_____ .

3 In a complete sentence, answer each question about your connection to sports.

1. ¿Cuál es tu deporte favorito?

   Answers will vary: **Mi deporte favorito es el béisbol.**

2. ¿Cuál es tu equipo favorito?

   Answers will vary: **Mi equipo favorito es los Yankees.**

3. ¿Tu equipo favorito gana siempre?

   Answers will vary: **No, pero mi equipo favorito gana muchas veces.**

Vocabulario C

> **¡AVANZA!** **Goal:** Talk about sports.

1 The baseball game is today. Use the words in the box to complete the dialog between two students.

los partidos	aficionado	nadar
las piscinas	un guante	campo

Jorge: ¡Hola, Pablo! ¿Eres **1.** ___aficionado___ al béisbol?

Pablo: ¡Hola, Jorge! Sí, me gusta mucho ver **2.** ___los partidos___ en el estadio.

Jorge: ¿Y tú practicas béisbol? ¿Tienes **3.** ___un guante___ ?

Pablo: Sí, y tengo un bate también. Todos los días voy al **4.** ___campo___

a jugar al béisbol.

Jorge: ¡Qué bueno! Yo juego béisbol de vez en cuando, pero prefiero

5. ___nadar___ . Me gusta la natación.

Pablo: ¡Es un buen deporte! A mí también me gusta mucho nadar en

6. ___las piscinas___ .

2 Define the following sports-related terms in your own words.

modelo: un(a) atleta: **Es una persona que practica deportes.**

1. los ganadores:

Answers will vary: **Son personas que no pierden el partido.** _____

2. los aficionados:

Answers will vary: **Son personas que miran los partidos.** _____

3. la cancha de tenis:

Answers will vary: **Es un lugar donde podemos jugar al tenis.** _____

3 Write three sentences that describe what you use to play your favorite sport. Use complete sentences.

Answers will vary: **Para jugar al béisbol uso un guante y un bate. También**

necesito un equipo. Jugamos en el campo. _____

Gramática A *The present tense of **Jugar***

> ¡AVANZA! **Goal:** Use the verb **jugar** to talk about sports.

1 Juan and his friends play many sports. Underline the correct form of the verb.

1. Ernesto (<u>juega</u> / jugamos) al voleibol.

2. Luis y Jimena (juega / <u>juegan</u>) al básquetbol.

3. Miriam y yo (<u>jugamos</u> / juegas) al tenis.

4. Yo (juega / <u>juego</u>) al béisbol.

5. Tú (<u>juegas</u> / juega) al fútbol americano.

2 Ana and her friends play sports, too. Complete the following sentences with the correct form of the verb **jugar**.

1. Julio y María, ¿ustedes _____ juegan _____ en un equipo de fútbol americano?

2. Señor Martín, ¿usted _____ juega _____ al béisbol?

3. Lucas y Marta _____ juegan _____ al voleibol.

4. Alejandra _____ juega _____ al tenis todos los sábados.

5. Javier y yo _____ jugamos _____ como campeones.

3 Use each element in the table at least once to create sentences using the necessary form of **jugar**.

ustedes	al béisbol	en un equipo
María	al voleibol	los sábados
usted	al tenis	en la cancha de la escuela

modelo: Ustedes juegan al tenis los sábados.

1. *Answers will vary:* **¿Ustedes juegan al béisbol en un equipo?**

2. *Answers will vary:* **¿María juega al tenis en la cancha de la escuela?**

3. *Answers will vary:* **Señor Moreno, ¿usted juega al voleibol los sábados?**

Gramática B *The present tense of Jugar*

> **¡AVANZA!** **Goal:** Use the verb **jugar** to talk about sports.

1 There are many sports to play. Complete the sentences with the correct form of **jugar**.

1. Los jugadores de tenis __d__ en las canchas al lado de la escuela.

   a. juegas **b.** juega **c.** juego **d.** juegan

2. ¿Tú __c__ al béisbol en el verano?

   a. juegan **b.** jugamos **c.** juegas **d.** juega

3. Yo no __b__ al fútbol americano.

   a. jugamos **b.** juego **c.** juegan **d.** tratamos

2 Describe when the people below play their sports. Complete the sentences using the correct form of **jugar**.

modelo: El equipo de la escuela / mañana / un partido
El equipo de la escuela juega un partido mañana.

1. Jaime y yo / siempre / al fútbol americano

   Jaime y yo siempre jugamos al fútbol americano.

2. Carolina y Guillermo / al tenis / temprano

   Carolina y Guillermo juegan al tenis temprano.

3. Nora / al béisbol / casi todos los días

   Nora juega al béisbol casi todos los días.

3 Answer the following questions about the sports that you play.

modelo: ¿ Tú juegas al béisbol? **Sí, (No, no) juego al béisbol.**

1. ¿Tus amigos juegan al béisbol?

   Answers will vary: **Sí (No), mis amigos (no) juegan al béisbol.**

2. ¿Tu familia y tú juegan al tenis?

   Answers will vary: **Sí (No), mi familia y yo (no) jugamos al tenis.**

3. ¿Tú juegas al voleibol?

   Answers will vary: **Sí, (No, no) juego al voleibol.**

Gramática C *The present tense of Jugar*

> **¡AVANZA!** **Goal:** Use the verb **jugar** to talk about sports.

1 Lucas is talking to a friend about sports. Complete the dialog with the correct form of **jugar**.

Lucas: Hola, Marcos. Mis amigos y yo **1.** ____jugamos____ al fútbol americano todos los sábados. ¿Tú también **2.** ____juegas____ ?

Marcos: No, yo no **3.** ____juego____ al fútbol americano. Me gusta más jugar al béisbol en el equipo de la escuela. Pedro también **4.** ____juega____ con el equipo.

Lucas: ¿Sí? Pedro, Miguel y Antonio **5.** ____juegan____ con nosotros los sábados. ¿Ustedes **6.** ____juegan____ bien?

Marcos: Yo no **7.** ____juego____ muy bien pero es divertido estar con ellos y aprender el deporte. Y ustedes, ¿**8.** ____juegan____ bien?

2 Where do these athletes play? Complete the following sentences with an appropriate phrase that includes the correct form of **jugar**.

modelo Los equipos de fútbol americano juegan en el campo o el estadio.

1. Un jugador de fútbol juega en el campo. _____

2. Un campeón de básquetbol juega en la cancha. _____

3. Los campeones de tenis juegan en la cancha. _____

3 Write a description of a sport that you or your friends like to play. Include information about where and when you play the sport and what equipment you need.

Answers will vary: **Me gusta el béisbol porque lo juego con mis amigos.**

Jugamos béisbol en las tarde en el estadio de la escuela. Usamos bates

guantes y pelotas para jugar.

_____

_____

Gramática A *The present tense of* **Saber** *and* **Conocer**

> **¡AVANZA!** **Goal:** Use the verbs **saber** and **conocer** to talk about sports.

1 Some of Marta's friends know a lot about sports. Complete the sentences below following the model.

a. Los amigos de Marta saben   **b.** Los amigos de Marta conocen

modelo: __b__ a muchos jugadores.

1. __a__ de béisbol y tenis.
2. __a__ que el equipo siempre gana.
3. __b__ muchos estadios.
4. __a__ patinar en línea.

2 Find out what these people know about sports. Underline the verb that completes each sentence below.

1. Camila (conoce / sabe) al campeón de tenis.
2. Los jugadores (conocen / saben) dónde está el campo.
3. Nosotros (conocemos / sabemos) a los atletas de la escuela.
4. Yo (conozco / sé) que la natación no es muy peligrosa.
5. ¿Tú (conoces / sabes) quiénes son los campeones?

3 What or whom do the following people know? Complete the sentences with the correct form of either **saber** or **conocer.**

1. Yo _____sé_____ unas historias muy divertidas de deportes.
2. Mi abuelo _____conoce_____ a un jugador de béisbol dominicano.
3. ¿Ustedes _____conocen_____ muchos países donde juegan al béisbol?
4. Nosotros _____sabemos_____ patinar muy bien.
5. Yo _____conozco_____ a su hermana Mirella.
6. ¿Tú _____sabes_____ a qué hora juega el equipo de fútbol americano?

Gramática B *The present tense of Saber and Conocer*

> **¡AVANZA!** **Goal:** Use the verbs **saber** and **conocer** to talk about sports.

1 Today's game is very important. Complete the following sentences by choosing the correct verb in parentheses.

1. Los aficionados no (<u>saben</u> / conocen) cómo llegar al estadio nuevo.

2. Los aficionados no (saben / <u>conocen</u>) el estadio nuevo.

3. Los jugadores (saben / <u>conocen</u>) bien a los atletas del otro equipo.

4. La atleta (<u>sabe</u> / conoce) patinar en línea.

5. Nosotros (sabemos / <u>conocemos</u>) a todos los jugadores.

2 Two teams are playing today. Complete the sentences using the correct form of **saber** or **conocer**.

1. Los jugadores no _____ saben _____ con quienes juegan.

2. Los atletas no _____ conocen _____ a los jugadores del otro equipo.

3. El equipo _____ sabe _____ que el partido es a las tres.

4. El equipo _____ conoce _____ bien la cancha.

5. Nosotros no _____ sabemos _____ quién gana.

3 Answer the following questions in complete sentences.

1. ¿Conoces tú Los Ángeles?

   Answers will vary: **Sí (No), yo (no) conozco Los Ángeles.** _____

2. ¿Tú sabes patinar?

   Answers will vary: **Sí (No), yo (no) sé patinar.** _____

   _____

3. ¿Sabes quiénes son los campeones de béisbol?

   Answers will vary: **Sí (No), yo (no) sé quiénes son los** _____

   campeones de béisbol. _____

4. ¿Tu amigo(a) quiere conocer a los campeones de fútbol americano?

   Answers will vary: **Sí (No), él (ella) (no) quiere conocer a los campeones de** ___

   fútbol americano. _____

Gramática C *The present tense of Saber and Conocer* Level 1, pp. 312-314

> **¡AVANZA!** **Goal:** Use the verbs **saber** and **conocer** to talk about sports.

1 Ernesto and Sofía talk about a football game. Complete the conversation with the correct forms of **saber** or **conocer**.

Ernesto: Hola, Sofía. ¿ _____Sabes_____ tú que hoy tu equipo juega un partido de fútbol americano?

Sofía: Sí. Yo _____sé_____ que vamos a ganar. ¿Sabes por qué?

Ernesto: No, no _____sé_____ . ¿Por qué?

Sofía: Porque Guillermo juega con nosotros.

Ernesto: No lo _____conozco_____ , ¿quién es?

Sofía: Es el campeón de fútbol americano. Él _____sabe_____ jugar bien.

Ernesto: ¿Tu hermano _____conoce_____ a los jugadores del otro equipo?

Sofía: Sí, él _____conoce_____ a todos los jugadores.

2 Which sports or athletes are you familiar with? Answer the following questions.

1. ¿Conoces a un jugador de fútbol americano?

Answers will vary: **Sí, (No, no) conozco a un jugador de fútbol americano.**

2. ¿Sabes las reglas del voleibol?

Answers will vary: **Sí, (No, no) sé las reglas del voleibol.**

3. ¿Saben patinar tú y tus amigos?

Answers will vary: **Sí, (No, no) sabemos patinar.**

4. ¿Conoces a un(a) aficionado(a) al béisbol?

Answers will vary: **Sí, (No, no) conozco a un(a) aficionado(a) al béisbol.**

5. ¿Sabes cuánto cuestan unos patines en línea nuevos?

Answers will vary: **Sí, (No, no) sé cuánto cuestan.**

3 Write about an athlete that you know. Use **saber** and **conocer**.

Answers will vary: **Conozco a Mariano. Es un buen jugador de béisbol. Él...**

Integración: Hablar

Level 1, pp. 315–316
WB CD 03 track 21

Alejandro has just moved to a new city and wants to practice all the sports he likes. He sees an Athletic club's Web page and decides to call and leave a message to express his interest in their sports facilities.

Fuente 1 Leer
Read Club Arco iris's Web site's main page...

¡Practica deportes en el **Club Arco iris**!

Las personas que saben de deportes dicen que practicarlos es muy bueno. Encuentra el deporte que más te gusta y puedes practicarlo en nuestro club (con amigos es más divertido). Una o dos veces por semana es bueno, pero si puedes más veces, mejor. Puedes patinar en línea los lunes.

- **¿Juegas al tenis? Puedes tomar clases los martes, los sábados y domingos.**

- **¿Juegas al béisbol? Tenemos partidos para los jugadores de nuestro club los miércoles y los sábados.**

Y también todos los días puedes nadar en la piscina del nuestro club.

Fuente 2 Escuchar *CD 03 track 22*
Listen to Alejandro's telephone message to Club Arco iris. Take notes.

_____

_____

_____

Hablar
What days can Alejandro practice the sports he likes at Club Arco iris?

modelo: Los lunes, Alejandro puede... Él también puede...

Answers will vary: **Los lunes, Alejandro puede patinar en línea. Él también puede**

nadar en la piscina todos los días. No va a tomar clases de tenis porque no le

gusta. Puede jugar al béisbol los miércoles y los sábados.

Integración: Escribir

Level 1, pp. 315–316
WB CD 03 track 23

Mauricio's friend, Gustavo, plays for the state's volleyball team. He sends an e-mail to a friend to express his views about the team, one day before the final championship match. On the day of the match, he changes his mind about having to be the winner, when he listens to Gustavo's coach talking about sportsmanship.

Fuente 1 Leer

Read Mauricio's e-mail to his friend Gustavo a day before the championship match...

De: Mauricio   A: Gustavo

Tema: ¡Vamos equipo!

¡Hola, Gustavo!

Pienso que ustedes tienen el mejor equipo, porque saben que comprender las reglas es importante, pero es más importante ganar. Ustedes casi nunca pierden, y ¡no pueden perder mañana! Son el mejor de todos los equipos. En mi escuela estamos muy contentos, porque ustedes son los favoritos y van a ganar. Todos somos aficionados al voleibol. Mañana a las ocho, mis amigos y yo miramos el partido en la televisión. Es casi una fiesta en la sala de mi casa.

Mauricio

Fuente 2 Escuchar   *CD 03 track 24*

Listen to Gustavo's coach speaking about the championship match on a radio show. Take notes.

_____

_____

_____

Escribir

Mauricio listened to Gustavo's coach on the radio, and then changed his mind about winning and losing. Why did he change his mind from one day to the other?

modelo: Un día antes, Mauricio piensa que...Pero después, comprende que...

Answers will vary: **Un día antes, Mauricio piensa que su equipo favorito tiene**

que ganar siempre. Pero después, comprende que su equipo favorito no puede

ganar todos los días. Los jugadores pueden estar contentos si pierden.

_____

_____

Escuchar A

¡AVANZA! **Goal:** Listen to discussions about sports.

1 Listen to Ernesto. Place an "x" next to the things he says he needs for his favorite sport.

1. ____ una piscina

2. ____ un libro de reglas

3. _X_ una pelota de béisbol

4. _X_ un guante de béisbol

5. ____ una raqueta

6. ____ unos patines en línea

7. _X_ un bate

8. _X_ un casco nuevo

2 Listen to Ángel. Then, complete the sentences by filling in the correct word.

1. Al hijo de Ángel le gustan muchos _____deportes_____ .

2. El deporte que le gusta más es _____el béisbol_____ .

3. El hijo de Ángel necesita cosas para _____jugar_____ al béisbol.

4. Ángel quiere comprar _____un guante_____ nuevo.

Escuchar B

| ¡AVANZA! | **Goal:** Listen to discussions about sports. |

1 Listen to Julio. Complete the table with the sport that each student plays.

Lucas y Susana	el básquetbol
Marcos	el fútbol americano
Andrea	patinar en línea
Ana	la natación
Miguel y Jimena	el béisbol

2 Listen to the conversation between Ana and Jorge. Take notes. Then, answer the questions below in complete sentences:

1. ¿Adónde quiere ir Ana?

Ana quiere ir al estadio.

2. ¿Quién juega?

Juega el equipo de básquetbol del hermano de Ana.

3. ¿Quién es un aficionado?

El hermano de Ana es un aficionado.

4. ¿Mira Ana muchos partidos en la televisión?

No, no mira muchos partidos en la televisión.

Escuchar C

Level 1, pp. 322-323
WB CD 03 tracks 29-30

> ¡AVANZA! **Goal:** Listen to discussions about sports.

1 Listen to Lucas and take notes. Then, write what day(s) he does the following activities.

1. jugar al básquetbol _____los lunes_____

2. patinar en línea _____los miércoles_____

3. jugar al voleibol _____los viernes y los martes_____

4. jugar al tenis _____los domingos_____

5. jugar al fútbol americano _____los sábados_____

6. jugar al béisbol _____los jueves_____

2 Listen to the conversation between Débora and her mother. Take notes. Then, answer the following questions:

1. ¿Por qué no está el hermano de Débora?

   Porque los lunes practica deportes todo el día.

2. ¿Qué encuentra la mamá de Débora?

   La mamá de Débora encuentra los patines de su hijo.

3. ¿Quiénes patinan en línea?

   Los chicos del equipo patinan en línea.

4. ¿Quién sabe dónde Nicolás patina?

   Débora sabe dónde Nicolás patina.

5. ¿Por qué Jorge no patina en línea?

   Porque piensa que es peligroso.

Leer A

¡AVANZA!	**Goal:** Read about sports.

The following is a flyer hanging in the hall and the cafeteria of the school.

Partido de béisbol

¡Atención, aficionados!

Nuestro equipo sabe jugar bien y ahora lo van a
hacer en su nuevo estadio.
Ven a conocer el Estadio Martínez de Punta Cana.

¿Sabes cuándo?: Hoy, el 2 de Mayo
¿Sabes dónde?: El Estadio Martínez

Globos para los chicos
Pelotas con los nombres de los jugadores para todos

¡Ven con toda la famila a celebrar con nuestro equipo!

¿Comprendiste?

Read the note about the game. Then, read each sentence below and answer **Cierto** (*True*) or **Falso** (*False*).

Ⓒ F   **1.** El partido es hoy.

C Ⓕ   **2.** El equipo juega mal.

C Ⓕ   **3.** El equipo juega en una cancha vieja.

Ⓒ F   **4.** El Estadio Martínez es un estadio de béisbol.

C Ⓕ   **5.** Los chicos reciben globos porque es un cumpleaños.

¿Qué piensas?

Read the note about the game. Answer the following question in a complete sentence.

1. ¿Conoces un estadio donde tú vives? ¿Cuál?

Answers will vary: **Sí, cerca de mi casa está el estadio Vidal López.**

2. ¿Hay un equipo de béisbol en tu escuela? ¿Dónde juegan?

Answers will vary: **Sí, juegan en el estadio de la escuela.**

Leer B

 Goal: Read about sports.

Laura writes a letter to her friends about her friend Ana.

> Hola chicos:
>
> Tengo que salir temprano hoy. ¿Saben que esta tarde Ana juega un partido de béisbol? Ella está muy nerviosa porque no conoce a las jugadoras del otro equipo y no sabe cómo juegan. A ella no le gusta perder. Siempre digo que también debe saber que no tiene que ganar siempre. A veces ganas y a veces pierdes. Pero ella no entiende. Siempre quiere ser campeona.
>
> ¿Vienen hoy al partido? Deben venir. Ana y el equipo necesitan tener muchos aficionados allí. Quiero verlos a ustedes en el partido.
>
> Hasta luego,
>
> Laura

¿Comprendiste?

Read Laura's letter. Then, place an "x" next to the things that are true.

1. __X__ Ana juega un partido de béisbol.

2. _____ Laura juega un partido de béisbol.

3. _____ Ana nunca pierde.

4. __X__ Laura quiere ver a sus amigos.

5. __X__ A Ana no le gusta perder.

6. _____ A Laura no le gusta perder.

7. __X__ Ana está nerviosa.

8. _____ Laura está nerviosa.

¿Qué piensas?

Read Laura's letter. Answer the following questions in complete sentences.

1. ¿Es importante saber perder? ¿Por qué?

   Answers will vary: **Sí, porque yo sé que a veces ganamos y otras veces perdemos.**

2. ¿Es importante ir a los partidos de tus amigos? ¿Por qué?

   Answers will vary: **Sí, porque a mis amigos les gusta tener aficionados en los partidos cuando ganan.**

Leer C

> **¡AVANZA!** **Goal:** Read about sports.

A brief article about the school's championship basketball team appears in the school newspaper.

¡GANAMOS OTRA VEZ!

Nuestro equipo es el campeón de básquetbol una vez más. Si conoces a los jugadores, sabes que ellos son serios y saben jugar muy bien. Los chicos del equipo también saben que es importante sacar buenas notas en clase. Ellos son trabajadores en la escuela y en la cancha. También, todos los jugadores saben que sus aficionados siempre van a venir a los partidos.

Con nuestro equipo, ¡siempre ganamos!

¿Comprendiste?

Read the article in the school newspaper. Then, read each sentence below and answer **Cierto** (*True*) or **Falso** (*False*).

Ⓒ F **1.** Los jugadores saben que las buenas notas son importantes.

C Ⓕ **2.** Los jugadores no saben el deporte bien.

Ⓒ F **3.** Los jugadores son serios.

C Ⓕ **4.** Ellos saben que sus aficionados nunca van a los partidos.

C Ⓕ **5.** El equipo nunca gana.

¿Qué piensas?

Read the article in the school newspaper. Then, answer the first question in a complete sentence and give an example explaining your reason in a second sentence.

1. ¿Piensas que es difícil practicar un deporte y sacar buenas notas en la escuela? ¿Por qué?

Answers will vary: **Sí, es muy difícil sacar buenas notas en la escuela,**

porque cuando practicas mucho, no puedes estudiar mucho.

2. ¿Conoces a un(a) atleta que es un(a) buena estudiante?

Answers will vary: **Si, mi amiga Carolina practica voleibol y es muy buena**

estudiante.

Escribir A

> ¡AVANZA! **Goal:** Write about sports.

Step 1

List 5 sports that are played on a court or in a field.

en una cancha	en un campo
1. *Answers will vary:* **básquetbol**	4. *Answers will vary:* **fútbol americano**
2. *Answers will vary:* **voleibol**	5. *Answers will vary:* **béisbol**
3. *Answers will vary:* **tenis**	

Step 2

Answer the following questions in complete sentences.

1. ¿Qué sabes de béisbol?

Answers will vary: **Yo sé que jugamos al béisbol en un campo grande y**

usamos un bate, un guante y una pelota.

2. ¿Qué jugador de béisbol conoces?

Answers will vary: **Yo conozco a Mariano Rivera.**

Step 3

Evaluate your writing using the information in the table below.

Writing Criteria	Excellent	Good	Needs Work
Content	You have responded to the questions completely.	You have responded to the questions partially.	You have not responded to the questions.
Communication	Most of your response is clear.	Some of your response is clear.	Your message is not very clear.
Accuracy	You make few mistakes in grammar and vocabulary.	You make some mistakes in grammar and vocabulary.	You make many mistakes in grammar and vocabulary.

Escribir B

Level 1, pp. 322-323

 Goal: Write about sports.

Step 1

Complete the first column with three sports that you play all the time and the second column with three sports that you do not know how to play.

Deportes que juegas	**Deportes que no sabes jugar**
Answers will vary: **béisbol**	*Answers will vary:* **voleibol**
Answers will vary: **fútbol americano**	*Answers will vary:* **patinar en línea**
Answers will vary: **básquetbol**	*Answers will vary:* **tenis**

Step 2

Write three sentences saying which sports you know how to play and one thing that you know you need for each. Then, write a sentence saying which sports you do not know how to play.

modelo: Yo juego al béisbol y sé que necesito un bate. Yo no sé jugar al voleibol.

Answers will vary: **Yo juego al fútbol americano y sé que necesito un**

casco. Yo no sé patinar en línea. Yo juego al básquetbol y sé que necesito

una cancha. No sé jugar al tenis.

_____

_____

_____

Step 3

Evaluate your writing using the information in the table below.

Writing Criteria	Excellent	Good	Needs Work
Content	You include all of the information.	You include some of the information.	You include little information.
Communication	Most of your message is organized and easy to follow.	Parts of your message are organized and easy to follow.	Your message is disorganized and hard to follow.
Accuracy	You make few mistakes in grammar and vocabulary.	You make some mistakes in grammar and vocabulary.	You make many mistakes in grammar and vocabulary.

Escribir C

> **¡AVANZA!** **Goal:** Write about sports.

Step 1

Complete the following table about a few sports. *Answers will vary:*

Deportes que conoces	Lugares donde los juegan	Cosas que usamos para jugarlos
béisbol	campo	pelota, guante y bate
fútbol americano	cancha	pelota
básquetbol	cancha	pelota
natación	piscina	ropa de natación
tenis	cancha	pelota y raqueta

Step 2

In six complete sentences, write an article about one of your school's athletic events for the school newspaper. Use the verbs **jugar, saber,** and **conocer.**

Answers will vary: **Hoy jugamos un partido de básquetbol con el equipo de la escuela Martínez. Todos sabemos que es un partido difícil porque ellos son los campeones de todas las escuelas. Pero nosotros conocemos a nuestro equipo y tenemos que estar tranquilos. Nuestro equipo juega muy bien y siempre sabe ganar.**

Step 3

Evaluate your writing using the information in the table below.

Writing Criteria	Excellent	Good	Needs Work
Content	You include all of the verbs in your article.	You include some of the verbs in your article.	You do not include any of the verbs in your article.
Communication	Most of your message is organized and easy to follow.	Parts of your message are organized and easy to follow.	Your message is disorganized and hard to follow.
Accuracy	You make few mistakes in grammar and vocabulary.	You make some mistakes in grammar and vocabulary.	You make many mistakes in grammar and vocabulary.

Cultura A

> **¡AVANZA!** **Goal:** Review cultural information about the Dominican Republic.

1 **The Dominican Republic** Read the following sentences and answer *true* or *false*.

T ⓕ **1.** Professional baseball in the Dominican Republic is played from March through July.

ⓣ F **2.** The currency of the Dominican Republic is the Dominican peso.

T ⓕ **3.** The national sport of the Dominican Republic is soccer.

ⓣ F **4.** The capital of the Dominican Republic is Santo Domingo.

ⓣ F **5.** The Dominican Republic is part of an island.

2 **Famous Dominicans** Draw lines to match the names of some famous Dominicans with their professions.

Oscar de la Renta   writer

Pedro Martínez   singer

Juan Luis Guerra   designer

Julia Álvarez   baseball player

3 **Serie del Caribe** Describe the **Serie del Caribe.** What sport is played and who participates? When does it take place? Is it similar to any other sporting events you know of? Explain.

Answers will vary. **The *Serie del Caribe* is a baseball championship that takes**

place in February. Four countries participate: the Dominican Republic, Puerto

Rico, Venezuela, and Mexico. Many U.S. major league players also take part.

It reminds me of the World Series, except *the Serie del Caribe* has four teams

participating, rather than two.

_____

_____

Cultura B

> ►¡AVANZA! **Goal:** Review cultural information about the Dominican Republic.

1 **Dominican Culture** Complete the sentences about the Dominican Republic.

1. The Dominican Republic shares the island of Hispaniola with ___Haiti___ .

2. Many tourists enjoy going to the _beaches_ of the Caribbean Sea in the Dominican Republic.

3. The _Altar de la Patria_ in Santo Domingo is a memorial dedicated to the heroes of the Dominican Republic's fight for freedom from Haiti.

4. The capital of the Dominican Republic is _Santo Domingo_ .

5. Cazabe is a typical _food_ of the Dominican Republic.

2 **People and professions** Write down the professions of the following famous Dominicans.

Famous Dominicans	Their Professions
Julia Álvarez	writer
Oscar de la Renta	designer
Juan Luis Guerra	singer
Pedro Martínez	baseball player

3 **The national sport** Describe the national sport of the Dominican Republic. What is it and when is it played? In your description, talk about a special Dominican sporting event.

Answers will vary: The national sport of the Dominican Republic is baseball. It is played

throughout the year, but professional baseball is played from October through February.

The _Serie del Caribe_ is a championship that takes place every February, between Mexico,

Puerto Rico, Venezuela, and the Dominican Republic.

_____

_____

Cultura C

Level 1, pp. 322-323

> ¡AVANZA! **Goal:** Review cultural information about the Dominican Republic.

1 **The Dominican Republic** Complete the following sentences with the missing words.

1. The Dominican Republic has a ___warm___ climate.

2. The Dominican baseball fans can go to see professional baseball games from October until the month of __February__ .

3. The __beaches__ of the Dominican Republic are popular with tourists.

4. Santo Domingo is the ___capital___ of the Dominican Republic.

2 **Dominican Culture** Answer these questions with complete sentences.

1. What are some typical foods of the Dominican Republic? _Some typical Dominican_

   foods are tropical fruits, **mangú, cazabe,** and **la bandera.**

2. What is the **Altar de la Patria** located in Santo Domingo? _The Altar de la Patria_

   of Santo Domingo is a monument to the Dominican heroes who fought in the

   battle of 1844.

3 **Serie del Caribe** Compare the **Serie del Caribe** to another sporting event you have seen or know about. Include information about what sport is involved and when it is played. Also mention where the event is held or which countries participate, along with any famous players who have competed in the event.

   Answers will vary.

   _____

   _____

   _____

   _____

   _____

   _____

   _____

   _____

Vocabulario A

| ¡AVANZA! | **Goal:** Talk about parts of the body. |

1 Match each part of the body below with the activity associated with it.

_c_	**1.**	ojos	**a.**	hablar
_e_	**2.**	orejas	**b.**	escribir
_a_	**3.**	boca	**c.**	mirar
_d_	**4.**	piernas	**d.**	caminar
_b_	**5.**	manos	**e.**	escuchar

2 Javier and his friends are at the beach. Complete the following sentences using the words in the box.

pesas	enferma	salud	bloqueador de sol	estómago

1. Es peligroso tomar el sol si no usas _____bloqueador de sol_____ .

2. Susana está _____enferma_____ y no puede ir a la playa.

3. A Susana le duele el _____estómago_____ porque bebe muchos refrescos.

4. Pedro levanta _____pesas_____ en la playa.

5. Caminar en la playa es una buena actividad para la _____salud_____ .

3 Answer the following questions in complete sentences.

1. ¿Te duelen las piernas cuando caminas mucho?

Answers will vary: **Sí, (No, no) me duelen las piernas cuando camino mucho.**

2. ¿Descansas mucho cuando estás enfermo(a)?

Answers will vary: **Sí, (No, no) descanso cuando estoy enfermo(a).**

3. Cuando nadas, ¿usas más las piernas o los brazos?

Answers will vary: **Cuando nado uso más las piernas.**

Vocabulario B

┌───┐
│ ¡AVANZA! **Goal:** Talk about parts of the body. │
└───┘

1 Alicia and her friends go to the beach. Complete each sentence with the correct word in parentheses.

1. Los chicos nadan en _____ el mar _____ . (las pesas / el mar / la salud)

2. Alicia usa bloqueador de sol en la _____ piel _____ . (ojo / playa / piel)

3. Los amigos de Alicia hacen _____ esquí acuático _____ . (esquí acuático / una cabeza / un corazón)

2 Inés and Carlos are also at the beach. Complete their conversation with the words from the box.

┌───┐
│ la piel   el sol   fuerte │
│ bloqueador de sol   enfermo │
└───┘

Inés: ¡Qué buen día! Tomamos **1.** _____ el sol _____ toda la mañana.

Carlos: ¿Usas **2.** _____ bloqueador de sol _____ ? En la playa, tienes que usarlo.

Inés: Sí, lo uso. Pero me duele un poco **3.** _____ la piel _____ .

El sol está muy **4.** _____ fuerte _____ .

Carlos: Es verdad. Yo no tengo sombrero y ya estoy un poco

5. _____ enfermo _____ .

3 The following people are sick. Write complete sentences to describe what hurts.

1. 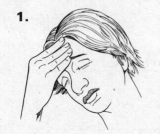   **2.**    **3.**

Answers will vary: **A Susana le duele la cabeza.**

A Luis le duele el estómago.

A Norma y a Martín les duelen los brazos.

Vocabulario C

> ¡AVANZA! **Goal:** Talk about parts of the body.

1 Place each word from the box in the appropriate category.

herido	sano	la boca	el esquí acuático
enfermo	las orejas	dolor	el mar
los ojos	el sol	el bloqueador de sol	la nariz

	La salud	La playa	La cabeza
1	sano	el mar	los ojos
2	enfermo	el sol	las orejas
3	dolor	el bloqueador de sol	la nariz
4	herido	el esquí acuático	la boca

2 We all get sick sometimes. Complete the following sentences with the reasons why. Follow the model:

modelo: Me duelen las piernas cuando **camino mucho**.

1. Me duelen los brazos cuando *Answers will vary:* **levanto pesas**.

2. Me duele la mano cuando *Answers will vary:* **escribo mucho**.

3. Me duele el estómago cuando *Answers will vary:* **tomo muchos refrescos**.

4. Me duele la piel cuando *Answers will vary:* **tomo sol sin bloqueador de sol**.

3 Write three complete sentences to describe what you do at the beach. Describe the beginning of your day, the things you do at the beach, and the end of your day.

Answers will vary: **Cuando comienza el día, llego a la playa. Traigo**

el bloqueador de sol y un sombrero. En el día, nado en el mar, tomo sol

y hago esquí acuático. Cuando termina el día, vuelvo a mi casa y limpio

todas las cosas que uso en la playa.

¡Avancemos! 1
Cuaderno: Práctica por niveles

UNIDAD 6 • Vocabulario C
Lección 2

Unidad 6, Lección 2
Vocabulario C **271**

Gramática A *Preterite of –ar Verbs*

> **¡AVANZA!** **Goal:** Use the preterite of **–ar** verbs to talk about a day at the beach.

1 Andrea and her friends spent the day at the beach. Underline the correct form of the verb in the following sentences.

1. Andrea (invitó / invité) a sus amigos a la playa.

2. Los amigos de Andrea (nadaste / nadaron) todo el día.

3. Andrea y yo (hablaron / hablamos) de los chicos en la clase.

4. Andrea y tú (llevaron / llevó) unos sombreros muy grandes.

5. ¿Tú (ayudó / ayudaste) a Andrea a bucear?

6. Andrea (comenzaste / comenzó) a levantar pesas.

2 The following students had fun at the beach. Complete the sentences using the preterite of the verbs in parentheses.

1. Lucas y yo _____caminamos_____ por la playa. (caminar)

2. En la noche, yo _____canté_____ en la playa. (cantar)

3. A Antonio le duelen las piernas. Él _____caminó_____ mucho con Inés. (caminar)

4. ¿Ustedes _____llevaron_____ bloqueador de sol? (llevar)

5. Antonio _____usó_____ un sombrero. (usar)

6. Inés está cansada. Ella _____buceó_____ mucho en la tarde. (bucear)

3 Answer the following questions about what you did yesterday in complete sentences.

1. ¿Levantaste pesas?

   Answers will vary: **Sí, levanté pesas.** _____

2. ¿Caminaron tú y tus amigos a la escuela?

   Answers will vary: **No caminamos. Tomamos el autobús.** _____

3. ¿Qué estudiaste?

   Answers will vary: **Yo estudié el español.** _____

Gramática B *Preterite of –ar Verbs*

> ¡AVANZA! **Goal:** Use the preterite of **–ar** verbs to talk about a day at the beach.

1 Alejandro and his friends went to the beach. The people who went are listed in one column and the things they did are listed in the other. Put them together to create sentences. Follow the model.

Jimena	llevamos los refrescos.
Jimena y Jorge	levanté pesas en la playa y me duelen los brazos.
Jorge y yo	hablaron de las tareas de la escuela.
Tú	escuchó su música favorita.
Yo	preparaste la comida.

modelo: Jimena escuchó su música favorita.

1. Jimena y Jorge hablaron de las tareas de la escuela.

2. Jorge y yo llevamos los refrescos.

3. Tú preparaste la comida.

4. Yo levanté pesas en la playa y me duelen los brazos.

2 Write three sentences to describe what happened at the beach. Use the information given.

1. Yo/ llevar la guitarra de Juan Yo llevé la guitarra de Juan.

2. Ana y yo/ nadar en el mar Ana y yo nadamos en el mar.

3. Guillermo y Carina/ mirar el sol en la tarde Guillermo y Carina miraron el sol en la tarde.

4. Ustedes/ tocar la guitarra en la playa Ustedes tocaron la guitarra en la playa.

3 Complete the following sentences about what you and the people you know did yesterday. Follow the model.

modelo: (mirar) Mi amigo(a) Mi amigo José miró la televisión ayer.

1. (celebrar) Yo *Answers will vary:* **Yo celebré mi cumpleaños.**

2. (llevar) Mis amigos *Answers will vary:* **Mis amigos llevaron pantalones cortos.**

3. (enseñar) Mi maestro(a) *Answers will vary:* **Mi maestra enseñó el español.**

Gramática C *Preterite of –ar Verbs*

> **¡AVANZA!** **Goal:** Use the preterite of **–ar** verbs to talk about a day at the beach.

1 Julia spent the day at the beach with her friends. Complete the following sentences with the correct form of the verbs from the box.

| hablar | cantar | bucear | caminar | llevar |

Ayer, nosotros pasamos un rato en la playa. Primero, Juan, Armando

y yo **1.** _____caminamos_____ por la playa. Hoy me duelen las

piernas. Después, los chicos **2.** _____bucearon_____ en el mar.

Ana y Manuel **3.** _____hablaron_____ del equipo de béisbol de la

escuela y del partido. Lucía **4.** _____llevó_____ su guitarra y

nosotros **5.** _____cantamos_____ por horas al lado del mar.

2 Write about the last time you went to the beach or pool with your friends. Use the preterite of the following verbs.

1. pasar *Answers will vary:* **Mis amigos y yo pasamos el día en la playa.**

2. usar *Answers will vary:* **Yo usé bloqueador de sol.**

3. hablar *Answers will vary:* **Jorge habló con Paula.**

4. comprar: *Answers will vary:* **Mis padres compraron sándwiches para todos.**

5. nadar: *Answers will vary:* **Nosotros nadamos todo el día.**

3 Write an e-mail message to a classmate. Say what you did yesterday. *Answers will vary:*

Hola Marcos:

Ayer escuché música con Ramiro. Estudié toda la tarde y ayudé a mi mamá

a preparar la cena. Preparamos una comida muy rica. Más tarde, en la noche,

celebramos el cumpleaños de Inés y yo bailé mucho.

Adiós

Carla

Gramática A Stem-Changing Verbs: –car, –gar

¡AVANZA! **Goal:** Use –car and –gar verbs to talk about the past.

1 Yesterday Enrique and Ana Sofía went to the beach. Complete Ana Sofía's sentences with **yo**, **Enrique** or **nosotros**.

1. _____Nosotros_____ pasamos el día en la playa.

_____Enrique_____ llegó primero.

2. _____Yo_____ llegué cinco minutos después.

_____Yo_____ busqué un lugar cerca del mar.

3. _____Enrique_____ almorzó pizza después de nadar.

_____Yo_____ saqué un sándwich de mi mochila.

4. _____Nosotros_____ jugamos fútbol en la playa.

_____Enrique_____ tocó la guitarra y cantó.

2 Complete each sentence with the preterite form of the verb in parentheses.

1. Yo _____toqué_____ la guitarra el sábado. (toqué / tocamos)

2. Yo _____llegué_____ tarde al partido de fútbol. (llegó / llegué)

3. Tú _____practicaste_____ básquetbol y te duelen los brazos. (practiqué / practicaste)

4. Yo _____busqué_____ a mi hermanita en su escuela. (busqué / buscaron)

5. Mi mamá _____pagó_____ la ropa que compró mi hermano. (pagó / pagué)

3 Answer the following questions in complete sentences.

1. ¿Qué deporte practicaste ayer?

Answers will vary: **Yo practiqué fútbol.** _____

2. ¿A qué hora llegaste hoy a la escuela?

Answers will vary: **Hoy llegué a las siete.** _____

3. ¿Sacaste una buena nota en ciencias?

Answers will vary: **Sí, yo saqué una buena nota en ciencias.** _____

Gramática B *Stem-Changing Verbs: –car, –gar*

> ¡AVANZA! **Goal:** Use **–car** and **–gar** verbs to talk about the past.

1 What did everyone do yesterday? Choose the correct form of the verb for each sentence below.

1. Yo __c__ tarde a clases.

   a. llegaste   **b.** llegamos   **c.** llegué   **d.** llegó

2. Juan __b__ a sus amigos en la cafetería.

   a. busqué   **b.** buscó   **c.** buscaron   **d.** buscamos

3. Yo __c__ la guitarra en la fiesta de cumpleaños de Ana.

   a. tocaron   **b.** tocaste   **c.** toqué   **d.** tocó

4. Los estudiantes __c__ buenas notas en todas las clases.

   a. sacamos   **b.** saqué   **c.** sacaron   **d.** sacaste

5. Yo __d__ natación ayer.

   a. practicó   **b.** practicaste   **c.** practicaron   **d.** practiqué

2 Complete the sentences with the preterite form of one of the verbs in the box.

1. Yo _____practiqué_____ el básquetbol y ahora me duele todo

   el cuerpo.

2. Yo _____toqué_____ el piano en casa de un amigo.

3. Mi hermana _____sacó_____ toda la ropa vieja del armario.

4. Nosotros _____buscamos_____ un buen lugar para cenar.

5. Yo _____llegué_____ primero a la piscina.

> tocar
> sacar
> llegar
> practicar
> buscar

3 Create sentences about what you did yesterday. Use the preterite of the verbs provided.
Answers will vary.

1. pagar Yo pagué la cena. _____

2. buscar Yo busqué a mis amigos. _____

3. llegar Yo llegué a la escuela a las siete. _____

Gramática C *Stem-Changing Verbs: –car, –gar*

> ¡AVANZA! **Goal:** Use **–car** and **–gar** verbs to talk about the past.

1 Find out what everyone did yesterday by completing the sentences with the preterite form of the verb in parentheses.

1. Yo _____llegué_____ a la escuela en autobús. (llegar)

2. Mis amigos _____buscaron_____ un lugar para comer. (buscar)

3. Yo _____pagué_____ los libros que compraste. (pagar)

4. Luis _____sacó_____ la basura para su padre. (sacar)

5. Yo _____practiqué_____ con el bate y el guante de béisbol. (practicar)

2 Write complete sentences to tell if you did or did not do the following activities.

1. comenzar la tarea tarde *Answers will vary:* **Yo no comencé la tarea tarde.**

2. practicar un deporte *Answers will vary:* **Yo practiqué un deporte.**

3. llegar a casa temprano *Answers will vary:* **Llegué a casa temprano.**

4. tocar la guitarra *Answers will vary:* **Yo no toqué la guitarra.**

5. jugar videojuegos *Answers will vary:* **Yo jugué videojuegos.**

3 Write a paragraph about a recent trip to the mall. Be sure to tell when you arrived, what you looked for and how much you paid.

Answers will vary: **Llegué a las cinco de la tarde al centro comercial.**

Busqué dónde venden camisas y encontré una tienda muy buena. Compré

una camisa y no pagué mucho.

Integración: Hablar

Level 1, pp. 339–340
WB CD 03 track 31

Miriam's friend Rodrigo loves sports, but he has not been feeling well lately. Rodrigo calls Miriam to ask if her father can help him. Miriam's father is a doctor who writes articles about health issues for an online publication.

Fuente 1 Leer
Read Dr. Salinas's Web page article on health issues...

La salud es importante

¡Hola! Soy el doctor José Salinas. Hoy voy a hablar de la salud y de las actividades para estar sano. También quiero hablar sobre las cosas que hacen doler el cuerpo, como actividades y alimentos peligrosos para la salud. Si juegas mucho al tenis, debes levantar pesas para tener los brazos siempre fuertes. Tienes que comer muchas frutas porque son nutritivas. Debes comer bien todos los días. Si haces actividades sanas como correr dos o más veces por semana y tienes dolor en las piernas, debes correr más despacio o caminar por quince minutos y después, correr.

Fuente 2 Escuchar   CD 03 track 32
Listen to Rodrigo's voicemail for Miriam. Take notes.

_____

_____

_____

_____

Hablar
What advice will Miram's father, Dr. Salinas, give to Rodrigo?

modelo: A Rodrigo le duele(n)..., el doctor Salinas va a decir que debe...

Answers will vary: **A Rodrigo le duelen las piernas cuando corre.**

El doctor Salinas va a decir que debe caminar primero. A Rodrigo le duelen

los brazos. El doctor va a decir que debe levantar pesas. También debe comer

comidas nutritivas.

Integración: Escribir

Gabriela and Beatriz went to Puerto Plata, Dominican Republic on vacation, but Gabriela is from Arkansas and did not know much about the beach, while Beatriz is from southern California and has spent a lot of time at the beach.

Fuente 1 Leer

Read Gabriela's e-mail to Beatriz...

> ¡Hola Beatriz!
>
> Me duelen la piel y la cabeza pero no es importante porque estoy muy contenta. Ayer, Norberto, mis amigas y yo pasamos el día en la playa. Tú sabes cuánto me gusta tomar el sol. Todos hablamos por horas y horas. Caminamos por la playa y nadamos en el mar. Tomamos el sol y escuchamos música. Tengo las piernas, los brazos y la nariz rojos como tomates, pero pasamos un día muy divertido en la playa. ¿Qué hicieron ustedes?
>
> Gabriela

Fuente 2 Escuchar   *CD 03 track 34*

Listen to Beatriz's voice message to Gabriela. Take notes.

_____

_____

_____

_____

Escribir

Explain why Gabriela is in pain but Beatriz is not.

modelo: A Gabriela le duelen...Pero Beatriz está bien porque...

Answers will vary: **A Gabriela le duelen la piel y la cabeza porque tomó el sol**

todo el día sin bloqueador de sol. Pero Beatriz está bien. No le duelen la

piel y la cabeza porque ella tomó el sol con el bloqueador de sol.

_____

_____

_____

_____

Escuchar A

> **¡AVANZA!** **Goal:** Listen to discussions about the body and past activities.

1 Listen to Graciela. Then, read each sentence and answer **Cierto** (*True*) or **Falso** (*False*).

Ⓒ F **1.** Graciela pasó el día en la playa.

Ⓒ F **2.** Miriam tomó sol.

C Ⓕ **3.** Miriam usó mucho bloqueador de sol.

C Ⓕ **4.** A Miriam le duelen las piernas.

C Ⓕ **5.** Graciela caminó con Miriam por la playa.

2 Listen to Miriam. Then, complete the sentences with the correct word.

1. Ayer, Miriam tomó mucho _____sol_____ . (sol / refrescos)

2. El sol en la playa es muy _____fuerte_____ . (sano / fuerte)

3. La amiga de Miriam la llamó para saber de su _____salud_____ . (salud / amigo)

4. Miriam hoy está _____enferma_____ . (enferma / tranquila)

Escuchar B

¡AVANZA! **Goal:** Listen to discussions about the body and past activities.

1 Listen to Lourdes and take notes. Then, match the people with what they did at the beach. People may have done more than one thing.

1. <u>b, e</u> Todos   **a.** caminar por la playa

2. <u>g</u> Las chicas   **b.** cantar en la noche

3. <u>h</u> Juan   **c.** bailar

4. <u>a</u> Norma   **d.** tocar la guitarra

5. <u>d</u> Marcos   **e.** celebrar el cumpleaños de Lourdes

6. <u>c</u> Julia y Diego   **f.** llegar a casa tarde

7. <u>f</u> Lourdes   **g.** preparar un pastel

                                h. practicar esquí acuático

2 Listen to Marcos. Take notes. Then, complete the sentences below:

1. Marcos y sus amigos pensaron en _____ *ir a la playa* _____ .

2. Allí, ellos __ *celebraron el cumpleaños* __ de la amiga de Marcos.

3. Marcos tocó _____ *la guitarra* _____ y _____ *tocó* _____ música rock.

4. A Marcos le duelen _____ *las manos* _____ .

5. Todos _____ *terminaron* _____ el día muy felices.

Escuchar C

> **¡AVANZA!** **Goal:** Listen to discussions about the body and past activities.

1 Listen to the doctor and take notes. Then, complete the table with the causes of each person's pain.

Dolor de	Qué hicieron
Estómago	cenar comida poco nutritiva
Piel	tomar el sol sin bloqueador de sol
Cabeza u ojos	estudiar toda la noche
Brazos	levantar pesas
Orejas	escuchar música fuerte

2 Listen to Luis' conversation with the doctor. Take notes. Then, answer the following questions:

1. ¿Por qué va Luis a ver al doctor?

Porque le duele el estómago.

2. ¿Por qué está enfermo Luis?

Porque almorzó mucha comida.

3. ¿Por qué el doctor le preguntó cuándo celebraron el cumpleaños de la hermana de Luis?

Porque Luis almorzó el pastel de cumpleaños y el doctor necesita saber si el

pastel está malo.

4. ¿Qué tiene que hacer Luis?

Tiene que pensar más en su salud.

UNIDAD 6 Lección 2 • Escuchar C

Leer A

 Goal: Read about past events.

Jaime wrote an e-mail message to his friends inviting them to spend the day at the beach.

> Hola chicos:
>
> Les escribo para invitarlos mañana a pasar el día en la playa. Yo pasé todo el sábado en la playa con mi familia y es una actividad muy divertida. Todavía me duelen los brazos porque levanté pesas. También practiqué esquí acuático. No llevé sombrero ni bloqueador de sol y todavía me duele la piel. Pero tengo ganas de ir otra vez. Pensé que si vamos todos, va a ser más divertido todavía. Voy a traer bloqueador de sol para todos.
>
> ¿Qué dicen?

¿Comprendiste?

Read Jaime's e-mail message. Then, write **sí** next to the things that Jaime said he did at the beach and **no** next to the things he didn't mention.

1. _Sí_ ir a la playa con su familia
2. _No_ llevar bloqueador de sol
3. _Sí_ levantar pesas
4. _No_ nadar toda la tarde
5. _No_ mirar el mar
6. _Sí_ practicar esquí acuático
7. _No_ cantar con sus amigos.
8. _Sí_ no llevar sombrero

¿Qué piensas?

Read Jaime's e-mail message. Then write two sentences describing what you did the last time you went to the beach or pool with your friends.

Answers will vary: **En el día de playa con mis amigos traje bloqueador de sol y nadé mucho. Mi papá miró el mar y cantó toda la tarde.**

_____

Leer B

> **Goal:** Read about past events.

The basketball team players are sick. Before they leave the gym, they are given the following informational leaflet:

¡Atención chicos!

Muchos jugadores están enfermos. Ayer, ganamos el partido y a muchos chicos hoy les duele el estómago. Después del partido celebraron en el parque. Cocinaron una comida poco nutritiva y hoy están enfermos. No jugaron el partido de la tarde.

La salud es muy importante y tenemos que hacer las cosas necesarias para estar sanos.

¡Tenemos que comer comida sana!

¿Comprendiste?

Read the leaflet. Then, complete the following sentences.

1. Los chicos no jugaron el partido de hoy porque *están enfermos.*

2. A los chicos les duele *el estómago.*

3. Les duele porque *cocinaron una comida poco nutritiva.*

4. Una de las cosas más importantes es *la salud.*

5. Tenemos que hacer todo para *estar sanos.*

¿Qué piensas?

Read the leaflet. Answer the first question in a complete sentence then explain your answer.

1. ¿Piensas que es importante comer comida nutritiva? ¿Por qué?

   Answers will vary: **Sí, pienso que es muy importante comer comida**

   nutritiva porque es buena para la salud.

2. ¿Qué cosas hiciste ayer para estar sano(a)?

   Answers will vary: **Ayer comí una comida nutritiva y también hice ejercicios.**

   _____

Leer C

 Goal: Read about past events.

This morning, Claudia's mother found this note on the table.

> *Mamá:*
>
> *Hoy no voy a la escuela porque me duele mucho la cabeza. Ayer estudié toda la noche y hoy no puedo abrir los ojos. Ya hablé con Susana y ella me trae la tarea en la tarde.*
>
> *Ya preparé el desayuno; está en la mesa de la cocina. Mi papá me ayudó y cocinó unos huevos. También están en la mesa.*
>
> *Encontré el libro que tú buscaste ayer en el armario del primer piso. Está encima de la mesita de la sala.*
>
> *Hablamos después*
>
> *Claudia*

¿Comprendiste?

Read Claudia's note. Then answer the questions.

1. ¿Por qué Claudia no va a la escuela?

Porque a ella le duele la cabeza.

2. ¿Qué buscó Claudia?

Ella buscó un libro de su mamá.

3. ¿Quién ayudó a Claudia? ¿Cómo?

Su papá la ayudó a preparar el desayuno y cocinó unos huevos.

4. ¿Por qué Susana llevó la tarea a la casa de Claudia en la tarde?

Porque Claudia no va a la escuela y necesita su tarea.

¿Qué piensas?

Read Claudia's note. Write a short description about what you did the last time you stayed home from school because you were sick.

Answers will vary: **Por la mañana bebí jugo de naranja y después**

descansé. También miré la televisión.

Escribir A

> **¡AVANZA!** **Goal:** Write about past events.

Step 1

In the first column, list the top parts of the body. In the second column, list the bottom parts of the body.

En la parte de arriba	En la parte de abajo
Order will vary: **cabeza**	*Order will vary:* **piernas**
Order will vary: **ojos**	*Order will vary:* **pies**
Order will vary: **brazos**	*Order will vary:* **tobillos**
Order will vary: **orejas**	*Order will vary:* **rodillas**

Step 2

Answer the following questions about your life in complete sentences:

1. ¿Qué celebraste el último mes?

Answers will vary: **Yo celebré el cumpleaños de un amigo.**

2. ¿Qué música escuchaste ayer?

Answers will vary: **Yo escuché música rock.**

3. ¿Qué estudiaste esta semana?

Answers will vary: **Yo estudié ciencias y matemáticas.**

Step 3

Evaluate your writing using the information in the table below.

Writing Criteria	Excellent	Good	Needs Work
Content	You have responded to the questions completely.	You have responded to the questions partially.	You have not responded to the questions.
Communication	Most of your response is clear.	Some of your response is clear.	Your message is not very clear.
Accuracy	You make few mistakes in grammar and vocabulary.	You make some mistakes in grammar and vocabulary.	You make many mistakes in grammar and vocabulary.

Escribir B

> ¡AVANZA! **Goal:** Write about past events.

Step 1

Read the definitions and write them in the spaces below. Then, write down each of the letters in the circles and you will discover the hidden word.

1. Parte del cuerpo con la que escribimos.

2. Partes del cuerpo con las que caminamos.

3. Parte del cuerpo que recibe la comida.

4. Parte del cuerpo con la que vemos.

5. Parte del cuerpo con la que hablamos y comemos.

1. m   a   n   (o)

2. p   i   e   (r)   n   a   s

3. (e)   s   t   ó   m   a   g   o

4. o   (j)   o

5. b   o   c   (a)

Hidden word: _____ oreja _____

Step 2

Complete the following sentences using the words from the previous activity and the preterite:

1. mano /escribir *Answers will vary:* **Con mi mano escribí una nota.**

2. ojos / ver *Answers will vary:* **Con los ojos vi la televisión.**

3. oreja / escuchar *Answers will vary:* **Con las orejas escuché música.**

Step 3

Evaluate your responses to Actividad 2 using the information in the table below.

Writing Criteria	Excellent	Good	Needs Work
Content	You include all of the information.	You include some of the information.	You include little information.
Communication	Most of your message is organized and easy to follow.	Parts of your message are organized and easy to follow.	Your message is disorganized and hard to follow.
Accuracy	You make few mistakes in grammar and vocabulary.	You make some mistakes in grammar and vocabulary.	You make many mistakes in grammar and vocabulary.

Escribir C

> **¡AVANZA!** **Goal:** Write about past events.

Step 1

Complete the table with the parts of the body and what we do with each of them.

Partes del cuerpo	¿Qué hacemos con ellas?
Answers will vary: **boca**	*Answers will vary:* **comer y hablar**
Answers will vary: **mano**	*Answers will vary:* **escribir**
Answers will vary: **pierna**	*Answers will vary:* **caminar**
Answers will vary: **ojos**	*Answers will vary:* **mirar**
Answers will vary: **brazos**	*Answers will vary:* **levantar pesas**

Step 2

You are in bed, sick. Write a four-sentence letter to a classmate telling him or her why you are sick and did not go to school. Use the preterite. *Answers will vary:*

Hola, Nicolás.

Estoy enfermo en mi casa. De verdad, me duele todo. Hoy voy al médico. Ayer, en

la playa, tomé el sol por dos horas. Cuando terminé de tomar el sol, miré mi

piel: ¡roja como un tomate! ¡No usé bloqueador de sol! También me duelen la

cabeza y los brazos, creo que esto es porque ayer también levanté pesas por

primera vez. Mejor nos vemos mañana.

Pedro

Step 3

Evaluate your writing using the information in the table below.

Writing Criteria	Excellent	Good	Needs Work
Content	You include all of the information.	You include some of the information.	You include little information.
Communication	Most of your message is organized and easy to follow.	Parts of your message are organized and easy to follow	Your message is disorganized and hard to follow.
Accuracy	You make few mistakes in grammar and vocabulary.	You make some mistakes in grammar and vocabulary.	You make many mistakes in grammar and vocabulary.

Cultura A

> ¡AVANZA! **Goal:** Review cultural information about the Dominican Republic.

1 Dominican Republic Complete the following sentences with one of the multiple-choice answers.

1. The Dominican Republic shares the island of Hispaniola with __b__.

   a. Puerto Rico   **b.** Haití   **c.** Cuba

2. The Festival del Merengue includes music and __c__.

   a. baseball   **b.** surfing   **c.** cart races

3. The Dominican Republic is in the __a__.

   a. Caribbean Sea   **b.** Pacific Ocean   **c.** Gulf of Mexico

2 Dominican culture Complete the following sentences by choosing the correct word.

1. The Festival del Merengue is celebrated every (winter / summer) in Santo Domingo.

2. The athlete Félix Sánchez won a (gold / silver) medal in the 2004 Olympic games.

3. The Dominican Republic has a (warm / cold) climate.

4. The **Altar de la** (**Nación** / **Patria**) is a monument to the Dominican heroes from the battle of 1844.

3 Merengue Merengue is considered to be a symbol of the Dominican Republic. Describe what instruments are used in playing merengue and what occurs at the Festival del Merengue. What would you enjoy most at the festival and why?

Answers will vary: **The merengue is played using the maracas, accordion, saxophone, drums, and the *güiro*. At the Festival del Merengue, people can listen and dance to merengue music, see parades, and look at arts and crafts. I would most enjoy listening to the merengue music because I enjoy hearing live music.**

Cultura B

¡AVANZA! **Goal:** Review cultural information about the Dominican Republic.

1 **Dominican culture** Draw lines to match the phrases and names on the left with their explanation on the right.

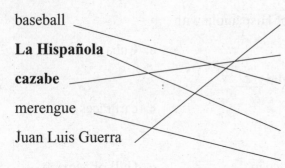

baseball   famous Dominican singer

La Hispañola   typical Dominican food

cazabe   national sport of the Dominican Republic

merengue   island of the Dominican Republic

Juan Luis Guerra   music of the Dominican Republic

2 **The Dominican Republic** Answer the following questions about the Dominican Republic.

1. What is the capital of the Dominican Republic? _The capital is Santo Domingo_

2. What are some events at the Festival del Merengue? _Some events include parades,_ _arts and crafts fairs, cart races, and merengue concerts._

3. What instruments are used to play merengue? _The maracas, accordion, saxophone,_ _drums, and the **güiro** are used to play merengue._

3 **Atletas famosos** Compare the athletes Félix Sánchez and Daniela Larreal with an athlete you admire or are familiar with. Mention where each athlete is from, which sport they participate in, and any championships they have competed in or awards they have won.

Answers will vary: **Félix Sánchez is from the United States, but is of Dominican**

heritage. He competes in track-and-field and has won a gold medal in the

Olympics. Daniela Larreal is a cyclist from Venezuela. She won four gold medals

in *los Juegos Bolivarianos*. Lance Armstrong is an athlete I admire, who

is also a cyclist. He is from the United States and has won the Tour de

France more times than any other person.

Cultura C

> **¡AVANZA!** **Goal:** Review cultural information about the Dominican Republic.

1 **Dominican Republic** Read the following sentences and answer *true* or *false*.

Ⓣ F **1.** The Festival del Merengue of Santo Domingo is held during the summer.

T Ⓕ **2.** The athlete Félix Sánchez was born in the Dominican Republic.

Ⓣ F **3.** One of the instruments used to play merengue is the accordion.

T Ⓕ **4.** Paella is a typical food of the Dominican Republic.

Ⓣ F **5.** The Dominican Republic is located in the Caribbean Sea.

2 **Dominican Culture** Answer the following questions with complete sentences.

1. What did the athlete Félix Sánchez promise he would do until he won a gold metal?

The athlete Félix Sánchez promised to wear the bracelet that he wore in

Sydney until he won a gold medal.

2. What is the currency of the Dominican Republic? The currency of the Dominican

Republic is the Dominican peso.

3. What can people do at the Festival del Merengue?

Answers will vary. **People can watch parades or cart races, listen to merengue**

music, and eat Domincan foods.

3 Look at the painting on page 332 of your book. Describe the images and style of the painting. What feelings does it evoke? What does it tell you about the climate and landscape of the Dominican Republic?

Answers will vary.

_____

_____

_____

_____

_____

UNIDAD 6
Lección 2

•

Cultura C

Comparación cultural: Deportes favoritos Level 1, pp. 349–350

Lectura y escritura

After reading the paragraphs about the favorite sports of Felipe, Gloria, and Agustín, write a paragraph about your favorite sport. Use the information on your sports chart to write sentences, and then write a paragraph that describes your favorite sport.

Step 1

Complete the sports chart describing as many details as possible about your favorite sport.

Categoría	Detalles
nombre del deporte	
lugar	
participantes	
equipo necesario	
ropa apropiada	

Step 2

Now take the details from your sports chart and write a sentence for each topic on the chart.

_____

_____

_____

_____

_____

_____

_____

_____

_____

UNIDAD 6 • Comparación Lección 2 • cultural

Comparación cultural: Deportes favoritos *Level 1, pp. 349–350*

Lectura y escritura (continued)

Step 3

Now write your paragraph using the sentences you wrote as a guide. Include an introduction sentence and use the verbs **jugar** and **saber** to write about your favorite sport.

_____

_____

_____

_____

_____

_____

_____

Checklist

Be sure that…

☐ all the details about your favorite sport from your sports chart are included in the paragraph;

☐ you use details to describe where the sport is played, as well as the participants and necessary equipment and clothing.

☐ you include new vocabulary words and the verbs **jugar** and **saber.**

Rubric

Evaluate your writing using the rubric below.

Writing criteria	Excellent	Good	Needs Work
Content	Your description includes many details about your favorite sport.	Your description includes some details about your favorite sport.	Your description includes little information about your favorite sport.
Communication	Most of your description is organized and easy to follow.	Parts of your description are organized and easy to follow.	Your description is disorganized and hard to follow.
Accuracy	Your description has few mistakes in grammar and vocabulary	Your description has some mistakes in grammar and vocabulary.	Your description has many mistakes in grammar and vocabulary.

Comparación cultural: Deportes favoritos *Level 1, pp. 349–350*

Compara con tu mundo

Now write a comparison about your favorite sport and that of one of the three students from page 349. Organize your comparison by topics. First, write the name of the sport, then describe where is played and who participates, and lastly the clothing and equipment.

Step 1

Use the chart to organize your comparison by topics. Write details for each topic about your favorite sport and that of the student you chose.

Categoría	Mi deporte	El deporte de _____
nombre del deporte		
lugar		
participantes		
ropa apropiada		

Step 2

Now use the details from the mind map to write a comparison. Include an introduction sentence and write about each category. Use the verbs **jugar** and **saber** to describe your favorite sport, and that of the student you chose.

_____
_____
_____
_____
_____
_____
_____
_____

Unidad 6
Comparación cultural: Deportes favoritos
294
¡Avancemos! 1
Cuaderno: Práctica por niveles

Vocabulario A

> ¡AVANZA! **Goal:** Talk about technology.

1 Place an "x" next to words related to computers and the Internet.

1. __X__ la pantalla
2. _____ los jeans
3. __X__ el mensajero instantáneo
4. __X__ el teclado
5. __X__ el sitio web

6. _____ la alfombra
7. __X__ el icono
8. __X__ el ratón
9. _____ las decoraciones
10. __X__ la dirección electrónica

2 Early in the morning, Lucas connected to the Internet. Complete the following sentences with the correct word from the ones in parentheses:

1. Lucas conecta a Internet para _____ estar en línea _____ . (estar en línea / estar enfermo)

2. Para mandar un correo electrónico a su amiga, Lucas necesita

   ___ la dirección electrónica ___ . (la cámara digital / la dirección electrónica)

3. Lucas usa ___ el mensajero instantáneo ___ para hablar con amigos. (el mensajero instantáneo /

   quemar un disco compacto)

4. Lucas hace clic en _____ el icono _____ . (la pantalla / el icono)

5. Lucas escribe correos electrónicos con _____ el teclado _____ . (el teclado /

   la cámara digital)

3 Complete the following sentences about using the computer:

1. Necesito buscar algo. ¿Tú sabes _____ navegar por Internet _____ ?

2. Me gusta la música salsa pero no la tengo. Mi amigo la tiene y va a

   ___ quemar un disco compacto ___ .

3. Yo tomo fotos con mi _____ cámara digital _____ .

Vocabulario B

> ¡AVANZA! **Goal:** Talk about technology.

1 Nicolás wants to send a few pictures to his friends. Put the steps below in logical order from a (for the first step) to e (for the last step).

1. Hacer clic en un icono para mandarlas _____ *e* _____ .

2. Conectar a Internet _____ *b* _____ .

3. Poner la dirección electrónica de su amigo _____ *Order will vary: c / d* _____ .

4. Escribir un correo electrónico con las fotos _____ *Order will vary: c / d* _____ .

5. Tomar las fotos con su cámara digital _____ *a* _____ .

2 Nicolás goes to the library to connect to the Internet. Complete the sentences using words from the box.

quemar un disco compacto	la pantalla teclado	en línea el sitio web

1. _____ *La pantalla* _____ está muy bien.

2. _____ *El sitio web* _____ es muy interesante, encuentro muchas cosas.

3. Quiero música nueva. Necesito _*quemar un disco compacto*_ , pero en la casa no puedo.

4. Me gusta escribir pero no me gusta usar el lápiz. Es más fácil escribir en mi _____ *teclado* _____ . Me gusta más.

5. Mi computadora conecta a Internet. Estoy _____ *en línea* _____ en un minuto.

3 Answer the following questions about your life in complete sentences:

1. ¿Quemaste un disco compacto la semana pasada?

   Answers will vary: **Sí, (No, no) quemé un disco compacto la semana pasada.**

2. ¿Usaste el mensajero instantáneo anteayer?

   Answers will vary: **Sí, (No, no) usé el mensajero instantáneo anteayer.**

3. ¿Tomaste fotos con la cámara digital el año pasado?

   Answers will vary: **Sí, (No, no) tomé fotos con la cámara digital el año pasado.**

Vocabulario C

¡AVANZA! **Goal:** Talk about technology.

---

1 Mariela wants to send pictures in an e-mail to her mother. Underline the correct word of the ones in parentheses to complete each sentence.

1. Mariela toma fotos con (una pantalla / un icono / una cámara digital).

2. Para mandar las fotos por correo electrónico, primero tiene que (hacer clic / conectar a Internet / quemar un disco compacto).

3. Después, pone (la dirección electrónica / el Internet / el teclado) de su madre.

4. Mariela manda un correo electrónico con (las fotos / el ratón / la pantalla).

5. Mariela quiere tener siempre las fotos. Entonces ella piensa (un sitio web / quemar un disco compacto / la computadora).

2 Mariela connected to the Internet from a friend's house. Complete the following sentences:

1. Mariela navega *Answers will vary:* **en sitios web muy interesantes.**

2. Mariela conecta *Answers will vary:* **a Internet todos los días.**

3. Mariela manda *Answers will vary:* **correos electrónicos a sus amigos.**

4. Mariela toma *Answers will vary:* **fotos con su cámara digital.**

3 Write three sentences about your own computer use. Use the words from the box.

anteayer	por fin	la dirección electrónica
luego	el ratón	conectar a Internet

1. *Answers will vary:* **Anteayer, no usé el ratón de mi computadora.**

2. *Answers will vary:* **Por fin, conecté a Internet.**

3. *Answers will vary:* **¿Luego escribes tu dirección electrónica?**

Gramática A *Preterite of Regular –er and –ir Verbs*

> **¡AVANZA!** **Goal:** Talk about what you and others did in the past.

1 Circle the correct verb form in the sentences below:

1. Ayer, Lorena (perdí / (perdió)) el dinero en el centro comercial.

2. Anteayer, Lorena y Carmen ((volvieron) / volvió) muy tarde.

3. Ernesto y yo ((salimos) / salieron) a beber un refresco.

4. Yo (subió / (subí)) las escaleras.

5. Tú ((viste) / vimos) la camisa que quieres.

2 Inés and her friends went shopping. Answer the questions with the correct form of the verb and the element in parentheses.

1. ¿A qué hora salieron ustedes de tu casa? (3:00) Nosotros salimos de mi casa a

   las tres.

2. ¿Qué vieron Inés y Cecilia? (zapatos) Inés y Cecilia vieron unos zapatos muy bonitos.

3. ¿Dónde perdió Inés el dinero? (en la tienda de deportes) Inés perdió el dinero en la

   tienda de deportes.

4. ¿Volviste a la tienda para buscarlo? (Sí) Sí, yo volví a la tienda para buscarlo.

3 Create sentences using the following elements. Conjugate the verbs in the preterite tense. Follow the model:

modelo: ayer / nosotros / comer / para celebrar el cumpleaños de mi tía:
Ayer nosotros comimos para celebrar el cumpleaños de mi tía.

1. mi tía y Norberto / compartir / el postre: Mi tía y Norberto compartieron el postre.

2. luego / ella / abrir / los regalos: Luego, ella abrió los regalos.

3. por fin /nosotros / volver / a casa: Por fin, nosotros volvimos a casa.

Gramática B *Preterite of Regular –er and –ir Verbs*

¡AVANZA! **Goal:** Talk about what you and others did in the past.

1 Several friends went to the park the day before yesterday. Choose the correct form of the verb to complete the sentences.

1. Inés __b__ por una hora.

  a. corriste   **b.** corrió   **c.** corrí   **d.** corrimos

2. ¿Tú __d__ temprano?

  a. volví   **b.** volvieron   **c.** volvió   **d.** volviste

3. Inés y yo __a__ nuestras chaquetas.

  a. perdimos   **b.** perdió   **c.** perdí   **d.** perdieron

4. Ustedes __a__ su almuerzo.

  a. compartieron   **b.** compartió   **c.** compartí   **d.** compartimos

5. Yo __d__ a las diez.

  a. salimos   **b.** salió   **c.** saliste   **d.** salí

2 Lorena and her friends did a lot of things the day before yesterday. Complete the sentences with the correct form of the verb in parentheses.

1. Yo_____*escribí*_____ un correo electrónico. (escribir)

2. Lorena y Armando _____*salieron*_____ al cine. (salir)

3. ¿Señora Barros, usted _____*barrió*_____ el suelo de su casa? (barrer)

4. Tú _____*corriste*_____ en el parque. (correr)

5. ¿Lorena y tú _____*recibieron*_____ el mensaje instantáneo de la fiesta? (recibir)

3 Write three sentences to describe what this family did last year. Use the preterite of the verbs in parentheses.

  modelo: Nosotros (vivir): Nosotros vivimos en otra casa.

1. Mis padres (salir): *Answers will vary:* **Mis padres salieron a comprar un coche.**

2. Yo (volver): *Answers will vary:* **Yo volví a la escuela después del verano.**

3. Mi madre (vender): *Answers will vary:* **Mi madre vendió su coche.**

Gramática C *Preterite of Regular –er and –ir Verbs*

¡AVANZA! **Goal:** Talk about what you and others did in the past.

1 Ernesto and his friends played a baseball game the day before yesterday. Complete the following text with the correct form of the verbs in the box:

Mi equipo de béisbol **1.** _____ recibió _____ muchos regalos ayer.

Nosotros **2.** _____ salimos _____ a jugar un partido de béisbol.

Yo **3.** _____ corrí _____ como nunca. Juan y Ariel no

4. _____ perdieron _____ ninguna pelota. Todos jugamos muy bien.

El otro equipo también jugó muy bien. Entonces, nosotros

5. _____ compartimos _____ los regalos con los chicos del otro equipo.

correr
perder
compartir
recibir
salir

2 Complete the following sentences about a sports event. Use the preterite of the verbs **correr, ver, perder, comprender las reglas,** and **recibir.**

1. Mis amigos y yo *Answers will vary:* **corrimos mucho en todos los partidos.**

2. Los chicos del equipo *Answers will vary:* **comprendieron las reglas.**

3. Yo *Answers will vary:* **vi el partido con mis amigas.**

4. ¿Tú *Answers will vary:* **viste todos los partidos?**

5. El equipo *Answers will vary:* **azul perdió el primer partido.**

3 Write three complete sentences to describe what happened at a soccer game. To begin, use one of these two expressions: **la semana pasada, el año pasado.**

Answers will vary: **El partido de fútbol de la semana pasada salió en**

televisión. Los jugadores corrieron todo el partido pero perdieron.

Los otros jugadores recibieron los regalos.

Gramática A   *Affirmative and Negative Words*

> **¡AVANZA!**   **Goal:** Talk about indefinite or negative situations.

1 Sofía and her family went to a restaurant and did not enjoy the experience. Draw a line from the question on the left to its correct answer on the right.

1. ¿Quién sirve la comida?   **a.** Ni el uno ni el otro.

2. ¿Hay sopa o pescado?   **b.** No, nunca tengo.

3. ¿Tiene algo con brócoli?   **c.** No, no hay nada.

4. ¿Siempre tiene carnes?   **d.** Tampoco hay.

5. No hay carne. ¿Hay pollo?   **e.** No hay nadie.

2 Valeria is not having a good day. Underline the word that best completes each sentence.

1. No quiere (<u>nada</u> / algo) de comer.

2. No quiere hablar con (alguien / <u>nadie</u>).

3. Valeria no quiere ni salir (<u>ni</u> / o) escuchar música.

4. Valeria no quiere ir al cine y, (<u>tampoco</u> / también) al teatro.

5. No quiere comprar (algunos / <u>ningunos</u>) jeans.

3 Ramiro is looking for something to do with his friends. Below are a few things they have decided not to do. Complete the sentences.

1. Ramiro no quiere ver _____ninguna_____ película en el cine.

2. Sus amigos no tienen hambre. No tienen ganas de comer _____nada_____ .

3. Las entradas para el teatro cuestan mucho. _____Nadie_____ puede comprarlas.

Gramática B *Affirmative and Negative Words*

> **¡AVANZA!** **Goal:** Talk about indefinite or negative situations.

1 Complete the following dialog using **o...o, tampoco, algo, ni...ni...** or **alguien.**

1. **Alejo:** Hola. ¿ _Alguien_ sabe quemar un disco compacto?
2. **Sara:** No, yo no sé y Rita _tampoco_ sabe.
3. **Rita:** Yo sé hacerlo. Necesitas usar_o_ el ratón_o_ el teclado.
4. **Sara:** No. Pienso que no necesitas _ni_ el ratón _ni_ el teclado.
5. **Rita:** ¡Pero él tiene que usar _algo_!

2 Osvaldo and Carmen are always opposites in what they do and want. Write complete sentences stating what Carmen does or wants. Follow the model.

modelo: Osvaldo quiere comprar algunos pantalones. Carmen no quiere comprar ningún pantalón.

1. Osvaldo prefiere un jugo o un refresco. Carmen _no prefiere ni un jugo ni un refresco._
2. Osvaldo siempre está contento. Carmen _nunca está contenta._
3. Osvaldo siempre habla con alguien por Internet. Carmen nunca _habla con nadie_

   por Internet.
4. A Osvaldo también le gusta usar el mensajero instantáneo. A Carmen _tampoco le_

   gusta usar el mensajero instantáneo.

3 Use the information in the table below to create three complete sentences about what Osvaldo does or does not do. Use each element once:

Nunca	comprar	nada
Siempre	recibir	alguna cosa
De vez en cuando	compartir	alguien

1. *Answers will vary:* **Osvaldo nunca compra nada.**
2. *Answers will vary:* **Osvaldo siempre recibe alguna cosa.**
3. *Answers will vary:* **De vez en cuando, Osvaldo comparte su**

   almuerzo con alguien.

Gramática C *Affirmative and Negative Words*

> **¡AVANZA!** **Goal:** Talk about indefinite or negative situations.

1 Elena is angry with Miriam. Rewrite the following sentences about what she is feeling, to make them negative.

1. Quiero saber algo de Miriam hoy.

No quiero saber nada de Miriam hoy.

2. Hay alguna persona tan enojada como yo ahora.

No hay ninguna persona tan enojada como yo ahora.

3. Ella siempre compartió sus libros y sus discos compactos.

Ella nunca compartió ni sus libros ni sus discos compactos.

4. Ella sale con alguien.

Ella no sale con nadie.

5. Ella quiere tener muchos amigos.

Ella no quiere tener ningún amigo.

2 Miriam is sad because one of her friends is angry with her. That's why she is not in the mood to do anything today. Complete the sentences. Use **ningún, nunca, nada, nadie** y **tampoco.**

1. Miriam no quiere *Answers will vary:* **hacer nada.**

2. Miriam *Answers will vary:* **nunca está tan triste como ahora.**

3. Miriam no quiere *Answers will vary:* **ver a nadie.**

4. Miriam *Answers will vary:* **tampoco quiere salir al cine.**

5. Miriam no tiene *Answers will vary:* **ningún amigo para hablar.**

3 Write two complete sentences about what you do at the times in parentheses. Use affirmative or negative expressions. Follow the model. *Answers will vary:*

modelo: (después de trabajar) Yo siempre como papas fritas después de trabajar.

1. (antes del desayuno) Yo nunca hablo con nadie antes del desayuno.

2. (los domingos) Yo estoy en el parque con alguien los domingos.

3. (después de las clases) Yo no veo televisión ni escucho música.

Integración: Hablar

Guillermo sends an e-mail to all his friends with pictures he took with his new digital camera.

Fuente 1 Leer

Read Guillermo's e-mail to all of his friends.

De: Guillermo   A: Todos mis amigos

Tema: Fotos nuevas

¡Hola a todos!

Estoy muy contento porque anteayer recibí regalos. ¡Qué fantástico! Mi papá me compró una cámara digital y también otra cosa. Cuando volví de la escuela, ¡mi papá abrió una computadora nueva! Ayer tomé algunas fotos con la cámara digital y las mando con este correo electrónico. Ustedes son los primeros que las ven, pero más tarde voy a ponerlas en un sitio web. Hoy mando más fotos a todos los chicos de la escuela.

Guillermo

Fuente 2 Escuchar   *CD 04 track 02*

Listen to the message Luis left on Guillermo's voicemail. Take notes.

_____

_____

_____

Hablar

Tell what Luis is trying to do and what problem he encounters.

modelo: Luis quiere... Pero...

Answers will vary: **Luis quiere ver las fotos de Guillermo por Internet.**

Pero no puede verlas porque no puede navegar por Internet.

Integración: Escribir

Soledad has a digital camera and repeatedly tries to send pictures attached in her e-mails without success. She goes to a Web site to get instructions. Still, she doesn't seem to be able to do what she wants, so she calls and leaves a message with customer service.

Fuente 1 Leer

Read Soledad's digital camera Web site instructions...

Para mandar fotos de su cámara digital por correo electrónico usted debe...

1. tomar las fotos con una cámara digital
2. poner las fotos en la computadora
3. conectar a Internet
4. escribir su dirección electrónica
5. escribir la dirección electrónica de la otra persona
6. hacer clic en el icono para poner las fotos en el correo electrónico
7. hacer clic en las fotos que quiere mandar
8. hacer clic en «mandar» el correo electrónico

Si todavía tiene problemas, llame gratis al 1-800-4-DIGITA

Fuente 2 Escuchar   *CD 04 track 04*

Listen to Soledad's message to a customer service department. Take notes.

_____

_____

_____

_____

Escribir

Explain why Soledad's pictures are not being sent in her e-mails.

modelo: Soledad no... Ella tampoco...

Answers will vary: **Soledad no escribe la dirección electrónica de la otra**

persona para mandar el correo. Tampoco hace clic en las fotos que

quiere mandar.

_____

_____

_____

Escuchar A

> **¡AVANZA!** **Goal:** Listen to discussions of various activities.

1 Listen to Viviana. Then, read each sentence below and answer **cierto** (true) or **falso** (false).

C (F) **1.** Viviana no tiene una casa nueva.

(C) F **2.** Viviana tiene una cámara digital.

(C) F **3.** Viviana tomó fotos de personas.

C (F) **4.** Viviana mandó las fotos el viernes pasado.

(C) F **5.** Viviana quiere mandar las fotos a sus amigos.

2 Listen to Julio. Then complete the sentences.

1. En su cumpleaños, la amiga de Julio recibió _____una cámara digital_____ .

2. Viviana recibió el regalo de _____sus amigos_____ .

3. La amiga de Julio manda fotos de _____su nueva casa_____ .

4. Julio y su amiga hablan por _____mensajero instantáneo_____ .

UNIDAD 7
Lección 1

Escuchar A

Unidad 7, Lección 1
Escuchar A

306

¡Avancemos! 1
Cuaderno: Práctica por niveles

Escuchar B

Level 1, pp. 376-377
CD 04 tracks 07-08

> ¡AVANZA! **Goal:** Listen to discussions of various activities.

1 Listen to Sebastián and take notes. Then, draw a line between the people and the photos they take.

1. Nicolás   **a.** de coches y autobuses
2. Miriam   **b.** del mar y la playa
3. Sebastián   **c.** de parques
4. Silvana   **d.** de personas
5. Pedro   **e.** de casas viejas

2 Listen to the conversation between Pedro and Silvana. Take notes. Then, complete the following sentences:

1. Pedro no mandó las fotos al sitio web.

2. Pedro piensa que a nadie le gustan sus fotos.

3. Anteayer, Silvana mandó a Pedro fotos de Answers will vary: **coches y autobuses.**

4. Cuando Pedro vio las fotos, nunca pensó en alguien que puede ganar una competición.

Escuchar C

Level 1, pp. 376-377
CD 04 tracks 09-10

| ¡AVANZA! | **Goal:** Listen to discussions of various activities. |

1 Listen to Armando and take notes. Then complete the following table with the information:

Persona que trae el regalo	Regalos	¿Para qué usa el regalo?
padre	computadora	navegar por Internet y quemar discos compactos
tío	cámara digital	tomar fotos
hermano	tocadiscos compactos	escuchar música

2 Listen to the conversation between Javier and Sandra. Take notes. Then answer the following questions:

1. ¿Por qué tiene el hermano de Javier muchos regalos?

Porque el año pasado no recibió ninguno.

2. ¿Dónde vivió el hermano de Javier el año pasado?

Él vivió en la casa de su abuela.

3. ¿Quién vivió en la casa de la abuela: Javier o su hermano?

Los dos chicos vivieron en la casa de la abuela.

4. ¿Por qué alguien tiene que estar con la abuela?

Porque está enferma.

5. ¿Cuándo es el cumpleaños de Javier?

Es el mes que viene.

Unidad 7, Lección 1
Escuchar C

308

¡Avancemos! 1
Cuaderno: Práctica por niveles

UNIDAD 7
Lección 1 • Escuchar C

Leer A

> **¡AVANZA!** **Goal:** Read about various activities.

Soledad is on vacation in Argentina. She sends this e-mail to her friend Agustín.

Hola, Agustín:

Estoy muy contenta. Ayer tomé muchas fotos y las mando con este correo electrónico. No sé la dirección electrónica de Jimena. ¿Puedes mandar tú las fotos? O mejor, ¿puedes mandar su dirección electrónica? Yo voy a mandar las fotos de ayer y las que mandé la semana pasada.

Ayer, comí una carne muy rica y salí a caminar por unos parques muy grandes.

¿Recibiste mi correo electrónico anteayer?

¿Vas a contestar algún día? Todavía no mandas ningún correo electrónico.

Adiós,

Soledad

¿Comprendiste?

Read Soledad's e-mail. Then place an "x" next to the things she did.

1. tomar fotos __X__

2. ir al centro comercial ____

3. comer __X__

4. caminar __X__

5. escribir a Jimena ____

6. ir a la playa ____

7. almorzar en un restaurante muy grande ____

8. estar enferma una semana ____

¿Qué piensas?

Read Soledad's e-mail. Then answer the following questions:

¿Quieres ir a otros países y tomar fotos ¿Por qué?

Answers will vary: **Sí, quiero tomar fotos para mis padres.**

_____

_____

UNIDAD 7
Lección 1 • Leer A

Leer B

> **¡AVANZA!** **Goal:** Read about various activities.

Santiago uses the instant messaging every day with a group of friends from other countries.

Santiago dice:

> ¡Hola a todos! ¿Cómo están? Estoy triste. Ayer hablé con los chicos de Argentina pero no vi a ninguno en el mensajero instantáneo.

Sofía dice:

> ¡Hola, Santiago! Yo ayer no hablé por mensajero instantáneo porque salí con algunas amigas al cine.

Ernesto dice:

> ¡Hola, Santiago! ¿Cómo estás? Yo tampoco hablé por mensajero instantáneo porque estudié toda la tarde.

Viviana dice:

> ¡Hola, Santiago! Yo no hablé por mensajero instantáneo porque salí a almorzar con mis padres y después salimos a comprar algunas cosas para mi cuarto. Nadie habló ayer por mensajero instantáneo.

¿Comprendiste?

Read the instant messenger conversation. Then, choose the correct answer about what each person did.

1. Ernesto: _d_
2. Viviana: _a_
3. Santiago: _c_
4. Sofía: _b_

a. comió en un restaurante
b. pasó un rato con amigas
c. conectó a Internet
d. estudió mucho

¿Qué piensas?

¿Te gusta hablar con amigos por mensajero instantáneo? ¿Por qué?

Answers will vary: **Sí, me gusta hablar con amigos por mensajero instantáneo,**

porque me gusta pasar un rato con amigos.

Leer C

¡AVANZA!	**Goal:** Read about various activities.

Víctor is on a trip. He writes a diary to remember everything he did in each place.

15 de marzo: Hoy paseé por parques muy grandes. Salí a caminar con unos amigos nuevos. Comí una carne muy rica y bebí jugos de frutas de aquí.

16 de marzo: Hoy no salí con amigos. Volví a los parques porque ayer perdí mi cámara digital en el parque. Por fin, la encontré.

Después comí pescado y ensalada.

17 de marzo: Hoy abrí la puerta de mi cuarto y encontré a todos mis amigos. Algunos prepararon una fiesta porque mañana voy a volver a mi país.

¿Comprendiste?

Read Victor's diary and imagine that today is March 17th. Then, list the things he did in the appropriate column.

Hoy	Ayer	Anteayer
1. Abrió la puerta de su cuarto.	1. No salió con amigos.	1. Paseó por parques muy grandes.
2. Encontró a todos sus amigos.	2. Volvió a los parques.	2. Salió a caminar con unos amigos.
3. Algunos prepararon una fiesta.	3. Encontró su cámara digital.	3. Perdió su cámara digital.
		4. Comió una carne muy rica y bebió jugos de frutas.

¿Qué piensas?

Read Victor's diary. Answer the first question in a complete sentence. Then, explain your answer.

1. ¿Piensas que puedes viajar solo?

   Answers will vary: **Sí, creo que puedo viajar solo.**

2. ¿Por qué?

   Answers will vary: **Porque sé hablar y puedo comunicarme con otras personas.**

Escribir A

> **¡AVANZA!** **Goal:** Write about various activities.

Step 1

List three places where you have taken photos with a digital camera.

1. *Answers will vary:* **el parque**
2. *Answers will vary:* **mi casa**
3. *Answers will vary:* **la escuela**

Step2

Write three sentences about the places where you have taken photos and what you did there. Include the words **hoy**, **ayer**, and **anteayer**:

Answers will vary: **Hoy almorcé temprano en mi casa. Ayer salí con amigos** _____

al parque. Anteayer navegué por Internet en la escuela. _____

_____

_____

_____

Step 3

Evaluate your writing using the information in the table below.

Writing Criteria	Excellent	Good	Needs Work
Content	You have included three sentences about the places you have been and what you did there.	You have included two sentences about the places you have been and what you did there.	You have included one sentence or less about the places you have been and what you did there.
Communication	Most of your response is clear.	Some of your response is clear	Your message is not very clear.
Accuracy	You make few mistakes in grammar and vocabulary.	You make some mistakes in grammar and vocabulary.	You make many mistakes in grammar and vocabulary.

UNIDAD 7 • Escribir A
**UNIDAD 7
Lección 1**

Unidad 7, Lección 1
Escribir A
312

¡Avancemos! 1
Cuaderno: Práctica por niveles

Escribir B

> **¡AVANZA!** **Goal:** Write about various activities.

Step 1

Write a list of four activities you do during the summer.

1. *Answers will vary:* **correr en el parque**
2. *Answers will vary:* **comer en la playa**
3. *Answers will vary:* **ir a la playa**
4. *Answers will vary:* **escribir correos electrónicos**

Step 2

Write four complete sentences that describe what you did last summer. Use the preterite of three different **–er** and **–ir** verbs.

Answers will vary: **El verano pasado yo tomé el sol en la playa. Luego, salí a comer con amigos en la playa. Yo escribí muchos correos electrónicos. Corrí en el parque con mi amiga.**

Step 3

Evaluate your writing using the information in the table.

Writing Criteria	Excellent	Good	Needs Work
Content	You included four sentences that describe what you did last summer.	You included three sentences that describe what you did last summer.	You included two or fewer sentences that describe what you did last summer.
Communication	Most of your message is organized and easy to follow.	Parts of your message are organized and easy to follow.	Your message is disorganized and hard to follow.
Accuracy	You make few mistakes in grammar and vocabulary.	You make some mistakes in grammar and vocabulary.	You make many mistakes in grammar and vocabulary.

Escribir C

Level 1, pp. 376-377

> ¡AVANZA! **Goal:** Write about various activities.

Step 1

Write a list of four things you and your friends buy at the mall.

1. *Answers will vary:* **camisas**
2. *Answers will vary:* **una blusa**
3. *Answers will vary:* **zapatos**
4. *Answers will vary:* **pantalones**

Step2

The day before yesterday you went to the mall with your friends. Use the list above to write five complete sentences that describe what all or some of you did. Include the words **alguna** and **ninguna.**

Answers will vary: Anteayer, mis amigos y yo salimos de compras al centro comercial.

Marta compró algunas camisas y pantalones en la tienda de ropa. Jimena buscó

una blusa azul pero no encontró ninguna. En la tienda de deportes, compré zapatos.

Después, comimos en un restaurante. Luis perdió el dinero en el restaurante y

todos volvimos a buscarlo.

Step3

Evaluate your writing using the information in the table below.

Writing Criteria	Excellent	Good	Needs Work
Content	You include five sentences that describe what you and your friends did at the mall.	You include three to four sentences that describe what you and your friend did at the mall.	You include two sentences or less that describe what you and your friend did at the mall.
Communication	Most of your message is organized and easy to follow.	Parts of your message are organized and easy to follow.	Your message is disorganized and hard to follow.
Accuracy	You make few mistakes in grammar and vocabulary.	You make some mistakes in grammar and vocabulary.	You make many mistakes in grammar and vocabulary.

UNIDAD 7 • Escribir C
Lección 1

314

Unidad 7, Lección 1
Escribir C

¡Avancemos! 1
Cuaderno: Práctica por niveles

Cultura A

> ¡AVANZA! **Goal:** Review cultural information about Argentina.

1 **Argentina** Read the following sentences about Argentina and answer *true* or *false*.

(T)　F　**1.** The capital of Argentina is Buenos Aires.

(T)　F　**2.** Argentina is located in South America.

T　(F)　**3.** Jorge Luis Borges was a famous Argentine painter.

(T)　F　**4.** The **bandoneón** is an Argentine musical instrument similar to the accordion.

(T)　F　**5.** Many Argentines use **vos** instead of **tú**.

2 **Argentine culture** Draw lines to match the names or phrases on the left with their explanation on the right.

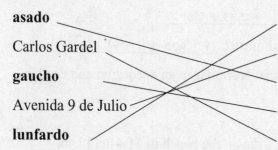

asado — typical Argentine food

Carlos Gardel — famous tango singer

gaucho — Argentine cattleman

Avenida 9 de Julio — the widest street in the world

lunfardo — a variety of slang from Buenos Aires

3 **Visiting Argentina** In Argentina there are many places to visit and many interesting things to see. Write down the interesting things to see in the following places in Argentina.

Places to visit

el Barrio de San Telmo

las **pampas**

Plaza de la República

the city of Mar del Plata

Interesting things to see

Answers will vary: **Tango dancers**

Answers will vary: **Gauchos**

Answers will vary: **The Obelisk, Avenida 9**

de Julio

Answers will vary: **Beautiful beaches**

UNIDAD 7
Lección 1 • Cultura A

Cultura B

> ¡AVANZA! **Goal:** Review cultural information about Argentina.

1 **Argentina** Choose the correct word to complete the sentences.

1. The city of Mar del Plata is famous for its ____beaches____ .

2. The ____tango____ is a popular Argentine dance.

3. Many Argentines don't use **tú,** but instead use____vos____ .

4. The capital of Argentina is ____Buenos Aires____ .

5. The ____gauchos____ raise cattle and are cultural icons in Argentina.

2 **About Argentina** Answer the following questions about Argentina in complete sentences.

1. What was the profession of Carlos Gardel? ____tango singer____

2. What do the **lunfardo** terms **gomias** and **zapi** mean? ____amigos (friends); pizza____

3. What is the name of the musical instrument that is similar to an accordion and used in

   tango music? ____The bandoneón____

3 Write a description of how you would spend a day at the beach in Mar del Plata, Argentina. What time of year would you travel there and why? What activities would you participate in? What might you see there?

Answers will vary: I would visit Mar del Plata in January because the

weather would be warm. I would go surfing and scuba diving. The beach

would be very crowded and there would be many people sunbathing there.

There would also be people riding bikes and walking dogs along the beach.

_____

_____

_____

Cultura C

> ¡AVANZA! **Goal:** Review cultural information about Argentina.

1 **Sites in Argentina** In Argentina, there are many interesting things to see. Write down what can be seen at the following famous sites of Argentina.

Famous sites of Argentina	What to see
Barrio de San Telmo	*Answers will vary:* **tango dancers**
Las pampas	*Answers will vary:* **gauchos, cattle**
Plaza de la República	*Answers will vary:* **the Obelisk, Avenida 9 de Julio**
Mar del Plata	*Answers will vary:* **miles of beaches**

2 **Argentina** Answer these questions about Argentina using complete sentences.

1. What do some people call the city of Buenos Aires because of its European architecture?

Some people call the city of Buenos Aires "The Paris of America".

2. Which avenue in Argentina is considered to be the widest in the world?

The Avenida 9 de Julio in Argentina is considered to be the widest in the world.

3. What people of Argentina are considered to be cultural icons? The gauchos are

considered to be cultural icons of Argentina.

3 **Lunfardo** Describe what **lunfardo** is. How and where did it develop? What are some examples of **lunfardo?**

Answers will vary: **Lunfardo is a type of slang that developed in Buenos**

Aires within the immigrant populations. Many words are influenced by

Italian and other languages. Examples of lunfardo words are *gomías* and

***zapi,* which mean *amigos* and *pizza.* Lunfardo usage spread to the general**

public through tango music by popular singers such as Carlos Gardel.

Vocabulario A

> **¡AVANZA!** **Goal:** Discuss where you like to go with your friends.

1 Griselda and Raúl go to fun places. Place an X next to the logical sentences.

1. Griselda prepara la comida en el acuario. _____

2. Raúl y Griselda aprenden mucho en el museo. _X_

3. Griselda y sus amigos leen mucho en el parque de diversiones. _____

4. A Griselda le gustan los animales y va mucho al zoológico. _X_

5. Raúl compra el boleto de los autitos chocadores. _X_

6. Griselda aprende de animales del mar en la vuelta al mundo. _____

2 It was fun! Look at the drawings and complete the following sentences.

1.  **2.**  **3.**  **4.**  **5.**

1. A Griselda le gustan ___los autitos chocadores___ .

2. Raúl mira el arte en ___el museo___ .

3. Raúl y Griselda tienen miedo de subir a ___la vuelta al mundo___ .

4. A Griselda le gusta ir ___al acuario___ .

5. Raúl siempre va ___al zoológico___ .

3 Answer the following questions about your life in complete sentences.

1. ¿Te gustaría conocer museos de otros países?

Answers will vary: **Sí, me gustaría conocer museos de otros países.**

2. ¿Tus amigos dejan el mensaje cuando llaman y tú no estás?

Answers will vary: **Sí, mis amigos dejan el mensaje.**

3. ¿Adónde invitas a tus amigos para pasar un rato divertido?

Answers will vary: **Yo invito a mis amigos al cine.**

Vocabulario B

> **¡AVANZA!** **Goal:** Discuss where you like to go with your friends.

1 Laura and her friends want to have fun. List related words from the box in the appropriate columns of the table.

parque de diversiones	biblioteca	acuario
museo	autitos chocadores	zoológico

Para pasar un rato divertido	Para aprender de animales	Para aprender otras cosas
parque de diversiones	acuario	museo
autitos chocadores	zoológico	biblioteca

2 Laura wants to ask Tomás to go to the amusement park. She calls him on the phone. Complete their conversation with an appropriate expression.

Laura: **1.** ¿_____Aló_____? **2.** ¿_____Puedo_____ hablar con Tomás?

Madre de Tomás: ¿Laura? ¿Cómo estás? Un momento, a ver... no, él no

3. _____está_____. Quieres dejar un mensaje?

Laura: ¿No está? **4.** ¡_____Qué lástima_____! Sí. Quiero dejar un mensaje.

Quiero saber si **5.** _____le gustaría_____ ir al parque de diversiones.

Madre de Tomás: ¡Claro que sí! Él invitó a su hermano Diego, pero Diego no puede ir.

Yo pienso que **6.** _____le encantaría_____.

3 **¿Qué prefiere?** Complete the first part of the following sentences with something each person does not want to do and the second part with what each person prefers instead. *Answers will vary:*

1. A Lucas no le gustaría ir a _____los museos_____, prefiere

_____el parque de diversiones_____.

2. Carina tiene miedo de _____la vuelta al mundo_____, le gustaría más

_____los autitos chocadores_____.

3. Norma no quiere subir a _____los autitos chocadores_____, pero le encantaría

_____la vuelta al mundo_____.

Vocabulario C

Level 1, pp. 380-384

> **¡AVANZA!** **Goal:** Discuss where you like to go with your friends.

1 My friends do many fun things. Draw a line between the activity they want and the place for it.

1. Los chicos quieren ver animales.   **a.** Van al parque de diversiones.

2. Los chicos quieren ver animales del mar.   **b.** Van al zoológico.

3. Los chicos quieren subir a la vuelta al mundo.   **c.** Van al museo.

4. Los chicos quieren ver el arte.   **d.** Van al acuario.

2 I went to the amusement park and other fun places with Gastón. Complete the following sentences with what you think happened.

1. Gastón subió a los autitos chocadores pero primero *Answers will vary:* **compró**

el boleto.

2. Gastón y yo vimos todo el parque de diversiones cuando *Answers will vary:* **subimos**

a la vuelta al mundo.

3. A Gastón no le gustan los lugares peligrosos, entonces *Answers will vary:* **tiene miedo**

de subir a la vuelta al mundo.

4. También, en el zoológico *Answers will vary:* **vimos muchos animales interesantes.**

5. «¡Qué aburrido!» dice Gastón cuando *Answers will vary:* **va al museo.**

3 Write three complete sentences describing fun activities that you would like to do with your friends this weekend.

Answers will vary: **Me gustaría mucho ir al cine y a caminar en el parque.**

También me gustaría ir al parque de diversiones con mis amigos. Ir a la

casa de alguno de mis amigos para escuchar música también es divertido.

Gramática A *Preterite of ir, ser, hacer*

> **¡AVANZA!** **Goal:** Say where you went, what you did, and how it was.

1 Fabiana and her friends did many things. Underline the correct form of each verb below.

1. Fabiana (fueron / <u>fue</u>) al museo.

2. Fabiana y yo (<u>hicimos</u> / hizo) algunas llamadas a nuestros amigos.

3. Adrián y Fabiana (hizo / <u>hicieron</u>) esquí acuático.

4. Subir a la vuelta al mundo (<u>fue</u> / fuimos) divertido.

5. ¿Tú (fue / <u>fuiste</u>) al acuario?

2 What did Fabiana's friends do? Complete the sentences with the preterite of the verbs in parentheses.

1. Fabiana _____fue_____ muy simpática con Jorge. (ser)

2. Fabiana y Josefina _____fueron_____ a comer a un restaurante bueno. (ir)

3. ¿Tú _____fuiste_____ el campeón de tenis el año pasado? (ser)

4. ¿Qué _____hicieron_____ ustedes anteayer? (hacer)

5. Pablo _____hizo_____ esquí acuático. (hacer)

6. Fabiana, Pablo y yo _____fuimos_____ al parque de diversiones. (ir)

7. Roberto y Patricio no fueron al parque de diversiones, ellos _____hicieron_____ las tareas. (hacer)

8. _____Fue_____ muy divertida la actividad. (ser)

3 Write three sentences about what happened last Saturday. Use the following elements.

1. Yo / ir / casa de mis amigos *Yo fui a la casa de mis amigos.*

_____

2. Yo / ser / estudioso *Yo fui estudioso.*

_____

3. Yo / hacer / la tarea *Yo hice la tarea.*

_____

Gramática B *Preterite of ir, ser, hacer*

> **¡AVANZA!** **Goal:** Say where you went, what you did, and how it was.

1 Fabio and his friends went out last week. Read the information in the table and write complete sentences with it.

Fabio	fui a la casa de Fabio.
Fabio y yo	hiciste una comida muy rica.
Yo	hicimos algunas compras.
Fabio y Soledad	fue al acuario.
Tú	fueron buenos amigos y compraron los boletos para nosotros.

1. Fabio fue al acuario.

2. Fabio y yo hicimos algunas compras.

3. Yo fui a la casa de Fabio.

4. Fabio y Soledad fueron buenos amigos y compraron los boletos para nosotros.

5. Tú hiciste una comida muy rica.

2 Federico and Agustina invited a friend to dinner. Complete the friend's sentences using the preterite of **ir, ser,** or **hacer**.

1. Federico _____hizo_____ una sopa nutritiva. ¡Qué rica!

2. Federico y Agustina _____fueron_____ a comprar las cosas para preparar la cena.

3. Federico y Agustina _____fueron_____ muy simpáticos en la cena.

4. Yo _____hice_____ el postre.

5. Agustina y yo _____fuimos_____ a comprar el jugo de naranja.

3 What did you do for fun last week? Write three complete sentences using the preterite of **ir, ser,** and **hacer**. Follow the model:

modelo: Yo hice esquí acuático.

1. *Answers will vary:* **Yo hice una pizza.**

2. *Answers will vary:* **Yo fui al centro comercial con mis amigas.**

3. *Answers will vary:* **Fue divertido jugar al fútbol.**

UNIDAD 7 • Gramática B
Lección 2

322
Unidad 7, Lección 2
Gramática B

¡Avancemos! 1
Cuaderno: Práctica por niveles

Gramática C *Preterite of ir, ser, hacer*

¡AVANZA! **Goal:** Say where you went, what you did, and how it was.

1 Emiliano spent a fun day with his friends. Complete the text with the correct form of **ir, ser,** or **hacer**.

Anteayer, mis amigos y yo **1.** _____fuimos_____ a pasar un día en

la playa. ¡Qué divertido! Fernando y Lupe **2.** _____hicieron_____

esquí acuático y también bucearon. Después, ellos y yo tocamos la guitarra

y cantamos. Por la tarde, **3.** _____hizo_____ mucho sol y calor,

entonces algunos chicos **4.** _____fueron_____ a buscar más refrescos

y los otros nadaron en el mar. **5.** ¡ _____Fue_____ un día perfecto!

2 Create five sentences about the activities and relationships of Emiliano and his friends, using the preterite of **ir, ser,** and **hacer.**

Emiliano
Fernando
yo
Marcos

1. *Answers will vary:* **Emiliano fue un amigo bueno en la escuela.**

2. *Answers will vary:* **Yo hice una sopa muy rica.**

3. *Answers will vary:* **Emiliano y Fernando fueron a la casa de Marcos.**

4. *Answers will vary:* **Yo fui a caminar al parque.**

5. *Answers will vary:* **Emiliano hizo esquí acuático.**

3 ¿Qué hiciste la semana pasada? Write an e-mail to a friend about last week's activities. Write four complete sentences using the preterite of **ir, ser,** and **hacer.**

Answers will vary:

Hola Vilma: Estoy muy contenta. Salí toda la semana con Octavio. El lunes

fuimos al cine y el martes fuimos al parque. Él fue muy simpático y habló de.

cosas interesantes El viernes salimos y mañana también. ¿Qué piensas? Inés

Gramática A Pronouns after Prepositions

> **¡AVANZA!** **Goal:** Talk about activities you did with friends.

1 Patricia invited her friends to the movies. Circle the correct pronoun for each sentence below.

1. Patricia buscó a Pablo y él fue con (ella / nosotros).

2. Nosotros fuimos al cine a las dos. Los chicos hablaron con (ellos / nosotros) a las dos y media.

3. Mi semana fue muy triste. Ir al cine fue muy bueno para (ti / mí).

4. Fui (contigo / conmigo) al cine porque tú eres una buena amiga.

5. ¡Qué divertido fue el día que tú fuiste (contigo / con nosotros) al cine!

2 Patricia and her friends had a good time at the movies. Complete each sentence with the correct pronoun.

1. A Patricia le gustó la película. Fue muy interesante para _____ella_____.

2. Yo invité a Matías porque me gusta estar con _____él_____.

3. Tú invitaste a Juana porque te gusta hablar con _____ella_____.

4. A _____mí_____ también me gustó la película.

5. No sabemos qué le gusta a Patricia. Nunca habla de _____ella_____.

3 Answer the following questions about your life in complete sentences. Use the same prepositions in your answer as in the question and the correct pronouns after them.

1. ¿A ti te gusta ir de compras?

Answers will vary: Sí, (No) a mí (no) me gusta ir de compras.

2. ¿Vas al cine con tus amigos el fin de semana?

Answers will vary: Sí, (No, no) voy con ellos el fin de semana.

3. ¿Tus padres van contigo al centro comercial?

Answers will vary: Sí, (No, no) van conmigo al centro comercial.

Unidad 7, Lección 2
Gramática A
324

¡Avancemos! 1
Cuaderno: Práctica por niveles

UNIDAD 7 • Gramática A
Lección 2

Gramática B   *Pronouns after Prepositions*

> **¡AVANZA!** **Goal:** Talk about activities you did with friends.

1 Sarita and her friends went shopping last weekend. Choose the correct pronoun to complete the sentences.

1. Al padre de Ana le gustan las camisas y Ana compró algunas para __a__ .

   a. él   **b.** nosotros   **c.** mí

2. Sandra compró un libro para __c__ , porque sabe que me gusta leer.

   a. ella   **b.** yo   **c.** mí

3. Sarita fue __b__ a la tienda de deportes porque yo sé de deportes.

   a. contigo   **b.** conmigo   **c.** con ella

2 Use the information given to create complete sentences. Exchange the correct pronoun for the information in parentheses.

   modelo: Yo / hablar con (Julia). Yo hablé con ella.

1. Yo / comprar un regalo para (mi hermano). *Yo compré un regalo para él.*

2. Mis amigos / compartir con (tú) su almuerzo. *Mis amigos compartieron contigo*
   su almuerzo.

3. Tú / no encontrar el disco compacto para (Soledad) y para (yo). *Tú no encontraste*
   el disco compacto para nosotros.

4. ¡Qué divertido! Nosotros / cantar "feliz cumpleaños" para (tú). *¡Qué divertido!*
   Nosotros cantamos "feliz cumpleaños" para ti.

3 Answer the following questions about your life in complete sentences. Use the correct pronoun after the prepositions given.

1. Para ti, ¿cuál es el deporte más peligroso?

   Answers will vary: **Para mí, el deporte más peligroso es el esquí acuático.**

2. ¿Quién va al cine contigo?

   Answers will vary: **Mis amigos siempre van al cine conmigo.**

3. En tu familia, ¿quién compra los regalos de cumpleaños para ustedes?

   Answers will vary: **En mi familia, mi mamá compra los regalos de cumpleaños**

   para nosotros.

Nombre _____ Clase _____ Fecha _____

Gramática C Pronouns after Prepositions

Level 1, pp. 390-392

¡AVANZA! **Goal:** Talk about activities you did with friends.

1 Yesterday, Silvia and some friends went to the museum. Read the sentences below and complete the second part with the correct pronoun after each preposition.

1. Yo invité a mis amigos al museo. A ___ellos___ les gusta el arte.
2. Mis amigos dicen que buscan a Norma y vienen con ___ella___ .
3. Joaquín, el autobús llega cerca de tu casa. Está cerca de ___ti___ .
4. El museo está al lado de la escuela. Está al lado de ___ella___ .
5. Silvia compra los boletos para Joaquín, para José, para Norma y para mí. Ella los compra para ___nosotros___ .

2 Our friends got to the museum late. Write complete sentences using the pronouns in parentheses after a preposition.

1. (mí) *Answers will vary:* **Para mí, quince minutos es llegar tarde.**
2. (ti) *Answers will vary:* **¿Qué piensas de ti?**
3. (nosotros) *Answers will vary:* **No llegaron con nosotros. Llegaron más tarde.**
4. (ella) *Answers will vary:* **Norma no llegó. No sé nada de ella.**
5. (conmigo) *Answers will vary:* **¿Estás enojado conmigo?**

3 Write three complete sentences about what you did last week. Use pronouns after prepositions.

1. *Answers will vary:* **Yo compré una blusa para mí.**
2. *Answers will vary:* **Yo vi a Jorge y hablé por teléfono con él.**
3. *Answers will vary:* **Yo fui al cine contigo.**

UNIDAD 7 • Gramática C
Lección 2

326 Unidad 7, Lección 2
Gramática C

¡Avancemos! 1
Cuaderno: Práctica por niveles

Integración: Hablar

Level 1, pp. 393-395
CD 04 track 11

Alejandra and Cecilia want to meet on Saturday. But they have different plans and are available at different times.

Fuente 1 Leer

Read Alejandra's e-mail to Cecilia...

> De: Alejandra   A: Cecilia
>
> Tema: Invitación para el sábado
>
> ¡Hola Cecilia!
>
> El fin de semana pasado fui al parque de diversiones y, ¡qué divertido! ¿Te gustaría venir conmigo el sábado? Hay una vuelta al mundo muy grande. Yo sé que te gustan mucho la vuelta al mundo y los autitos chocadores. ¿Puedes venir o por la mañana o por la tarde? Si vamos por la tarde, podemos almorzar en un café en el parque. Manda un correo electrónico o llama por teléfono. Si me llamas a casa y no estoy, me puedes dejar un mensaje en mi teléfono celular.
>
> Alejandra

Fuente 2 Escuchar   CD 04 track 12

Listen to Cecilia's message on Alejandra's cell phone. Take notes.

_____

_____

_____

_____

Hablar

According to their schedules, when can Alejandro and Cecilia meet on Saturday? What activities can they do together? What can't they do?

modelo: Alejandra y Cecilia pueden ir... Luego, ellas... No pueden...

Answers will vary: **Alejandra y Cecilia pueden ir al parque de diversiones por la**

mañana. Luego, ellas pueden cenar en el Restaurante Sol por la noche. No pueden

almorzar en un café por la tarde.

UNIDAD 7
Lección 2

Integración:
Hablar

Integración: Escribir

There is a new baseball museum in the city. It is advertised in newspapers and people are interested in going there.

Fuente 1 Leer

Read the Museum's newspaper ad...

MUSEO DEL BÉISBOL

¿Te gusta el béisbol?

¿Quieres saber más sobre los jugadores y la historia del deporte?

De vez en cuando algunos jugadores famosos vienen al museo para hablar. El fin de semana pasado, abrimos para ti un museo en el centro comercial de la calle Santa Fe, cerca del parque. Es un museo donde puedes aprender muchas cosas de tu deporte favorito.

En el museo hay premios de campeonatos. También tenemos muchas cosas de los jugadores.

Fuente 2 Escuchar *CD 04 track 14*

Listen to the explanations given through loudspeakers in the museum. Take notes.

_____

_____

_____

Escribir

Describe what people can see in the museum.

modelo: En el museo... También las personas pueden...

Answers will vary: **En el museo hay cosas de los jugadores, como cascos,**

camisetas y bates. También las personas pueden ver los premios de

los campeonatos. También pueden escuchar a jugadores famosos,

de vez en cuando.

Escuchar A

¡AVANZA! **Goal:** Listen to discussions about fun activities with friends.

1 Listen to Federico. Then, place an "x" next to the sentences that describe what happened.

1. Federico y sus amigos fueron al parque de diversiones. __X__

2. Federico y sus amigos fueron al zoológico. ____

3. Todos subieron a la vuelta al mundo pero Susana no subió. __X__

4. Raúl habló con sus amigos para subir a los autitos chocadores. ____

5. Raúl subió a los autitos chocadores pero nadie más subió. ____

6. Todos subieron a los autitos chocadores. __X__

2 Listen to Susana. Then, complete the sentences.

1. Susana tiene _____miedo_____ de los lugares peligrosos.

2. Susana cree que ___la vuelta al mundo___ es peligrosa.

3. Todos hablaron _____con ella_____ pero no subió.

4. Después del ___parque de diversiones___ , fueron a la casa de Noemí.

Escuchar B

Level 1, pp. 400-401
CD 04 tracks 17-18

> ¡AVANZA! **Goal:** Listen to discussions about fun activities with friends.

1 Listen to Teresa and take notes. Then, underline the word that completes each sentence.

1. Teresa invitó a Jaime al (acuario / zoológico).

2. A Teresa le gusta ir con (él / ella).

3. Jaime sacó buenas notas en ciencias el (mes pasado / año pasado).

4 Teresa aprendió cosas de (animales / buenas notas).

5. Teresa piensa que el zoológico es un lugar muy (aburrido / interesante).

2 Listen to Jaime and take notes. Then, complete the table below with the information requested.

¿Qué recibió Jaime?	¿De quién?	¿Cuándo?
el boleto	de Teresa	hoy
un libro de los zoológicos de todos los países	de su papá	el año pasado
un libro con fotos de todos los animales	de su mamá	el mes pasado

Unidad 7, Lección 2
Escuchar B
330

¡Avancemos! 1
Cuaderno: Práctica por niveles

UNIDAD 7 • Escuchar B
Lección 2

Escuchar C

Level 1, pp. 400-401
CD 04 tracks 19-20

¡AVANZA! **Goal:** Listen to discussions about fun activities with friends.

1 Listen to Luis. Then, write four things that happened in Catalina's house and four things that happened in the movie.

En la casa de Catalina	**En la película**
1. _Answers will vary:_ **Los chicos vieron una película.**	**1.** _Answers will vary:_ **Un chico conoce a una chica en la playa.**
2. _Answers will vary:_ **Catalina preparó sándwiches.**	**2.** _Answers will vary:_ **Los chicos van a un parque de diversiones.**
3. _Answers will vary:_ **Ramón compró refrescos.**	**3.** _Answers will vary:_ **Los padres de la chica los ven en la vuelta al mundo.**
4. _Answers will vary:_ **Los chicos escucharon música.**	**4.** _Answers will vary:_ **A los padres de la chica no les gusta el chico.**

2 Listen to Catalina's conversation and take notes. Then, answer the following questions:

1. ¿Quiénes fueron a la casa de Catalina?

Sus amigos.

2. ¿Cuándo fueron los chicos a comprar refrescos?

Después de ver la película.

3. ¿Qùe tiene Manuel?

Manuel tiene unos discos compactos de música rock.

4. ¿Por qué tocó Luis la guitarra para María?

Porque a Luis le gusta María.

5. ¿Qué piensa Catalina de recibir amigos en su casa?

Le gusta recibir a sus amigos en su casa.

Leer A

> **¡AVANZA!** **Goal:** Read about a few activities.

Vanesa has a diary. Yesterday, she went out with friends and she wrote about it in her diary.

> *Martes, 23 de septiembre.*
>
> *Hoy salí con Gastón y Julieta. Fuimos al parque de diversiones. ¡Qué divertido! A Julieta le gusta ir conmigo cuando sale. Dice que le encanta salir conmigo. Vamos a todos los lugares. También es muy divertido salir con Gastón. Gastón y yo subimos a la vuelta al mundo. Julieta fue a comprar algo de beber y no subió. Ella tiene miedo de subir tan alto. Gastón y Julieta subieron a los autitos chocadores y yo saqué mi teléfono celular y hablé con otro amigo. No me gustan los autitos chocadores. Les tengo miedo.*
>
> *Volvimos muy tarde pero contentos.*

¿Comprendiste?

Read Vanessa's diary. Draw a line from the people's names below to what each person did.

1. Julieta
2. Julieta, Vanesa y Gastón
3. Vanesa
4. Vanesa y Gastón
5. Vanesa y Julieta

a. Hizo una llamada.
b. Sale siempre con Vanesa.
c. Fue a comprar refrescos.
d. No tiene miedo de subir alto.
e. Salieron para divertirse.

¿Qué piensas?

Read Vanessa's diary. Answer the following question in a complete sentence.

1. ¿Qué te gustaría hacer: subir a la vuelta al mundo, a la montaña rusa o a los autitos chocadores?

   Answers will vary: **Me gustaría subir a la vuelta al mundo, pero a veces tengo miedo.**

2. ¿Con quién o quiénes te gustaría ir al parque de diversiones? ¿Por qué?

   Answers will vary: **Me gustaría ir al parque de diversiones con mis amigos porque me divierto con ellos.**

Leer B

¡AVANZA! **Goal:** Read about a few activities.

Ramiro writes an e-mail to his best friend to tell him what he did over the weekend.

> Hola, Carlos.
>
> Este fin de semana fue muy divertido. El sábado salí con Lucía. Ella es muy simpática. Fuimos a un lugar a ver animales muy interesantes. Después, fuimos a otro lugar a ver los animales del mar. A Lucía le gusta el mar y todos los animales que viven en él. Aprendí muchas cosas nuevas con Lucía. En la noche, nos subimos a la vuelta al mundo y a la montaña rusa. ¡Ella no le tiene miedo de nada!
>
> Voy a llamarla por teléfono para ver si ella quiere salir conmigo mañana también.
>
> Ramiro

¿Comprendiste?

Read Ramiro's e-mail. Then, circle the words that best complete each sentence, based on the text.

1. El primer lugar al que fueron Ramiro y Lucía es (el acuario /(el zoológico)).

2. A Lucía le gusta ir al ((acuario)/ parque de diversiones).

3. A Ramiro le gusta salir con Lucía porque aprende mucho con (él /(ella)).

4. El tercer lugar donde fueron Ramiro y Lucía fue ((el parque de diversiones)/ el museo)

5. Ramiro va a (dejar un mensaje /(hacer una llamada)) a Lucía para invitarla a salir el domingo.

¿Qué piensas?

Read Ramiro's e-mail. Answer the first question in a complete sentence. Then, give an example of your answer.

1. ¿Alguna vez saliste e hiciste muchas cosas en un solo día?

   Answers will vary: **Sí, una vez hice muchas cosas y salí con mis amigos.**

   _____

2. Ejemplo:

   Answers will vary: **El mes pasado, fuimos de compras, a comer, al**

   parque, al cine y después fuimos a cenar en mi casa.

Leer C

¡AVANZA! **Goal:** Read about a few activities.

Ester didn't go to school today and wrote this note to her friend Carina. She sends it with her brother.

> Carina:
>
> Hoy no fui a la escuela porque me duelen las piernas. Ayer corrí en la mañana, jugué al tenis a las doce y levanté pesas a las cuatro. Gustavo y yo salimos a las siete y volví a mi casa después de ocho horas. También fui con él al parque y encontramos una feria del libro. Tú sabes que a Gustavo le encanta leer de todo y compró libros de muchos temas. Él fue muy buen amigo y me regaló uno de salud y ejercicios muy interesante. Son los que más me gustan. Después del almuerzo también subimos a la montaña rusa. ¡Él no le tiene miedo! Y Gustavo compró los boletos para nosotros. Me encantó el día.
>
> Besos,
> Ester

¿Comprendiste?

Read Ester's note. Then, draw a line from the beginning of each sentence in the left column to the correct ending in the right, based on the text.

1. A Ester le duelen las piernas porque   **a.** al parque de diversiones con ella.

2. Al parque Ester y Gustavo encontraron   **b.** una feria del libro.

3. Gustavo también fue   **c.** hizo muchos deportes ayer.

4. Gustavo pagó   **d.** fue divertido.

5. Para Ester, el día   **e.** los boletos para los dos.

¿Qué piensas?

Read Ester's note. Answer the following question in two complete sentences:

¿Piensas que es divertido ir a una feria del libro? ¿Por qué?

Answers will vary: **Sí, pienso que es muy divertido ir a una feria del libro.**

Para mí, comprar libros es una actividad interesante.

_____

_____

Escribir A

> **¡AVANZA!** **Goal:** Write about various activities.

Step 1

List three places where you had fun on your summer vacation last year.

1. *Answers will vary:* la feria _____
2. *Answers will vary:* el cine _____
3. *Answers will vary:* el zoológico _____

Step 2

Use the list above to write three sentences about what you did at those places.

Answers will vary: _____

Fui al cine y compré un refresco. También fui a la feria, y compré algo para

mi amiga. Mi amigo y yo fuimos al zoológico.

Step 3

Evaluate your writing using the information in the table.

Writing Criteria	Excellent	Good	Needs Work
Content	You have included three sentences about what you did on your vacation last year.	You have included two sentences about what you did on your vacation last year.	You have included only one sentence about what you did on your vacation last year.
Communication	Most of your response is clear.	Some of your response is clear.	Your message is not very clear.
Accuracy	You make few mistakes in grammar and vocabulary.	You make some mistakes in grammar and vocabulary.	You make many mistakes in grammar and vocabulary.

UNIDAD 7
Lección 2 • Escribir A

Escribir B

> ¡AVANZA! **Goal:** Write about various activities.

Step 1

Complete the following table with places where you can go in the left column. In the other column, write what you do there.

Lugares	¿Qué haces allí?
Answers will vary: **museo**	*Answers will vary:* **ver y aprender**
Answers will vary: **zoológico**	*Answers will vary:* **ver animales**
Answers will vary: **playa**	*Answers will vary:* **nadar y tomar sol**
Answers will vary: **parque**	*Answers will vary:* **caminar**

Step 2

Using the information you listed above, write an e-mail to your friends telling them where you went and what you did.

Answers will vary: Hola, chicos. Fui todos los días a la playa con Berta

porque a ella le gusta nadar. El domingo en la noche ella fue al cine

conmigo. Nosotros fuimos al zoológico. Fui con mi hermano al museo.

Hablamos después. Santiago.

Step 3

Evaluate your writing using the information in the table.

Writing Criteria	Excellent	Good	Needs Work
Content	You include several sentences that tell where you went and what you did.	You include some sentences that tell where you went and what you did.	You include few sentences that tell where you went and what you did.
Communication	Most of your message is organized and easy to follow.	Parts of your message are organized and easy to follow.	Your message is disorganized and hard to follow.
Accuracy	You make few mistakes in grammar and vocabulary.	You make some mistakes in grammar and vocabulary.	You make many mistakes in grammar and vocabulary.

Escribir C

> ⊳ ¡AVANZA! **Goal:** Write about various activities.

Step 1

List four fun things you did last summer. *Answers will vary.*

1. Miré arte de Argentina.

2. Subí a la montaña rusa.

3. Hice esquí acuático.

4. Aprendí del mar.

Step 2

Write a paragraph about your activities last summer using the list, with an introductory sentence.

Answers will vary: **El verano pasado me gustó mucho. Fui al museo con**

mi mamá. También fui al parque de diversiones con mis amigas de la

escuela. Yo subí a la montaña rusa pero ellas no. Otro día, mi amigo

Joaquín fue a la playa conmigo, y yo hice esquí acuático.

Step 3

Evaluate your writing using the information in the table.

Writing Criteria	Excellent	Good	Needs Work
Content	You include six sentences about your activities.	You include four to five sentences about your activities.	You include three or fewer sentences about your activities.
Communication	Most of your message is organized and easy to follow.	Parts of your message are organized and easy to follow.	Your message is disorganized and hard to follow.
Accuracy	You make few mistakes in grammar and vocabulary.	You make some mistakes in grammar and vocabulary.	You make many mistakes in grammar and vocabulary.

Cultura A

> **¡AVANZA!** **Goal:** Review cultural information about Argentina.

1 **Argentina** Complete the following questions with one of the multiple-choice answers.

1. The **Museo al Aire Libre** of Argentina is on which street? __c__

   a. El Pueblito   **b.** El Vallecito   **c.** El Caminito

2. In Argentina, the people who are from Buenos Aires are called __a__

   a. porteños   **b.** norteños   **c.** costeños

3. The Obelisk of Buenos Aires is in the Plaza de __b__

   a. la Patria   **b.** la República   **c.** la Independencia

2 **Argentine culture** Read the following sentences about Argentina and answer *true* or *false*.

(T) F   **1.** The currency of Argentina is the Argentine peso.

T (F)   **2.** The Argentine painter Benito Quinquela Martín grew up in the neighborhood of San Telmo.

(T) F   **3.** **Matambre** is a typical Argentine dish.

(T) F   **4.** In the neighborhood La Boca there are many multicolored houses.

T (F)   **5.** Argentina is located in Central America.

3 **Argentine cuisine** Argentina's landscape includes the **pampas,** or sprawling grasslands. Many immigrants also came to Argentina from Italy. Explain how each of these factors have influenced the type of cuisine popular in Argentina today.

Answers will vary: **Because of the pampas, many ranches were developed to raise cattle.**

Thus, beef and steak are very popular in Argentina, often eaten twice a day. Because of

the Italian immigrants, Italian foods such as pizza and pasta are also common in

Argentina.

_____

_____

_____

UNIDAD 7 • Cultura A
Lección 2

Unidad 7, Lección 2
Cultura A

338

¡Avancemos! 1
Cuaderno: Práctica por niveles

Nombre _____ Clase _____ Fecha _____

Cultura B

Level 1, pp. 400-401

> **¡AVANZA!** **Goal:** Review cultural information about Argentina.

1 **Argentina** Choose the correct word to complete the following sentences.

1. **El Parque de la Costa** is the largest (national / <u>amusement</u>) park in South America.

2. Argentina is located in (<u>South</u> / North) America.

3. La Boca was the first (<u>port</u> / skyscraper) of Buenos Aires.

4. Benito Quinquela Martín is a famous Argentine (writer / <u>painter</u>).

5. In Argentina, (French / <u>Italian</u>) food is very popular in addition to meat.

2 **In Argentina** Answer the following questions about Argentina in complete sentences.

1. What are **estancias?** _____ranches_____

2. What is the capital of Argentina? _____Buenos Aires_____

3. On which famous Argentine street can you find the **Museo al Aire Libre?**
_____El Caminito_____

4. What is the Argentine curency? _____The Argentine peso_____

3 **Museums** Write a comparison of **El Museo al Aire Libre** and **El Museo de Instrumentos Musicales.** Where is each museum located and what can you find there? Which museum would you prefer to visit and why?

<u>Answers will vary:</u> **El Museo al Aire Libre** is located in the neighborhood of La Boca in

Buenos Aires, Argentina. It is an open-air museum on the famous street El Caminito.

It has many sculptures, murals, and paintings, with many multi-colored houses in

the background. El Museo de Instrumentos Musicales is located in La Paz, Bolivia. It is

an interactive museum, where you can play different instruments. There are many types

of instruments in the museum, such as drums, wind instruments, and el charango. I

would prefer to visit the museum in Bolivia because I am interested in music and I would

like to try playing some of the instruments there.

_____

_____

_____

¡Avancemos! 1
Cuaderno: Práctica por niveles

Unidad 7, Lección 2
Cultura B **339**

Cultura C

> ¡AVANZA! **Goal:** Review cultural information about Argentina.

1 **In Argentina** Draw lines to match the words on the left with their explanation on the right.

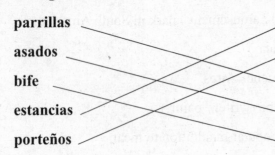

parrillas — restaurants where they sell meat

asados — open-air barbecues

bife — meat or steak

estancias — ranches

porteños — people from Buenos Aires

2 **Argentina** Answer the following questions with complete sentences.

1. Aside from meat or steak, what other foods are popular in Argentina? <u>In Argentina,</u>
   <u>Italian food is also popular, such as pizzas and pastas.</u>

2. Why is beef a common food in Argentina? <u>Beef is a common food because of</u>
   <u>Argentinas **pampas,** or grasslands, where many cattle ranches were developed.</u>

3. The painter Benito Quinquela Martín lived in which neighborhood, or **barrio,** of
   Argentina? <u>The painter Benito Quinquela Martín lived in La Boca.</u>

3 **Argentine life** The **gauchos** live in **las pampas** and earn a living raising cattle, while
   many Argentine artists live in the neighborhood La Boca where they sell and create their
   art. Which of these two lifestyles would you like to lead? Write a paragraph about how
   your life would be. Where would you live? What would you do every day?

   <u>Answers will vary.</u>

   _____

   _____

   _____

   _____

   _____

UNIDAD 7
Lección 2

Cultura C

Unidad 7, Lección 2
Cultura C

340

¡Avancemos! 1
Cuaderno: Práctica por niveles

Comparación cultural: ¿Conoces un lugar divertido?

Level 3, pp. 402-403

Lectura y escritura

After reading the paragraphs about the places that Luis, Liliana and Eva visited, write a paragraph about a place that you recently visited. Use the information on your activity timeline to write sentences and then write a paragraph that describes your visit.

Step 1

Complete the activity timeline, showing what you did first, second, third, and so on. Describe as many details as you can about the place you went and what you did.

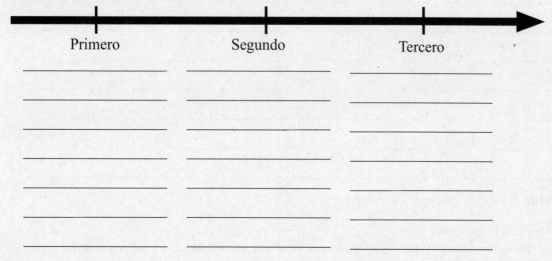

Primero   Segundo   Tercero

_____ _____ _____
_____ _____ _____
_____ _____ _____
_____ _____ _____
_____ _____ _____
_____ _____ _____
_____ _____ _____

Step 2

Now take the details from the activity timeline and write a sentence for each topic on the timeline.

_____
_____
_____
_____
_____
_____
_____
_____
_____
_____
_____

Comparación cultural: ¿Conoces un lugar divertido?

Lectura y escritura (continued)

Step 3

Now write your paragraph using the sentences you wrote as a guide. Include an introduction sentence and use **primero, más tarde, luego, después,** and **por fin** to write about the place you visited and what you did.

_____

_____

_____

_____

_____

_____

_____

Checklist

Be sure that…

☐ all the details about your visit from your timeline are included in the paragraph;

☐ you use details to describe, as clearly as possible, sequence of your activities;

☐ you include expressions of time and new vocabulary words.

Rubric

Evaluate your writing using the rubric below.

Writing criteria	Excellent	Good	Needs Work
Content	Your description includes many details about where you went.	Your description includes some details about where you went.	Your description includes little information about where you went.
Communication	Most of your description is organized and easy to follow.	Parts of your description are organized and easy to follow.	Your description is disorganized and hard to follow.
Accuracy	Your description has few mistakes in grammar and vocabulary.	Your description has some mistakes in grammar and vocabulary.	Your description has many mistakes in grammar and vocabulary.

Unidad 7
Comparación cultural: ¿Conoces un lugar divertido?
342
¡Avancemos! 1
Cuaderno: Práctica por niveles

Comparación cultural: ¿Conoces un lugar divertido?

Compara con tu mundo

Now write a comparison about your visit and that of one of the three students from page 403. Organize your comparison in chronological order. Describe what you did first, then second, and finally the last activities you did or places you visited.

Step 1

Use the table to organize your comparison in chronological order. Write details for each activity of your visit and that of the student you chose.

Categoría	Mis actividades	Las actividades de _____
Primero		
Después		
Luego		
Por fin		

Step 2

Now use the details from the table to write a comparison. Include an introduction sentence and write about each activity. Use the words **primero, más tarde, luego, después,** and **por fin** to describe your visit and that of the student you chose.

_____

_____

_____

_____

_____

_____

_____

Vocabulario A

> **¡AVANZA!** **Goal:** Talk about daily routines.

① Lucía and Lucas get up early to go to school. Place an "x" next to the activities they might do in the morning before going to school.

1. _____ acostarse

2. __X__ ducharse

3. __X__ afeitarse

4. __X__ cepillarse los dientes

5. __X__ maquillarse

6. __X__ peinarse

7. _____ dormirse

8. _____ quedarse en un hotel

② Look at the drawings below to see what people use to get ready for work. Then complete the sentences.

1.

2.

3.

4.

5.

1. Jaime usa _____*pasta de dientes*_____ para cepillarse los dientes.

2. Nora se baña con agua y _____*jabón*_____ .

3. Roberto usa _____*champú*_____ para lavarse el pelo.

4. María usa una _____*toalla*_____ para secarse.

5. Ángel se peina con un _____*peine*_____ .

③ Complete the sentences with what you might do on a trip.

1. Puedo ir de vacaciones a la ciudad o *Answers will vary:* **al campo.**

2. Puedo hacer un viaje en tren, en barco o *Answers will vary:* **en avión.**

3. Llego y busco un buen *Answers will vary:* **hotel** para dormir.

Unidad 8, Lección 1
Vocabulario A
344
¡Avancemos! 1
Cuaderno: Práctica por niveles

UNIDAD 8 • Vocabulario A
Lección 1

Vocabulario B

¡AVANZA! **Goal:** Talk about daily routines.

1 Irma's routine is the same every day. Draw a line from what she does to what she uses to do it.

1. peinarse

2. bañarse

3. cepillarse los dientes

4. maquillarse

5. vestirse

a. la pasta y el cepillo de dientes

b. el espejo

c. el peine

d. la ropa

e. el jabón y el champú

2 Andrea is going on a trip. Complete her conversation with her friend Gustavo.

Gustavo: ¡Hola, Andrea! ¿Ya vas **1.** _de vacaciones_ ?

Andrea: ¡Hola, Gustavo! Sí, voy al **2.** _campo_ , lejos de la ciudad. Tengo muchas cosas que hacer todavía.

Gustavo: ¿Vas en **3.** _avión_ ?

Andrea: No, voy en **4.** _tren_ . No es tan rápido pero puedo mirar lugares muy bonitos.

Gustavo: ¿Y sabes a qué **5.** _hotel_ vas?

Andrea: No, no voy a un hotel. Voy a casa de unos tíos.

3 Answer the following questions about your routine.

1. ¿A qué hora te acuestas generalmente?

Answers will vary: **Generalmente, me acuesto a las nueve.**

2. ¿A qué hora te despiertas generalmente?

Answers will vary: **Generalmente, me despierto a las siete.**

3. ¿Cuántas veces por día te cepillas los dientes?

Answers will vary: **Yo me cepillo los dientes tres veces por día.**

Vocabulario C

> **¡AVANZA!** **Goal:** Talk about daily routines.

1 Santiago has to wake up early; he's taking a trip. In one column, place words related to his daily routine and, in the other column, place words related to taking trips.

el hotel	el peine	el secador de pelo	el tren
la toalla	el campo	el viaje	el jabón
el avión	el cepillo de dientes	el champú	el barco

La rutina | **Las vacaciones**

1. la toalla
2. el champú
3. el peine
4. el jabón
5. el cepillo de dientes
6. el secador de pelo

7. el viaje
8. el campo
9. el tren
10. el barco
11. el avión
12. el hotel

2 Marcos woke up late and might miss his train. Complete the following sentences with what he needs to do.

1. Marcos va a llegar tarde. Tiene que *Answers will vary:* **despertarse más temprano.**

2. Marcos está sucio. Tiene que *Answers will vary:* **bañarse.**

3. Marcos acaba de lavarse el pelo. Necesita *Answers will vary:* **el secador de pelo.**

4. Marcos tiene diez años. No tiene que *Answers will vary:* **afeitarse.**

3 Write three complete sentences to describe your own daily routine.

1. *Answers will vary:* **De lunes a viernes me despierto a las siete de la mañana.**

2. *Answers will vary:* **Después, me baño y me lavo los dientes.**

3. *Answers will vary:* **Después, me peino y me visto.**

UNIDAD 8 • Vocabulario C
Lección 1

Unidad 8, Lección 1
Vocabulario C

346

¡Avancemos! 1
Cuaderno: Práctica por niveles

Gramática A *Reflexive Verbs*

¡AVANZA! **Goal:** Use reflexive verbs to talk about daily routines.

1 Laura and her friends all have the same routine. Circle the correct form of each verb.

1. Laura (**se acuesta**/ me acuesto) temprano.

2. Laura y Verónica (se maquilla /**se maquillan**) después de secarse el pelo.

3. Laura y yo (te lavas /**nos lavamos**) el pelo con un champú muy bueno.

4. Yo (se viste /**me visto**) .

5. Y tú, ¿ (se cepillan /**te cepillas**) los dientes antes o después de ducharte?

2 The following people start their day early. Complete the sentences with the correct form of the verbs in parentheses.

1. Mario _____*se despierta*_____ a las seis de la mañana. (despertarse)

2. Laura y yo _____*nos duchamos*_____ antes de ir a la escuela. (ducharse)

3. Laura y Patricia _____*se lavan*_____ el pelo antes de bañarse. (bañarse)

4. ¿Cuándo _____*se peina*_____ usted? (peinarse)

5. Yo_____*me seco*_____ el pelo antes de vestirme. (secarse)

3 Answer the following questions about daily routines.

1. ¿Qué haces después de despertarte?

Answers will vary: **Después de despertarme, me baño.**

2. ¿Qué haces después de bañarte?

Answers will vary: **Me afeito después de bañarme.**

3. ¿Qué hacen tus hermanos o los hermanos de tus amigos antes de vestirse?

Answers will vary: **Antes de vestirse, mis hermanos se secan el pelo y se peinan.**

¡Avancemos! 1
Cuaderno: Práctica por niveles

Unidad 8, Lección 1
Gramática A **347**

UNIDAD 8 • Gramática A
Lección 1

Gramática B *Reflexive Verbs*

> ¡AVANZA! **Goal:** Use reflexive verbs to talk about daily routines.

1 Francisco and his friends have a set daily routine from Monday to Friday. Choose the correct form of each verb below.

1. Francisco y yo __b__ a las siete de la mañana.

   a. te despiertas   **b.** nos despertamos   **c.** se despiertan   **d.** me despierto

2. Los amigos de Francisco __a__ antes de afeitarse.

   a. se duchan   **b.** te duchas   **c.** se ducha   **d.** nos duchamos

3. Yo nunca __d__ después de ducharme.

   a. te afeitas   **b.** se afeita   **c.** nos afeitamos   **d.** me afeito

4. ¿Tú __b__ el pelo con un secador de pelo?

   a. se secan   **b.** te secas   **c.** se seca   **d.** me seco

5. Todos los días, Francisco __a__ a las diez.

   a. se acuesta   **b.** nos acostamos   **c.** te acuestas   **d.** se acuestan

2 On Saturdays, their routines are a little different. Complete the following sentences with the verb in parentheses. *Answers will vary:*

1. Francisco _____ se despierta _____ a las diez de la mañana. (despertarse)

2. Francisco y Norberto _____ se afeitan _____ antes de ducharse. (afeitarse)

3. Norberto y yo ___ nos secamos el pelo ___ antes de vestirnos. (secarse el pelo)

4. ¿Ustedes _____ se visten _____ antes de desayunar? (vestirse)

5. Yo _____ me duermo _____ a medianoche. (dormirse)

3 Write three sentences to state at what time the following people wake up and go to bed.

1. Tus amigos: *Answers will vary:* **Mis amigos se despiertan a las siete y se acuestan tarde.**

2. Una persona en tu familia: *Answers will vary:* **Mi hermano se despierta a las ocho y se acuesta a las nueve.**

3. Tú: *Answers will vary:* **Yo me acuesto a las diez y me levanto a las siete.**

Gramática C *Reflexive Verbs*

| ¡AVANZA! | **Goal:** Use reflexive verbs to talk about daily routines. |

1 Javier's friends play soccer on the weekends. Complete the text with the correct form of the verbs in parentheses.

Hoy es sábado y nosotros (despertarse) **1.** ___nos despertamos___

muy temprano. Estoy cansado porque los viernes yo (dormirme)

2. ___me duermo___ tarde. Antes de ir al partido, mi hermano

(ducharse) **3.** ___se ducha___ y (lavarse)

4. ___se lava___ el pelo. Todos los chicos del equipo

(ponerse) **5.** ___se ponen___ pantalones cortos negros y

camisetas anaranjadas para el partido.

2 What is your routine? Use reflexive verbs to complete the following sentences.

1. Normalmente, yo *Answers will vary:* **me despierto a las siete.**

2. Todos los días, yo *Answers will vary:* **me lavo los dientes antes de acostarme.**

3. Los fines de semana, yo *Answers will vary:* **me duermo más tarde.**

4. Yo nunca *Answers will vary:* **me seco el pelo con un secador de pelo.**

5. De vez en cuando, yo *Answers will vary:* **me ducho por la tarde.**

3 Use reflexive verbs to write an e-mail to your penpal about your Monday routine. Write three sentences. *Answers will vary:*

Hola, Marcos:

Todos los lunes, yo me despierto a las siete pero puedo hacerlo antes si

tenemos que estudiar. Me baño y me afeito por la mañana. Después me

visto y voy a la escuela. Por la tarde me quedo en casa para estudiar.

_____

_____

_____

¡Avancemos! 1
Cuaderno: Práctica por niveles

Unidad 8, Lección 1
Gramática C **349**

UNIDAD 8 • Gramática C
Lección 1

Gramática A *Present Progressive*

Level 1, pp. 42-44

> **¡AVANZA!** **Goal:** Use the present progressive to talk about what people are doing right now.

❶ Lorenzo's family is going on a trip. Draw a line from the people to what each of them are doing right now to get ready.

1. Los hermanos de Lorenzo   **a.** está afeitándose.

2. Lorenzo   **b.** estamos hablando del hotel.

3. La madre de Lorenzo y yo   **c.** están sacando las maletas.

4. Tú _____ **d.** estás pidiendo la comida.

❷ The following people are busy doing many things. Complete each sentence with the present progressive of the verb in parentheses.

1. Javier ____está hablando____ por teléfono. (hablar)

2. Nora y Carla ____están caminando____ en el bosque. (caminar)

3. Yo ____estoy haciendo____ las maletas. (hacer)

4. ¿Usted ____se está vistiendo / está vistiéndose____? (vestirse)

5. ¿Chicos, ustedes ____están durmiendo____? (dormir)

❸ Look at the drawings below and write what each person is doing right now.

1.  2.  3.

1. **Mauro está limpiando su cuarto.**

2. Víctor y Ana están tomando fotos.

3. Marcela está escribiendo correos electrónicos.

350

Unidad 8, Lección 1
Gramática A

¡Avancemos! 1
Cuaderno: Práctica por niveles

UNIDAD 8 • Gramática A
Lección 1

Gramática B *Present Progressive*

> **¡AVANZA!** **Goal:** Use the present progressive to talk about what people are doing right now.

1 These friends are doing a few things to get ready for their trip. Complete these sentences with the present progressive form of the verbs in parentheses.

1. Camila les _____está diciendo_____ a todos los chicos qué tienen que hacer. (decir)

2. Ariadna y Fernanda ____se están bañando / están bañándose____ . (bañarse)

3. Abel y yo ____estamos comprando____ los boletos del tren. (comprar)

4. Tú _____estás leyendo_____ información sobre los hoteles. (leer)

5. Yo____estoy vistiéndome / me estoy vistiendo____ para ir de vacaciones. (vestirse).

2 The people below are on vacation. Write sentences using the present progressive.

1. Los chicos / viajar en tren.

Los chicos están viajando en tren.

2. Armando y yo / hablar del viaje.

Armando y yo estamos hablando del viaje.

3. Tú / tomar fotos.

Tú estás tomando fotos.

2. Yo / no dormir.

Yo no estoy durmiendo.

3 Using the information in the table below, write three sentences about what each of the students are doing right now.

Camila	mirar	el parque
Camila y yo	caminar	el campo
Camila y Armando	correr	la playa

1. *Answers will vary:* **Camila está mirando el campo.**

2. *Answers will vary:* **Camila y yo estamos caminando por la playa.**

3. *Answers will vary:* **Camila y Armando están corriendo por el parque.**

Gramática C *Present Progressive*

¡AVANZA!	**Goal:** Use the present progressive to talk about what people are doing right now.

1 We have just returned from vacation and are now doing several things. Complete the following sentences with the present progressive of the verb in parentheses.

1. Marcos y yo _____*estamos llegando*_____ a nuestras casas. (llegar)

2. Marcos _____*está lavando*_____ su ropa con jabón. (lavar)

3. Yo _____*estoy quemando*_____ un disco compacto con las fotos de las vacaciones. (quemar)

4. Marcos y Mariela _____*están leyendo*_____ sus correos electrónicos. (leer)

5. Tú *te estás bañando / estás bañándote* antes de dormir. (bañarse)

2 The following students just got back from a trip to the country. Complete these sentences with what you think they might be doing right now. Use the present progressive.

1. Marcos y Natalia *Answers will vary:* **están organizando sus cosas.** _____

_____

2. Natalia *Answers will vary:* **está lavando su ropa.** _____

_____

3. Natalia y yo *Answers will vary:* **estamos comiendo.** _____

_____

4. Yo *Answers will vary:* **estoy hablando con mis amigos.** _____

_____

5. Ustedes *Answers will vary:* **están viendo la televisión.** _____

3 Write three sentences about what your family members are doing right now. Use the present progressive.

Answers will vary: **Mi hermana está estudiando mucho para el examen**

de español. Mis hermanos están buscando un libro de ciencias en la

biblioteca. Mi mamá está preparando la cena.

_____

Integración: Hablar

Agustín decided to go on vacation to the countryside after reading an ad in the newspaper. He is having a really good experience and calls his roomates to let them know about it.

Fuente 1 Leer

Read the newspaper ad that Agustín read...

¿Vacaciones en el campo?

¿Estás pensando en pasar tus vacaciones en el campo?
Con nosotros, vas a pasar las mejores vacaciones.
Organizamos tu viaje completo.

Primero, te buscamos en coche en tu casa y te llevamos a tomar el tren. Después, te llevamos al hotel.

Organizamos todo para tu familia.

Puedes llamarnos al 555-4567

¡Tus vacaciones en nuestras manos son vacaciones de película!

Fuente 2 Escuchar   *CD 04 track 22*

Listen to Agustín's message for his roomates. Take notes.

_____

_____

_____

_____

Hablar

What did Agustín do in the first day of his vacation?

modelo: Antes de llegar al hotel, Agustín... Después de llegar al hotel, Agustín...

Answers will vary: **Antes de llegar al hotel, Agustín viajó en un tren. Después de llegar al hotel, Agustín se bañó y se lavó el pelo. Después, él tomó el sol y montó en bicicleta por el campo. Luego, se acostó temprano.**

Integración: Escribir

Level 1, pp. 45-47
WB CD 04 track 23

Vilma is on vacation and forgets some things at home. She e-mails her brother and he calls her back and teases her a bit in his message.

Fuente 1 Leer
Read the email that Vilma writes to her brother.

> De: Vilma   A: Roberto
>
> Tema: Mis vacaciones
>
> Hola Roberto:
>
> Estoy aburrida, no estoy haciendo nada divertido. Me desperté temprano. Me bañé pero no me maquillé. No hay champú en el hotel. No tengo un peine y tú me tienes que ayudar. Todas las cosas para maquillarme están en casa. ¡Mándame mis cosas ya! Las necesito para estar bonita, porque quiero salir a bailar. No quiero estar aburrida.
>
> Adiós,
>
> Vilma

Fuente 2 Escuchar   *CD 04 track 24*
Listen to Roberto's voicemail to Vilma. Take notes.

_____

_____

_____

_____

Escribir
What does Vilma need and why? What solutions does Roberto offer?

modelo: Vilma necesita... porque... Roberto es cómico y dice que Vilma puede... Por fin Roberto dice que va a...

Answers will vary: **Vilma quiere champú, un peine y algunas cosas para maquillarse por que quiere salir a bailar. Roberto dice que Vilma puede peinarse con el cepillo de dientes y también lavarse el pelo con jabón porque es cómico. Por fin Roberto dice que va a mandar las cosas a Vilma.**

Unidad 8, Lección 1
Integración: Escribir
354
¡Avancemos! 1
Cuaderno: Práctica por niveles

UNIDAD 8 • Lección 1
Integración: Escribir

Escuchar A

> ¡AVANZA! **Goal:** Listen to discussions about daily routines.

1 Listen to Fernando. Then, place an "x" next to the things that happen to him.

1. Casi siempre llega tarde a la escuela. __X__

2. No puede despertarse temprano. __X__

3. Todos los días, se acuesta temprano. _____

4. A Fernando no le gusta mirar la televisión. _____

5. La madre de Fernando está enojada. __X__

6. De vez en cuando, Fernando se levanta a las siete. __X__

2 Listen to Marta. Then, complete the sentences with the words from the box.

se viste	se acuesta	la rutina	despertarse

1. El hijo de Marta _____se acuesta_____ tarde.

2. El hijo de Marta no puede _____despertarse_____ .

3. El hijo de Marta _____se viste_____ después de afeitarse.

4. Mirar la televisión o escuchar música por la noche es _____la rutina_____ del hijo de Marta.

¡Avancemos! 1
Cuaderno: Práctica por niveles

UNIDAD 8
Lección 1

Unidad 8, Lección 1
Escuchar A **355**

Escuchar A

Escuchar B

| ¡AVANZA! | **Goal:** Listen to discussions of daily routines. |

1 Listen to Jorge. Then, complete the table with each person's routine.

Jorge	La hermana de Jorge
se despierta	se despierta temprano
se ducha	se lava el pelo
se cepilla los dientes	se cepilla los dientes
se lava el pelo	se baña
se afeita	se peina
se viste	se maquilla
	se viste

2 Listen to Daniela. Then, complete the following sentences:

1. Daniela comparte el baño con su hermano.

_____

2. Todas las mañanas, Daniela necesita llegar a la escuela temprano.

_____

3. Daniela le dice a su hermano que tiene que despertarse temprano.

_____

4. El hermano de Daniela dice que ella no debe maquillarse en el baño.

_____

5. Daniela no tiene un espejo en su cuarto.

_____

Unidad 8, Lección 1
Escuchar B

356

UNIDAD 8 · Escuchar B
Lección 1

¡Avancemos! 1
Cuaderno: Práctica por niveles

Escuchar C

> **¡AVANZA!** **Goal:** Listen to discussions of daily routines.

1 Listen to Gabriela and take notes. Then, put her routine below in order, numbering the sentences 1 through 8.

a. __3__ Se baña.

b. __5__ Se seca con la toalla y con el secador de pelo.

c. __2__ Se lava el pelo.

d. __1__ Se despierta temprano.

e. __7__ Se maquilla.

f. __4__ Se cepilla los dientes.

g. __8__ Se viste.

h. __6__ Se peina.

2 Listen to Gabriela's conversation with her mother. Take notes. Then, answer the following questions.

1. ¿Por qué llama la mamá a su hija?

La mamá llama a su hija para desayunar.

2. ¿Qué está haciendo Gabriela?

Gabriela está maquillándose.

3. ¿Cuántos minutos necesita ella para maquillarse?

Answers will vary: **Ella necesita quince minutos.**

4. ¿Qué están haciendo la mamá y el papá de Gabriela?

La mamá y el papá de Gabriela están saliendo a la oficina.

5. ¿Qué cosa importante necesita hacer Gabriela antes de salir?

Ella necesita desayunar antes de salir.

¡Avancemos! 1
Cuaderno: Práctica por niveles

**UNIDAD 8
Lección 1 • Escuchar C**

Unidad 8, Lección 1
Escuchar C **357**

Leer A

¡AVANZA! **Goal:** Read about people's routines and trips.

This hotel organizes trips to the country and placed this ad in the newspaper.

¡Vamos al campo!

¿Tienes vacaciones?
¿Estás pensando en viajar
y no sabes adónde?

El hotel "Cinco estrellitas" organiza viajes para toda la familia,
para grupos de amigos y también viajes individuales.

¿Te gusta el campo? ¿Quieres despertarte y ver
bellos lugares por tu ventana?

Puedes venir en tren o en avión.

**Nosotros organizamos las otras cosas
para unas vacaciones fantásticas.**

¿Comprendiste?

Read the hotel's ad. Then, read each sentence and answer **cierto** (true) or **falso** (false).

C (F) **1.** No pueden ir grupos de amigos.

(C) F **2.** Pueden ir familias.

(C) F **3.** El hotel está en el campo.

C (F) **4.** Puedes ver una escuela por la ventana del hotel.

C (F) **5.** Puedes llegar en barco.

¿Qué piensas?

¿A qué lugar prefieres ir de vacaciones, al campo o a la ciudad? ¿Por qué?

Answers will vary: Yo prefiero ir al campo porque me gusta caminar y tomar

el sol.

_____

_____

Leer B

> ¡AVANZA! **Goal:** Read about people's routines and trips.

Emiliano wrote this letter to his friend. In it, he describes what he is doing on his trip.

> *Hola Hugo.*
>
> *No sabes qué vacaciones fantásticas estoy pasando en el campo. Me despierto todos los días a las nueve de la mañana. Miro por la ventana y veo unos lugares muy bonitos. Este lugar es muy bueno para la salud. Mi familia y yo llegamos en tren. Cuando vi el campo, pensé que quiero vivir aquí para siempre. ¡El lugar es fantástico!*
>
> *Ahora me estoy durmiendo, mañana te escribo más.*
>
> *Emiliano*

¿Comprendiste?

Read Emiliano's letter. Then, place an "x" next to what he describes.

1. Las vacaciones de Emiliano son aburridas. _____

2. Las vacaciones de Emiliano son en la playa. _____

3. A Emiliano le gusta el campo. __X__

4. El campo es bueno para la salud. __X__

5. La rutina de Emiliano empieza temprano. __X__

6. Emiliano fue con sus padres. __X__

7. Emiliano fue con sus amigos. _____

¿Qué piensas?

1. ¿Qué haces cuando estás de vacaciones?

   Answers will vary: **Cuando estoy de vacaciones me quedo en hoteles y como**

   en restaurantes.

2. ¿Tienes una rutina cuando vas de vacaciones? ¿Cuál?

   Answers will vary: **Sí, tengo una rutina cuando voy de vacaciones. Me**

   levanto más tarde y normalmente me ducho después de desayunar.

¡Avancemos! 1
Cuaderno: Práctica por niveles

UNIDAD 8
Lección 1

Leer B

Unidad 8, Lección 1
Leer B **359**

Leer C

> **¡AVANZA!** **Goal:** Read about people's routines and trips.

Jimena went on a trip to another city. She writes an e-mail about it to her friend.

Hola, Viviana.

Mi familia y yo llegamos a la ciudad muy bien. El viaje en avión fue tranquilo. El hotel está muy bien. Yo prefiero las vacaciones en el campo pero mi papá fue a comprar los boletos de avión y compró boletos para la ciudad. Él prefiere la ciudad.

En la ciudad hay muchas cosas para ver: teatros, cines y parques. En el campo podemos hacer actividades que son buenas para la salud y los lugares son más bonitos.

Todos los días estamos almorzando en un restaurante del centro. El lugar es bonito. ¿Puedes conectarte a Internet a las tres? Hablamos por mensajero instantáneo.

Besos,

Jimena

¿Comprendiste?

Read Jimena's e-mail. Then, answer the questions below:

1. ¿Cómo llegó Jimena a la ciudad? Ella llegó a la ciudad en avión.

2. ¿Dónde se quedó Jimena? Jimena se quedó en un hotel.

3. ¿Dónde prefiere ir de vacaciones Jimena? Ella prefiere ir al campo.

4. ¿Por qué prefiere ir de vacaciones al campo? Ella prefiere ir al campo porque es mejor para la salud.

5. ¿Dónde comen? Comen en un restaurante del centro.

¿Qué piensas?

1. ¿Qué te gusta hacer cuando vas de vacaciones a una ciudad?

   Answers will vary: Cuando voy de vacaciones a una ciudad me gusta caminar y ver museos.

2. ¿A qué ciudades fuiste de vacaciones? ¿Cuál te gustó más?

   Answers will vary: Fui de vacaciones a Nueva York y San Francisco. Me gustó más San Francisco.

Escribir A

> **¡AVANZA!** **Goal:** Write about daily routines and trips.

Step 1

List the methods of transportation you know.

1. *Answers will vary:* **avión**
2. *Answers will vary:* **tren**
3. *Answers will vary:* **barco**
4. *Answers will vary:* **coche**
5. *Answers will vary:* **autobús**

Step 2

Complete the following sentences with your daily routine.

1. Yo, cuando me despierto, *Answers will vary:* **me baño.**
2. Después, yo *Answers will vary:* **me peino.**
3. Después, yo *Answers will vary:* **me visto.**
4. Cuando estoy viajando, yo *Answers will vary:* **no me maquillo.**

Step 3

Write three complete sentences about your daily routine when you are traveling by boat, airplane, or train.

modelo: Cuando hago un viaje en avión ...

Answers will vary: **Cuando hago un viaje en avión, yo siempre me cepillo los dientes.**

También me lavo la cara. Luego me baño en el hotel, me seco el pelo y me visto.

Step 4

Evaluate your writing using the information in the table.

Writing Criteria	Excellent	Good	Needs Work
Content	Your sentences include many details about your routine.	Your sentences include some details about your routine.	Your sentences include little information about your routine.
Communication	Most of your sentences are clear.	Some of your sentences are clear.	Your sentences are not very clear.
Accuracy	Your sentences have few mistakes in grammar and vocabulary.	Your sentences have some mistakes in grammar and vocabulary.	Your sentences have many mistakes in grammar and vocabulary.

Nombre _____ Clase _____ Fecha _____

Escribir B

Level 1, pp. 52-53

> **¡AVANZA!** **Goal:** Write about daily routines and trips.

Step 1

Complete the table with your daily routine.

Por la mañana	¿A qué hora?	Por la noche	¿A qué hora?
Answers will vary: me despierto	Answers will vary: 7:00 a.m.	Answers will vary: me baño.	Answers will vary: 8:00 p.m.
Answers will vary: me cepillo los dientes	Answers will vary: 7:05 a.m.	Answers will vary: me cepillo los dientes.	Answers will vary: 8:30 p.m.
Answers will vary: me visto	Answers will vary: 7:30 a.m.	Answers will vary: me acuesto.	Answers will vary: 9:00 p.m.

Step 2

Using the information in the table above, describe your daily routines. Write four complete sentences. Also describe how your routine changes when you are taking a trip. Follow the model.

modelo: Generalmente me despierto a las seis y media de la mañana ...

Answers will vary: Yo me despierto a las siete de la mañana, pero cuando

hago un viaje me despierto a las nueve. Generalmente me cepillo los dientes

a las siete y cinco de la mañana y después me visto a las siete y media.

Step 3

Evaluate your writing using the information in the table.

Writing Criteria	Excellent	Good	Needs Work
Content	You include all of the information.	You include some of the information.	You include little information.
Communication	Most of your sentences are clear.	Some of your sentences are clear.	Your sentences are not very clear.
Accuracy	Your sentences have few mistakes in grammar and vocabulary.	Your sentences have some mistakes in grammar and vocabulary.	Your sentence have many mistakes in grammar and vocabulary.

UNIDAD 8 Lección 1 • Escribir B

Unidad 8, Lección 1
Escribir B
362
¡Avancemos! 1
Cuaderno: Práctica por niveles

Escribir C

> **¡AVANZA!** **Goal:** Write about daily routines and trips.

Step 1

Complete the following sentences about your morning routine.

1. Antes de bañarme, yo *Answers will vary:* **me afeito.**

2. Después, yo *Answers will vary:* **me cepillo los dientes.**

3. Después de bañarme, yo *Answers will vary:* **me seco.**

4. Después, yo *Answers will vary:* **me visto.**

5. Después, yo *Answers will vary:* **me peino.**

6. Después, yo *Answers will vary:* **me maquillo.**

Step 2

You are on a trip. Write a five-sentence e-mail to your friend describing your routine there. Use the present progressive at least once.

Answers will vary: **Hola, Agustín:**

Estoy pasando unas vacaciones muy divertidas. Duermo mucho y me levanto

a las once. Después me ducho, me seco, me visto, me peino y voy a desayunar.

Normalmente vamos a pasear y comemos en el centro de la ciudad.

Cuando volvemos al hotel me cepillo los dientes y leo un rato. Por la noche

cenamos en el hotel y generalmente me acuesto a las doce.

Step 3

Evaluate your writing using the information in the table.

Writing Criteria	Excellent	Good	Needs Work
Content	Your email includes all of the information.	Your email includes some of the information.	Your email includes little information.
Communication	Most of your email is organized and easy to follow.	Parts of your email are organized and easy to follow.	Your email is disorganized and hard to follow.
Accuracy	Your email has few mistakes in grammar and vocabulary.	Your email has some mistakes in grammar and vocabulary.	Your email has many mistakes in grammar and vocabulary.

Cultura A

> **¡AVANZA!** **Goal:** Review cultural information about Costa Rica.

1 **Costa Rica** Complete the following questions with one of the multiple-choice answers.

1. The capital of Costa Rica is __b__

   a. San Juan   **b.** San José   **c.** San Luis

2. The __c__ of Tabacón are popular with tourists.

   a. carretas   **b.** beaches   **c.** hot springs.

3. The **carretas,** or oxcarts, which are a symbol of Costa Rica, were used to __a__

   a. transport coffee   **b.** transport sugarcane   **c.** transport bananas

2 **Costa Rican culture** Read the following sentences about Costa Rica and answer *true* or *false*.

   Ⓣ   F   **1.** Costa Rica was the headquarters of the Kayak Surf World Championship in 2005.

   Ⓣ   F   **2.** **Gallo pinto** is a typical dish from Costa Rica.

   T   Ⓕ   **3.** Costa Rica is located in South America.

   Ⓣ   F   **4.** Arenal is an active volcano in Costa Rica.

   T   Ⓕ   **5.** Costa Ricans use **tú** instead of **vos.**

3 **Costa Rican geography** Costa Rica has many varied landscapes. Write a description of some of the landscapes found in Costa Rica. Which land feature do you like most and why?

Answers will vary: **Costa Rica has high-altitude farmlands and beaches,**

as well as mountain ranges and active volcanoes, such as Arenal. There are

also rivers, mineral water pools, and rainforests. The land feature I like most

is the rainforests, because of the variety of animals and tropical plants that

live there.

_____

_____

Unidad 8, Lección 1
Cultura A

364

¡Avancemos! 1
Cuaderno: Práctica por niveles

UNIDAD 8
Lección 1

Cultura A

Cultura B

┌───┐
│ ¡AVANZA! **Goal:** Review cultural information about Costa Rica. │
└───┘

1 **Costa Rica** Draw lines to match the names or phrases on the left with their explanation on the right.

Arenal   were used to transport coffee

Sarchí   typical Costa Rican food

colón   active volcano

gallo pinto   Costa Rican currency

carretas   where the **carreta** festival is held

2 **Costa Rican culture** Answer the following questions about Costa Rica.

1. What is the name of the active volcano in Costa Rica? _____Arenal_____

2. Which aquatic sport can you do on Costa Rica's beaches? _____surfing_____

3. What is the capital of Costa Rica? _____San José_____

4. In general, Costa Ricans do not use **tú,** but instead use _____vos_____

5. In Costa Rica, family members often use _____usted_____ when speaking with each other.

3 **Costa Rican travel** You work at a travel agency and must create an advertisement to get tourists interested in traveling to Costa Rica. Write an ad describing the types of activities and scenery that the tourists could enjoy in Costa Rica.

Answers will vary: _____

_____

_____

_____

_____

_____

_____

_____

¡Avancemos! 1
Cuaderno: Práctica por niveles

Unidad 8, Lección 1
Cultura B **365**

UNIDAD 8
Lección 1 • Cultura B

Cultura C

> **¡AVANZA!** **Goal:** Review cultural information about Costa Rica.

1 **Costa Rica** Complete the sentences about Costa Rica.

1. Costa Rica is located in _____Central_____ America.

2. _____Arenal_____ is an active volcano in Costa Rica.

3. Costa Ricans use _____vos_____ rather than **tú,** but many family members use _____usted_____ with each other.

4. Casado is a typical Costa Rican _____dish_____.

5. _____San José_____ is the capital of Costa Rica.

2 **In Costa Rica** Answer the following questions using complete sentences.

1. What is the name of the Costa Rican town where the **carreta** festival is held every year?

The town in Costa Rica that holds the **carreta** festival every year is called Sarchí.

2. What is Costa Rica's landscape like? It is varied and includes rivers, rain forests, beaches, and volcanoes.

3. What is the name of Costa Rica's currency? The Costa Rican currency is the **colón.**

3 **Souvenirs** You work at a souvenir shop in Costa Rica. Write about a typical souvenir from Costa Rica that you would recommend for a tourist. What would you tell the tourist to convince them to buy the item? Describe what the souvenir looks like, as well as any interesting facts.

Answers will vary. I would recommend the **carreta,** or wooden oxcart. They are

handmade, with elaborate and colorful designs. They used to be used to

transport coffee in the 1800s and there is also a **carreta** festival in the town

of Sarchí every year. They are a unique item that represents Costa Rican

history and culture.

Unidad 8, Lección 1
Cultura C
366
¡Avancemos! 1
Cuaderno: Práctica por niveles

UNIDAD 8 Lección 1 • Cultura C

Nombre _____ Clase _____ Fecha _____

Vocabulario A

Level 1, pp. 434-438

> **¡AVANZA!** Read about what people do on vacation.

1 We like to go away on vacation and do lots of activities. Match the words in the left column with related words in the right column.

a. estar al aire libre — comprar cerámica

b. hacer una parrillada — surf de vela

c. buscar artesanía — preparar carne

d. hacer surfing — acampar

e. buscar joyas — comprar un collar

2 We do a lot of things on our vacation. Complete the following sentences with words from the box.

1. En el mercado de artesanías, compramos ____recuerdos____ para nuestras familias.

2. Me encantan los anillos de ____oro____ que compré ayer.

3. Este artículo de madera es muy ____barato.____ .

4. Nos divertimos mucho cuando vamos a ____montar a caballo____ .

5. Berta compró unos ____aretes____ de plata muy bonitos.

| aretes |
| oro |
| montar a caballo |
| recuerdos |
| barato |

3 Complete the sentences with what these people like to do on vacation.

modelo: (a mí) / acampar / vacaciones.

Me gusta acampar en vacaciones.

1. (a ti) / comprar / de madera

Answers will vary: **Te gusta comprar recuerdos de madera.**

2. (a / María) / regatear mercado

Answers will vary: **A María le gusta regatear en el mercado.**

3. (hermano) / comprar artículos / calidad

Answers will vary: **A mi hermano le gusta comprar artículos de calidad.**

¡Avancemos! 1
Cuaderno: Práctica por niveles

Unidad 8, Lección 2
Vocabulario A **367**

UNIDAD 8 • Vocabulario A
Lección 2

Vocabulario B

> ¡AVANZA! **Goal:** Read about what people do on vacation.

1 Martín and his friends go on vacation. Choose the correct word in parentheses to complete each sentence.

1. Martín da _____caminatas_____ al aire libre. (caminatas / mercados / aretes)

2. Martín compra artesanías en el _____mercado_____ . (surf / mercado / collar)

3. Los chicos tienen mucho _____tiempo libre_____ . (barato / recuerdo / tiempo libre)

4. Martín compra algunas _____joyas_____ para su mamá. (joyas / parrilladas / caminatas)

2 Martín goes to the handicrafts market. Complete the dialogue with words from the box.

lo dejo	le puedo ofrecer	me deja ver	Qué caro

Martín: ¡Buenos días! ¿ _____me deja ver_____ el anillo de plata?

Artesano: Claro. También_____le puedo ofrecer_____ algunos de oro. El precio está debajo de cada artículo.

Martín: ¡ _____Qué caro_____ !

Artesano: Bueno, _____lo dejo_____ más barato si compra dos.

3 Look at the pictures and complete the sentences.

1.    2.    3.

1. Claudia _____hace surf de vela_____ en la playa.

2. Alejandro _____hace una parrillada_____ en su casa.

3. Los chicos van a _____acampar_____ al aire libre.

Unidad 8, Lección 2
Vocabulario B
368
¡Avancemos! 1
Cuaderno: Práctica por niveles

UNIDAD 8 • Vocabulario B
Lección 2

Vocabulario C

> ¡AVANZA! **Goal:** Read about what people do on vacation.

1 Natalia and her friends went on a summer vacation. Write the related words in the correct column.

dar una caminata	hacer una parrillada	acampar
artesanías	anillos	artículos de madera
hacer surfing	aretes	comer al aire libre
recuerdos	artículos de cerámica	montar a caballo

Actividades	**Mercado**
dar una caminata	artesanías
hacer surfing	recuerdos
hacer una parrillada	anillos
comer al aire libre	aretes
montar a caballo	artículos de cerámica
acampar	artículos de madera

2 Do you like to go on vacation? Complete the sentences with things that you like to do when you go on vacation.

1. A mí me gusta *Answers will vary:* **dar caminatas.**

2. Normalmente yo *Answers will vary:* **monto a caballo.**

3. Yo prefiero *Answers will vary:* **acampar al aire libre.**

4. Cuando voy de vacaciones, yo *Answers will vary:* **voy a un mercado de artesanías.**

5. En mis vacaciones, yo siempre *Answers will vary:* **hago una parrillada para todos.**

3 Write a three-sentence text to describe what you did on your vacation.

Answers will vary: **El verano pasado fui de vacaciones a la playa. Unos**

amigos y yo acampamos cerca del mar. Dimos caminatas, jugamos,

hicimos surf de vela y montamos a caballo.

Gramática A *Indirect Object Pronouns*

Level 1, pp. 439-443

> ¡AVANZA! **Goal:** Use indirect object pronouns to talk about vacations.

1 Pablo's friends went on vacation together. Underline the correct pronoun for each sentence.

1. ¿Quieres ir de vacaciones? Yo (te / me) mando el nombre del hotel.

2. Susana no encuentra su peine. Yo (le / nos) doy mi peine.

3. Patricia y yo compramos artesanías. (Nos / Te) gustan las artesanías.

4. ¿Sabes hacer surfing? ¿(Me / Te) gusta hacerlo?

5. ¿(Me / Le) puedes comprar el bloqueador de sol?

2 These friends help each other. Complete the sentences with the correct pronoun.

1. Necesito el jabón. ¿ _____Me_____ lo das?

2. Claudia quiere unos aretes. ¿ _____Le_____ puedes comprar unos aretes de plata?

3. Mis padres no saben cómo estoy. ¿Puedes mandar_les_____ un correo electrónico?

4. ¿Estás enfermo? ¿Puedo dar_te_____ algo?

5. Álvaro y yo vamos a hacer una parrillada. ¿ _____Nos_____ puedes decir cómo hacerlo?

3 Complete the sentences with things you can buy at a handicrafts market.

modelo: Comprar un anillo (mamá).

Puedo comprarle un anillo a mamá.

1. Comprar recuerdos (amigos)

Answers will vary: **Puedo comprarles recuerdos a mis amigos.**

2. Comprar aretes (hermana)

Answers will vary: **Puedo comprarle aretes a mi hermana.**

3. Comprar artículos de madera (tú)

Answers will vary: **Puedo comprarte artículos de madera.**

UNIDAD 8 • Gramática A
Lección 2

370

Unidad 8, Lección 2
Gramática A

¡Avancemos! 1
Cuaderno: Práctica por niveles

Gramática B *Indirect Object Pronouns*

> **¡AVANZA!** **Goal:** Use indirect object pronouns to talk about vacations.

1 Everyone went to the handicrafts market. The following sentences are out of order; rewrite each one in the correct order.

1. madre algunas mi joyas compré a le

Le compré algunas joyas a mi madre.

2. los cerámica gustaron me de artículos

Me gustaron los artículos de cerámica.

3. algunos amigos llevo madera artículos de a les mis

Les llevo algunos artículos de madera a mis amigos.

4. muy recuerdos compré bonitos te unos

Te compré unos recuerdos muy bonitos.

5. unos chicos los compraron bonitos nos anillos muy

Los chicos nos compraron unos anillos muy bonitos.

2 After the handicrafts market, everyone did other activities. Rewrite the sentences, replacing the person with the correct indirect object pronoun.

1. Traemos un caballo para Lucas. *Le traemos un caballo.*

2. Hacemos una parrillada para todos los chicos. *Les hacemos una parrillada.*

3. Los chicos traen frutas para nosotros. *Los chicos nos traen frutas.*

4. Yo compro algo de comer para ustedes. *Yo les compro algo de comer.*

3 Answer the questions with a complete sentence.

1. ¿A quién le dices tus secretos?

Answers will vary: **Yo le digo todos mis secretos a mi mejor amiga.**

_____

2. ¿A quiénes les pides regalos de cumpleaños?

Answers will vary: **Yo les pido regalos de cumpleaños a mis padres.**

_____

Gramática C *Indirect Object Pronouns*

> ¡AVANZA! **Goal:** Use indirect object pronouns to talk about vacations.

1 Read the following sentences about a day at the handicrafts market. Complete each sentence using an indirect object pronoun.

1. Necesito saber cuánto cuesta el anillo. ¿Puedes decir<u>me</u> cuánto cuesta?

2. Quieres un collar y ____<u>te</u>____ compré un collar de plata.

3. A nosotros ____<u>nos</u>____ gustan las artesanías de madera.

4. Los chicos no vienen con nosotros, pero podemos comprar<u>les</u>

    algunos recuerdos.

5. ¿Quieres comprar<u>le</u>_____ algo a tu madre?

2 Write complete sentences about what happens at the handicrafts market. Use indirect object pronouns.

modelo (nosotros) buscar un regalo / para Armando:

Le buscamos un regalo muy bonito.

1. (ellos) / llevar recuerdos / para mis padres:

    Answers will vary: **Les llevan recuerdos de cerámica.**

2. (yo) comprar un anillo / para mí:

    Answers will vary: **Me compro un anillo de plata.**

3. (él) traer frutas / para nosotros:

    Answers will vary: **Nos trae frutas.**

3 Write a four-sentence e-mail to a friend. Tell your friend what things you buy at the handicrafts market. Use indirect object pronouns.

Answers will vary: **Hola Guillermo:**

Tienes que ir al mercado de artesanías porque es fantástico. Yo sé que

te gustan las artesanías y en el mercado puedes comprarte todas las

artesanías que quieres.

372

Unidad 8, Lección 2
Gramática C

¡Avancemos! 1
Cuaderno: Práctica por niveles

UNIDAD 8 • Gramática C
Lección 2

Gramática A *Demonstrative Adjectives*

> **¡AVANZA!** **Goal:** Use demonstrative adjectives to talk about vacations.

1 Mark with an "x" the sentences that describe things that are near.

1. Estos caballos son muy altos. __X__
2. Aquellas personas acampan cerca del parque. ____
3. Esos collares me gustan mucho. ____
4. Este anillo es de Carolina. __X__
5. Estos recuerdos son para mi familia. __X__
6. Aquel perro es de ese chico. ____

2 Choose the correct demonstrative adjective in the parentheses to complete each sentence.

1. Me gusta acampar en _____este_____ lugar. (esa / este)
2. _____Estos_____ aretes son muy caros. (estas / estos)
3. ¿Cuánto cuestan _____estas_____ artesanías de madera? (estas / esos)
4. La semana pasada hicimos una parrillada. _____Esa_____ parrillada fue muy divertida. (aquellos / esa)
5. La calidad de _____aquel_____ anillo es muy buena. (esa / aquel)

3 Answer each question with a complete sentence. Use demonstrative adjectives.

1. ¿Adónde vas en estas vacaciones?

   Answers will vary: **En estas vacaciones voy al campo.**

2. ¿Adónde compraste esa cerámica?

   Answers will vary: **Esa cerámica la compré en el mercado de artesanías.**

3. ¿Fue barata esa cerámica?

   Answers will vary: **Sí, esa cerámica fue barata.**

Gramática B *Demonstrative Adjectives*

> ¡AVANZA! **Goal:** Use demonstrative adjectives to talk about vacations.

1 We bought some things at the handicrafts market. Complete the sentences with the correct adjective.

1. Yo compré __b__ aretes.

    a. este   **b.** estos   **c.** esta   **d.** aquel

2. Luis compró __c__ collar de oro.

    a. esos   **b.** esta   **c.** aquel   **d.** aquella

3. Marta compró __c__ artesanías.

    a. estos   **b.** esta   **c.** estas   **d.** aquel

4. Mis amigos compraron __b__ joya.

    a. ese   **b.** esa   **c.** este   **d.** aquel

5. Mi hermana compró __d__ recuerdos para ustedes.

    a. esas   **b.** estas   **c.** aquel   **d.** aquellos

2 We all bought things at the handicrafts market. Complete the following sentences with **ese** (that) or **este** (this) in singular or plural, feminine or masculine, as appropriate.

1. Yo vi _____estos_____ recuerdos. (cerca)

2. Nosotros compramos _____estas_____ artesanías. (cerca)

3. Mi hermana compró _____esas_____ joyas. (lejos)

4. Ustedes compraron _____ese_____ anillo de plata. (lejos)

5. Iván compró _____este_____ artículo de madera. (cerca)

3 Write sentences about things we buy at the handicrafts market. Change the adjective to singular or plural, feminine or masculine, as appropriate.

1. Aquel / aretes: Compramos aquellos aretes.

2. Este / recuerdos: Compramos estos recuerdos.

3. Ese / artesanías: Compramos esas artesanías.

Gramática C Demonstrative Adjectives

> **¡AVANZA!** **Goal:** Use demonstrative adjectives to talk about vacations.

1 Yesterday, you went to the handicrafts market. Complete the following sentences with the correct demonstrative adjectives. Use the words in parentheses as clues.

1. Yo compré _____estos_____ aretes de plata. (cerca)

2. Mis amigos vieron _____aquellos_____ collares que tú quieres. (muy lejos)

3. Tú compraste _____esos_____ recuerdos muy baratos. (lejos)

4. Yo vi _____esas_____ artesanías muy bonitas. (lejos)

5. Ustedes compraron _____esta_____ joya de oro. (cerca)

2 What did you buy at the handicrafts market? Write sentences using the demonstrative adjectives in parentheses.

1. (este) *Answers will vary:* **Yo compré este lindo recuerdo.**

   _____

2. (aquellas) *Answers will vary:* **Yo compré aquellas artesanías**

   que nos gustaron el año pasado.

3. (esos) *Answers will vary:* **Yo compré esos aretes que quiere**

   tu mamá.

4. (esa) *Answers will vary:* **Yo compré esa joya muy cara.**

   _____

5. (estos) *Answers will vary:* **Yo compré estos anillos de oro.**

   _____

3 Write three sentences about things that are near to you and things that are far from you at this moment. Use demonstrative adjectives.

1. *Answers will vary:* **Este cuaderno está encima de mi escritorio.**

2. *Answers will vary:* **Esa tiza está debajo del pizarrón.**

3. *Answers will vary:* **Aquella ventana está cerca de la puerta.**

Integración: Hablar

Level 1, pp. 447-449
CD 04 track 31

Iván and his friends go on vacation, and decide to go to an arts and crafts fair. Ivan's friends are interested in shopping but he wants to do other activities in the area.

Fuente 1 Leer

Read the newspaper article on the **Feria de Artesanías**...

Feria de Artesanías

Todos los que pasan sus vacaciones en nuestra playa pueden ir a la Feria de Artesanías. Es un lugar fantástico. En la feria venden todas las cosas que las personas buscan. Después de un día de actividades al aire libre, pueden dar una caminata por la playa y llegar al Parque Victorino. En este parque pueden montar a caballo y comer al aire libre. Es un buen lugar para hacer una parrillada.

Fuente 2 Escuchar   *CD 04 track 32*

Listen to what the announcer says through the loudspeakers at the Feria de Artesanías. Take notes.

_____

_____

_____

_____

Hablar

What can Ivan's friends buy at the **Feria de Artesanías**? What other activities can Ivan and his friends do nearby? Tell when they should do each activity.

modelo: Primero, Iván y sus amigos pueden... Luego, también pueden...

Answers will vary: **Primero, Iván y sus amigos pueden comprar recuerdos o joyas como anillos, collares y aretes de oro y plata. Luego, deben ir al Parque Victorino para hacer una parrillada. También pueden montar a caballo.**

Integración: Escribir

Level 1, pp. 447-449
WB CD 04 track 33

Lucía went on vacation with her classmates. Olga couldn't join them for the trip.

Fuente 1 Leer

Read the email Olga sent to Lucía.

> Queridos amigos:
>
> Ya es de noche y les escribo porque no estoy triste. No ir de vacaciones fue mejor porque estoy enferma. Me duelen la cabeza y el estómago. Es cierto, no tengo ganas salir. Ahora quiero dormir. Pero voy a estar bien. Quisiera pedir una cosa pequeña. Si tienen tiempo y pueden, quiero que compren un recuerdo del lugar donde ustedes están. Si me traen un recuerdo de ese lugar, cuando lleguen voy a estar contenta.
>
> Adiós,
>
> Olga

Fuente 2 Escuchar *CD 04track 34*

Listen to Federico's voice message to Olga. Take notes.

_____
_____
_____
_____

Escribir

Now answer this question: Olga had to stay home, but what's going to happen for her to feel better? Explain why.

Modelo: Olga quiere...Entonces sus amigos

Answers will vary: **Olga quiere recuerdos del lugar donde están sus amigos.**

Entonces sus amigos traen recuerdos de las vacaciones para ella.

_____
_____
_____
_____

¡Avancemos! 1
Cuaderno: Práctica por niveles

Unidad 8, Lección 2
Integración: Escribir   377

UNIDAD 8 • Lección 2
Integración: Escribir

Escuchar A

Level 1, pp. 454-455
CD 04 tracks 36-37

¡AVANZA! **Goal:** Listen to people talking about vacation activities.

1 Listen to Cecilia talking about her vacation. Then, read each sentence and answer **cierto** (true) or **falso** (false).

Ⓒ F **1.** A Cecilia le gustan las actividades al aire libre.

C Ⓕ **2.** A Cecilia no le gusta montar a caballo.

Ⓒ F **3.** A los amigos de Cecilia les gusta montar a caballo.

C Ⓕ **4.** Estas vacaciones, Cecilia va al campo.

C Ⓕ **5.** Cecilia siempre va a la playa con su familia.

2 Listen to Inés. Then, complete the sentences using the correct word in parentheses.

1. Inés va de _____ vacaciones _____ (vacaciones / caballo) con sus amigos.

2. Los amigos de Inés son _____ divertidos _____ . (divertidos / baratos)

3. Inés tiene _____ una pelota _____ . (la calidad / una pelota)

4. Inés va a comprarle a su madre _____ unos aretes _____ como recuerdo. (unos aretes / artesanías)

Escuchar B

Level 1, pp. 454-455
CD 04 tracks 37-38

> ¡AVANZA! **Goal:** Listen to people talking about vacation activities.

1 Listen to Victoria. Then, draw lines to match each person with what he or she bought at the handicrafts market.

a. Verónica   Anillo

b. Hugo   Artículo de madera

c. Mauro   Recuerdos

d. Sandra   Aretes de plata

e. Victoria   Collar

2 Listen to Ernesto. Then, complete the following sentences.

1. Victoria le compró _____ recuerdos _____
   a Ernesto.

2. Este regalo es _____ un artículo de cerámica, una artesanía. _____

3. No fue cara porque _____ Victoria regateó. _____

4. La persona de la tienda las vendió baratas porque ____ Victoria compró muchas. ____

5. Victoria les compró estos artículos a _____ todos los chicos de la clase. _____

Escuchar C

¡AVANZA!	**Goal:** Listen to people talking about vacation activities.

1 Listen to the handicrafts seller and take notes. Then, complete the chart.

¿Quién compró?	¿Qué compró?	¿De qué es?
Unos chicos	artículos	de madera
Unas chicas	aretes	de plata
Otras chicas	anillos	de plata
Muchos chicos	recuerdos	de cerámica
Una chica	collar	de oro

2 Listen to Miriam and take notes. Then, answer the questions with complete sentences.

1. ¿Qué compró Miriam y para quién lo compró?

Miriam le compró un collar de oro a su mamá.

2. ¿Qué le gusta a la mamá de Miriam?

Answers will vary: **A ella le gustan estas joyas.**

3. ¿Cómo son las joyas que más le gustan a la mamá de Miriam?

A ella le gustan las artesanías de oro.

4. ¿Por qué Miriam no le compró nada a su padre?

Ella no le compró nada porque compró un collar caro y no tiene más dinero.

UNIDAD 8
Lección 2

Escuchar C

Unidad 8, Lección 2
Escuchar C

380

¡Avancemos! 1
Cuaderno: Práctica por niveles

Leer A

| ¡AVANZA! | **Goal:** Read about vacation activities. |

A campground places an ad in the local newspaper.

 ¿Te gusta acampar?

Si te gusta acampar, conocemos el lugar ideal para hacerlo.

• Puedes hacer muchas actividades al aire libre: puedes montar a caballo, hacer surfing o dar una caminata.

¿Quieres venir a un lugar fantástico?

• Este lugar es un lugar como los de las películas.

• Si vienen en grupo les podemos ofrecer precios muy baratos.

¿Comprendiste?

Read the ad from a campground. Mark with an "x" those sentences that name things you can do.

1. acampar _X_
2. hacer actividades en el agua _X_
3. montar a caballo _X_
4. caminar al aire libre _X_
5. comprar recuerdos ____
6. ver animales ____
7. hacer deportes en el agua _X_
8. llevar a tus amigos _X_

¿Qué piensas?

¿Te gustaría ir a un lugar como el que describe la publicidad? ¿Por qué?

Answers will vary: **Sí, me encantaría ir a un lugar como el de la publicidad**

porque me gusta acampar al aire libre, dar caminatas y montar a caballo.

Leer B

> **¡AVANZA!** **Goal:** Read about vacation activities.

Before going away on vacation with some friends, Andrea receives an e-mail.

Hola, Andrea:

Te escribo este correo electrónico porque sé que sales de viaje a las 2:45 pm y yo salgo de mi clase de ciencias a las 3:00 pm.

Las vacaciones son muy divertidas cuando vas con cuatro personas. ¿Puedes tomar fotos de todo el grupo? ¿Me mandas las fotos por correo electrónico?

Conozco un lugar bonito, donde pueden acampar y hacer parrilladas. ¡Es buenísimo! Está al lado del mercado de artesanías.

Adios,

Javier

¿Comprendiste?

Read Javier's e-mail. Then complete the sentences.

1. Javier le escribe un correo electrónico a Andrea porque Andrea sale de viaje.

2. Andrea va de vacaciones con un un grupo de amigos.

3. Javier le pide fotos de todos.

4. Javier le habla de un lugar muy bueno para acampar y hacer parrilladas.

5. Ese lugar está cerca del mercado de artesanías.

¿Qué piensas?

¿Te gusta ir de vacaciones en grupo o con pocas personas? ¿Por qué?

Answers will vary: **Me gusta más ir de vacaciones en grupo. Porque conoces**

a muchas personas y es más divertido hacer actividades en grupo.

UNIDAD 8
Lección 2

Leer B

Unidad 8, Lección 2
Leer B

382

¡Avancemos! 1
Cuaderno: Práctica por niveles

Leer C

 Goal: Read about vacation activities.

Verónica received a letter from her friend Raúl.

> Hola, Verónica.
>
> Todavía estoy en la playa. No encuentro una computadora para mandarte un correo electrónico, entonces te escribo esta carta.
>
> Ayer fui al mercado de artesanías y te compré un recuerdo. Vi un collar de plata que me gustó mucho pero no sé si te gustaría. Todo fue muy barato porque regateé y el señor me vendió todo a un buen precio.
>
> También hice surf de vela. Fue divertido. Como al aire libre todas las mañanas y leo un libro en mi tiempo libre por las tardes. Estoy muy contento, y tú, ¿cómo estás?
>
> Raúl

¿Comprendiste?

Read the letter from Raúl. Then answer the following questions using complete sentences.

1. ¿Por qué Raúl escribe una carta?

Porque no encuentra una computadora para mandar un correo electrónico.

2. ¿Qué hizo en el mercado?

Él le compró un recuerdo a Verónica.

3. ¿Por qué pagó poco dinero por las cosas que compró?

Porque él regateó y el vendedor le vendió todo muy barato.

4. ¿Qué más hace Raúl?

Él también hace surf de vela, come el desayuno al aire libre y lee un libro en su tiempo libre.

¿Qué piensas?

1. ¿Tú les escribes a tus amigos cuando estás de vacaciones?

Answers will vary: **Sí, les escribo a mis amigos cuando estoy de vacaciones.**

2. Da un ejemplo:

Answers will vary: **El año pasado fui a la playa y les escribí correos**

electrónicos todos los días a mis amigos.

Escribir A

> **¡AVANZA!** **Goal:** Write about vacation activities.

Step 1

Write a list of things you can buy in a handicrafts market.

1. *Answers will vary:* **collares**

2. *Answers will vary:* **aretes**

3. *Answers will vary:* **anillos**

4. *Answers will vary:* **joyas**

5. *Answers will vary:* **artículos de cerámica**

6. *Answers will vary:* **artículos de madera**

Step 2

Using the information from the list, write three sentences about which of these items you can buy for your friends and family, and why. Use indirect object pronouns.

> *Answers will vary:* **A mi madre le puedo comprar collares y aretes de**
>
> **plata porque le gusta mucho la plata. A mi amiga Laura le gustan mucho**
>
> **los anillos; le puedo comprar uno en el mercado de artesanías. A mi hermano**
>
> **Lucas le puedo comprar algo de madera porque le gustan los artículos**
>
> **de madera.**

Step 3

Evaluate your writing using the information in the table.

Writing Criteria	Excellent	Good	Needs Work
Content	Your sentences include many details and new vocabulary.	Your sentences include some details and new vocabulary.	Your sentences include little information or new vocabulary.
Communication	Most of your sentences are clear.	Some of your sentences are clear.	Your sentences are not very clear.
Accuracy	Your sentences have few mistakes in grammar and vocabulary.	Your sentences have some mistakes in grammar and vocabulary.	Your sentences have many mistakes in grammar and vocabulary.

UNIDAD 8
Lección 2

Escribir A

384

Unidad 8, Lección 2
Escribir A

¡Avancemos! 1
Cuaderno: Práctica por niveles

Escribir B

> ¡AVANZA! **Goal:** Write about vacation activities.

Step 1

Make a list about activities you can do on vacation.

1. *Answers will vary:* **dar caminatas** _____
2. *Answers will vary:* **hacer parrilladas para mis amigos** _____
3. *Answers will vary:* **montar a caballo** _____
4. *Answers will vary:* **hacer surf de vela en el mar** _____

Step 2

Using the information from the list, write four sentences about vacation activities.
Use indirect object pronouns and demonstrative adjectives.

Answers will vary: **Yo necesito hacer caminatas todas las mañanas**

cuando estoy de vacaciones. Me gusta ver a aquellos amigos que viven cerca

de la playa y hacer parrilladas con ellos. Cuando vamos de vacaciones a la

montaña, a mis padres les gusta montar a caballo por las tardes. Ese

lugar donde vamos le gusta mucho a mi hermano.

Step 3

Evaluate your writing using the information in the table.

Writing Criteria	Excellent	Good	Needs Work
Content	Your sentences include many details and new vocabulary.	Your sentences include some details and new vocabulary.	Your sentences include little information or new vocabulary.
Communication	Most of your sentences are organized and easy to follow.	Some of your sentences are organized and easy to follow.	Your sentences are disorganized and hard to follow.
Accuracy	Your sentences have few mistakes in grammar and vocabulary.	Your sentences have some mistakes in grammar and vocabulary.	Your sentences have many mistakes in grammar and vocabulary.

¡Avancemos! 1
Cuaderno: Práctica por niveles

UNIDAD 8
Lección 2 • Escribir B

Unidad 8, Lección 2
Escribir B **385**

Escribir C

> ¡AVANZA! **Goal:** Write about vacation activities.

Step 1

You are going to go shopping at a handicrafts market. Complete this chart with what you buy, what is made of, and who you buy it for. *Answers will vary.*

¿Qué?	¿De qué?	¿Para quién?
anillo	de plata	Laura
aretes	de oro	Irene
artículos	de madera	para mí

Step 2

Using the information from the chart, write a paragraph about a visit to a handicrafts market. Use demonstrative adjectives and indirect object pronouns.

Answers will vary: Ayer fui al mercado de artesanías y les compré muchos

regalos a mis amigos. Le compré este anillo de plata a Laura y aquelllos

aretes de oro a Irene. Yo me compré unos artículos de madera como estos

que están aquí. Todos esos regalos les gustaron mucho a mis amigas.

Quiero volver para comprarles más recuerdos.

Step 3

Evaluate your writing using the information in the table.

Writing Criteria	Excellent	Good	Needs Work
Content	Your text includes many details and vocabulary.	Your text includes some details and vocabulary.	Your text includes little information or vocabulary.
Communication	Most of your text is organized and easy to follow.	Parts of your text are organized and easy to follow.	Your text is disorganized and hard to follow.
Accuracy	Your text has few mistakes in grammar and vocabulary.	Your text has some mistakes in grammar and vocabulary.	Your text has many mistakes in grammar and vocabulary.

UNIDAD 8
Lección 2

Escribir C

386

Unidad 8, Lección 2
Escribir C

¡Avancemos! 1
Cuaderno: Práctica por niveles

Cultura A

> ¡AVANZA! **Goal:** Review cultural information about Costa Rica.

1 **Costa Rica** Complete the following sentences with one of the multiple-choice answers.

1. The taxis in Costa Rica are __c__

    a. blue   **b.** yellow   **c.** red

2. Costa Rica is located in __a__

    a. Central America   **b.** North America   **c.** South America

3. The **quetzal** and the **tucán** are examples of __b__ found in Costa Rica.

    a. typical dishes   **b.** tropical birds   **c.** tropical plants

2 **Costa Rican culture.** Choose the correct word to complete the following sentences.

1. (Gold / Coffee) is one of Costa Rica's most exported products.

2. In Costa Rica coffee is harvested between the months of (November and January / April and June).

3. Arenal is a well-known (volcano/ river) in Costa Rica.

3 **Markets** At San José's **Mercado Central** there are many stalls that sell a variety of things. Do you remember what is sold in this market? Write about the types of items that you can buy at the **Mercado Central.** Which items would you buy if you visited this market?

Answers will vary: At the market you can buy many items such as t-shirts,

fruit, coffee, medicinal plants, and flowers. I would be interested in buying

t-shirts and jewelry at this market.

_____

¡Avancemos! 1
Cuaderno: Práctica por niveles

UNIDAD 8
Lección 2 • Cultura A

Unidad 8, Lección 2
Cultura A **387**

Cultura B

┌───┐
│ ¡AVANZA! **Goal:** Review cultural information about Costa Rica.   │
└───┘

1 **Costa Rica** Read the following sentences about Costa Rica and answer *true* or *false*.

Ⓣ   F   **1.** The product that Costa Rica exports the most is coffee.

Ⓣ   F   **2.** At the **Mercado Central** in San José, you can buy fruit and flowers.

T   Ⓕ   **3.** Costa Rica is larger than México.

T   Ⓕ   **4.** Costa Rica has a very cold climate.

Ⓣ   F   **5.** **Casado** is a typical Costa Rican food.

2 **Costa Rican culture** Answer the following questions about Costa Rica.

1. What color are the airport taxis in Costa Rica? _____ orange _____

2. In which region of the Americas Costa Rica located? __ In Central America __

3. When is the coffee harvest in Costa Rica? __ between November and January __

4. What are three common transportation methods in Costa Rica? _taxis, bus, local airlines_

3 **Transportation** Compare the modes of transportation that are popular in Costa Rica with those that are popular in your city or state. How do people travel short and long distances, typically? What are the pros and cons of each type of transportation?

Answers will vary. **In Costa Rica, taxis, buses, and local airline flights are**

popular modes of transportation.

_____

_____

388   **Unidad 8, Lección 2**
Cultura B

¡Avancemos! 1
Cuaderno: Práctica por niveles

UNIDAD 8
Lección 2   •   Cultura B

Cultura C

> ¡AVANZA! **Goal:** Review cultural information about Costa Rica.

1 **Life in Costa Rica** In Costa Rica, there are many places to visit and many things to do. Where do you go in Costa Rica to do the following things?

Things to do	Places to go
Buy fruit, coffee, or flowers	at the Mercado central in San José
Surfing	on the Pacific beaches of Costa Rica
go to the *carreta* festival	in the town of Sarchí

2 **Costa Rica** Answer the following questions about Costa Rica using full sentences.

1. When is coffee harvested in Costa Rica? _Coffee is harvested between the months_
of November and January.

2. What is the currency of Costa Rica? The currency of Costa Rica is the **colón.**

3. What are three common transportation methods in Costa Rica? _____

In Costa Rica, taxis, buses, and local airline flights are popular modes of transportation.

3 **Markets** Write a comparison of Costa Rica's **Mercado Central** and Uruguay's **Mercado del Puerto.** In which cities are the markets located? What can you buy and where can you eat at each market?

Answers will vary: **The Mercado Central is in San José and the Mercado**

 del Puerto is in Montevideo. You can buy t-shirts, coffee, fruit, jewelry, and

medicinal plants at the Mercado Central. You can also eat in small

restaurants called sodas. The Mercado del Puerto has many handicrafts

and art from local artists. There are also restaurants serving meat and fish.

UNIDAD 8
Lección 2

Cultura C

Comparación cultural: ¡De vacaciones!

Lectura y escritura

After reading the paragraphs about how Ernesto, Isabel, and Osvaldo describe their vacations, write a short paragraph about a real or imaginary vacation. Complete the information in the three boxes and then write a paragraph that describes your vacation.

Step 1

Complete the boxes describing as many details as you can about your place, activities, and your opinion about the location.

Lugar	Actividades	Opinión

Step 2

Now take the details from the boxes and write a sentence for each one according to their category.

_____

_____

_____

_____

_____

_____

_____

_____

_____

_____

UNIDAD 8 • Comparación
Lección 2   cultural

Unidad 8
Comparación cultural: ¡De vacaciones!

390

¡Avancemos! 1
Cuaderno: Práctica por niveles

Comparación cultural: ¡De vacaciones!

Lectura y escritura (continued)

Step 3

Now write your paragraph using the sentences you wrote as a guide. Include an introductory sentence and use **hacer un viaje, quedarse** and **gustar** to write about your own vacation.

_____

_____

_____

_____

_____

_____

Checklist

Be sure that…

☐ all the details about your vacation from your boxes are included in the paragraph;

☐ you use details to describe, as clearly as possible, all of your activities;

☐ you include new vocabulary words and the verbs **hacer un viaje, quedarse, and gustar.**

Rubric

Evaluate your writing using the rubric below.

Writing criteria	Excellent	Good	Needs Work
Content	Your paragraph includes many details about your vacation.	Your paragraph includes some details about your vacation.	Your paragraph includes little information about your vacation.
Communication	Most of your paragraph is organized and easy to follow.	Parts of your paragraph are organized and easy to follow.	Your paragraph is disorganized and hard to follow.
Accuracy	Your paragraph has few mistakes in grammar and vocabulary.	Your paragraph has some mistakes in grammar and vocabulary.	Your paragraph has many mistakes in grammar and vocabulary.

Comparación cultural: ¡De vacaciones!

Level 1, pp. 456-457

Compara con tu mundo

Now write a comparison about your vacation and that of one of the three students from page 457. Organize your comparison by topics. First, compare the place where you go, then the activities, and lastly your opinions about the locations.

Step 1

Use the table to organize your comparison by topics. Write details for each topic about yourself and the student you chose.

Categoría	Mis vacaciones	Las vacaciones de _____
lugar(es)		
actividades		
opinión		

Step 2

Now use the details from your chart to write the comparison. Include an introductory sentence and write about each topic. Use **hacer un viaje, quedarse,** and **gustar** to describe your vacation and that of the student you chose.

_____

_____

_____

_____

_____

_____

_____

_____

_____

Greet People and Say Goodbye

GREETINGS

Buenos días.	Good morning.
Buenas tardes.	Good afternoon.
Buenas noches.	Good evening.
Hola.	Hello./Hi.

SAY GOODBYE

Adiós.	Goodbye.
Buenas noches.	Good night.
Hasta luego.	See you later.
Hasta mañana.	See you tomorrow.

SAY HOW YOU ARE

¿Cómo estás?	How are you? (familiar)
¿Cómo está usted?	How are you? (formal)
¿Qué tal?	How is it going?
Bien.	Fine.
Mal.	Bad.
Más o menos.	So-so.
Muy bien.	Very well.
Regular.	Okay.
¿Y tú?	And you? (familiar)
¿Y usted?	And you? (formal)
¿Qué pasa?	What's up?

Say Which Day It Is

¿Qué día es hoy?	What day is today?
Hoy es...	Today is...
Mañana es...	Tomorrow is
el día	day
hoy	today
mañana	tomorrow
la semana	week

Describe the Weather

¿Qué tiempo hace?	What is the weather like?
Hace calor.	It is hot.
Hace frío.	It is cold.
Hace sol.	It is sunny.
Hace viento.	It is windy.
Llueve.	It is raining.
Nieva.	It is snowing.

Say Where You Are From

¿De dónde eres?	Where are you (familiar) from?
¿De dónde es?	Where is he/she from?
¿De dónde es usted?	Where are you (formal) from?
Soy de...	I am from...
Es de...	He/She is from...

Make Introductions

¿Cómo se llama?	What's his/her/your (formal) name?
Se llama...	His/Her name is...
¿Cómo te llamas?	What's your (familiar) name?
Me llamo...	My name is...
Te/Le presento a...	Let me introduce you (familiar/formal) to...
El gusto es mío.	The pleasure is mine.
Encantado(a).	Delighted./Pleased to meet you.
Igualmente.	Same here./Likewise.
Mucho gusto.	Nice to meet you.
¿Quién es?	Who is he/she/it?\\
Es...	He/She/It is...

Exchange Phone Numbers

¿Cuál es tu/su número de teléfono?	What's your (familiar/formal) phone number?
Mi número de teléfono es...	My phone number is...

Other Words and Phrases

la clase	class
el (la) maestro(a) de español	Spanish teacher (male/female)
Perdón.	Excuse me.
el país	country
(Muchas) Gracias.	Thank you (very much).
el señor (Sr.)	Mr.
la señora (Sra.)	Mrs.
la señorita (Srta.)	Miss
sí	yes
no	no

Talk About Activities

alquilar un DVD	to rent a DVD
andar en patineta	to skateboard
aprender el español	to learn Spanish
beber	to drink
comer	to eat
comprar	to buy
correr	to run
descansar	to rest
dibujar	to draw
escribir correos electrónicos	to write e-mails
escuchar música	to listen to music
estudiar	to study
hablar por teléfono	to talk on the phone
hacer la tarea	to do homework
jugar al fútbol	to play soccer
leer un libro	to read a book
mirar la televisión	to watch television
montar en bicicleta	to ride a bike
pasar un rato con los amigos	to spend time with friends
pasear	to go for a walk
practicar deportes	to practice / play sports
preparar la comida	to prepare food / a meal
tocar la guitarra	to play the guitar
trabajar	to work

Say What You Like and Don't Like to Do

¿Qué te gusta hacer?	What do you like to do?
¿Te gusta...?	Do you like...?
Me gusta...	I like...
No me gusta...	I don't like...

Snack Foods and Beverages

el agua (fem.)	water
la fruta	fruit
la galleta	cookie
el helado	ice cream
el jugo	juice
las papas fritas	French fries
la pizza	pizza
el refresco	soft drink

Other Words and Phrases

la actividad	activity
antes de	before
después (de)	afterward, after
la escuela	school
más	more
o	or
pero	but
también	also

Describe Yourself and Others

¿Cómo eres?	What are you like?
PERSONALITY	
artístico(a)	artistic
atlético(a)	athletic
bueno(a)	good
cómico(a)	funny
desorganizado(a)	disorganized
estudioso(a)	studious
inteligente	intelligent
malo(a)	bad
organizado(a)	organized
perezoso(a)	lazy
serio(a)	serious
simpático(a)	nice
trabajador(a)	hard-working
APPEARANCE	
alto(a)	tall
bajo(a)	short (height)
bonito(a)	pretty
grande	big, large; great
guapo(a)	good-looking
joven (pl. jóvenes)	young
pelirrojo(a)	red-haired
pequeño(a)	small
viejo(a)	old
Tengo...	I have...
Tiene...	He / She has
pelo rubio	blond hair
pelo castaño	brown hair

People

el (la) amigo (a)	friend
la chica	girl
el chico	boy
el (la) estudiante	student
el hombre	man
la mujer	woman
la persona	person

Other Words and Phrases

muy	very
un poco	a little
porque	because
todos(as)	all

Subject Pronouns and ser

Ser means *to be*. Use **ser** to identify a person or say where he or she is from.

Singular		Plural	
yo	**soy**	nosotros(as)	**somos**
tú	**eres**	vosotros(as)	**sois**
usted	**es**	ustedes	**son**
él, ella	**es**	ellos(as)	**son**

Gustar with an Infinitive

Use **gustar** to talk about what people like to do.

A mí **me gusta** dibujar.
A ti **te gusta** dibujar.
A usted **le gusta** dibujar.
A él, ella **le gusta** dibujar.
A nosotros(as) **nos gusta** dibujar.
A vosotros(as) **os gusta** dibujar.
A ustedes **les gusta** dibujar.
A ellos(as) **les gusta** dibujar.

Nota gramatical: Use **de** with the verb **ser** to talk about where someone is from.
Yo soy de Miami. Ellos son de California.

Definite and Indefinite Articles

In Spanish, articles match nouns in gender and number.

		Definite Article	Noun	Indefinite Article	Noun
Masculine	Singular	el	chico	un	chico
	Plural	los	chicos	unos	chicos
Feminine	Singular	la	chica	una	chica
	Plural	las	chicas	unas	chicas

Noun-Adjective Agreement

In Spanish, adjectives match the gender and number of the nouns they describe.

	Singular	Plural
Masculine	el chico alto	los chicos altos
Feminine	la chica alta	las chicas altas

Nota gramatical: Use **ser** to describe what people are like.
Ella es alta. Mis amigos son simpáticos.

Tell Time and Discuss Daily Schedules

¿A qué hora es...?	At what time is...?
¿Qué hora es?	What time is it?
A la(s)...	At ... o'clock.
Es la.../ Son las...	It is ... o'clock.
de la mañana	in the morning (with a time)
de la tarde	in the afternoon (with a time)
de la noche	at night (with a time)
la hora	hour; time
el horario	schedule
menos	to, before (telling time)
el minuto	minute
...y cuarto	quarter past
...y (diez)	(ten) past
...y media	half past

Describe Classes

Other Words and Phrases

casi	almost
¿Cuántos(as)...?	How many...?
difícil	difficult
el examen (pl. los exámenes)	exam
en	in
fácil	easy
hay...	there is, there are...
muchos(as)	many
tarde	late
temprano	early
tener que	to have to

Describe Frequency

de vez en cuando	once in a while
muchas veces	often, many times
mucho	a lot
nunca	never
siempre	always
todos los días	every day

SCHOOL SUBJECTS

el arte	art
las ciencias	science
el español	Spanish
la historia	history
el inglés	English
las matemáticas	math

CLASSROOM ACTIVITIES

contestar	to answer
enseñar	to teach
llegar	to arrive
necesitar	to need
sacar una buena / mala nota	to get a good / bad grade
tomar apuntes	to take notes
usar la computadora	to use the computer

NUMBERS FROM 11 TO 100 p. 87

Describe Classes

aburrido(a)	boring
divertido(a)	fun
interesante	interesting

Describe Classroom Objects

el borrador	eraser
la calculadora	calculator
el cuaderno	notebook
el escritorio	desk
el lápiz (pl. los lápices)	pencil
el mapa	map
la mochila	backpack
el papel	paper
el pizarrón (pl. los pizarrones)	board
la pluma	pen
la puerta	door
el reloj	clock; watch
la silla	chair
la tiza	chalk
la ventana	window

Places in School

el baño	bathroom
la biblioteca	library
la cafetería	cafeteria
el gimnasio	gymnasium
la oficina del (de la) director(a)	principal's office
el pasillo	hall

Say Where Things Are Located

al lado (de)	next to
cerca (de)	near (to)
debajo (de)	underneath, under
delante (de)	in front (of)
dentro (de)	inside (of)
detrás (de)	behind
encima (de)	on top (of)
lejos (de)	far (from)

Other Words and Phrases

¿(A)dónde?	(To) Where?
¿Cuándo?	When?
cuando	when
el problema	problem

Talk about How You Feel

cansado(a)	tired
contento(a)	content, happy
deprimido(a)	depressed
emocionado(a)	excited
enojado(a)	angry
nervioso(a)	nervous
ocupado(a)	busy
tranquilo(a)	calm
triste	sad

The Verb tener

Use the verb **tener** to talk about what you have.

tener *to have*		
yo	**tengo**	nosotros(as)	**tenemos**
tú	**tienes**	vosotros(as)	**tenéis**
usted	**tiene**	ustedes	**tienen**
él, ella	**tiene**	ellos(as)	**tienen**

Tener + que + infinitive is used to talk about what someone has to do.

Present Tense of –ar Verbs

To form the present tense of a regular verb that ends in **–ar**, drop the **–ar** and add the appropriate ending.

hablar *to talk, to speak*		
yo	**habl**o	nosotros(as)	**habl**amos
tú	**habl**as	vosotros(as)	**habl**áis
usted	**habl**a	ustedes	**habl**an
él, ella	**habl**a	ellos(as)	**habl**an

Nota gramatical: For the numbers 21, 31, and so on, use **veintiún, treinta y un,** and so on before a masculine noun. Use **veintiuna, treinta y una,** and so on before a feminine noun.

The Verb estar

Use **estar** to indicate location and say how people feel.

estar *to be*		
yo	**estoy**	nosotros(as)	**estamos**
tú	**estás**	vosotros(as)	**estáis**
usted	**está**	ustedes	**están**
él, ella	**está**	ellos(as)	**están**

The Verb ir

Use **ir** to talk about where someone is going.

ir *to go*		
yo	**voy**	nosotros(as)	**vamos**
tú	**vas**	vosotros(as)	**vais**
usted	**va**	ustedes	**van**
él, ella	**va**	ellos(as)	**van**

Nota gramatical: To form a question, you can switch the position of the verb and the subject.

Talk About Foods and Beverages

MEALS		
el almuerzo	lunch	
la bebida	beverage, drink	
la cena	dinner	
compartir	to share	
la comida	food; meal	
el desayuno	breakfast	
vender	to sell	

FOR BREAKFAST		
el café	coffee	
el cereal	cereal	
el huevo	egg	
el jugo de naranja	orange juice	
la leche	milk	
el pan	bread	
el yogur	yogurt	

FOR LUNCH		
la hamburguesa	hamburger	
el sándwich de jamón y queso	ham and cheese sandwich	
la sopa	soup	

FRUIT		
la banana	banana	
la manzana	apple	
las uvas	grapes	

Describe Feelings

tener ganas de...	to feel like . . .
tener hambre	to be hungry
tener sed	to be thirsty

Ask Questions

¿Cómo?	How?
¿Cuál?	Which?; What?
¿Por qué?	Why?
¿Qué?	What?

Other Words and Phrases

ahora	now
Es importante.	It's important.
horrible	horrible
nutritivo(a)	nutritious
otro(a)	other
para	for; in order to
rico(a)	tasty; delicious

Talk About Family

la abuela	grandmother
el abuelo	grandfather
los abuelos	grandparents
la familia	family
la hermana	sister
el hermano	brother
los hermanos	brothers, brother(s) and sister(s)
la hija	daughter
el hijo	son
los hijos	son(s) and daughter(s), children
la madrastra	stepmother
la madre	mother
el padrastro	stepfather
el padre	father
los padres	parents
el (la) primo(a)	cousin
los primos	cousins
la tía	aunt
el tío	uncle
los tíos	uncles, uncle(s) and aunt(s)

Ask, Tell, and Compare Ages

¿Cuántos años tienes?	How old are you?
Tengo... años.	I am . . . years old.
mayor	older
menor	younger

Give Dates

¿Cuál es la fecha?	What is the date?
Es el... de...	It's the . . . of . . .
el primero de...	the first of . . .
el cumpleaños	birthday

Pets

el (la) gato(a)	cat
el (la) perro(a)	dog

Other Words and Phrases

¡Feliz cumpleaños!	Happy birthday!
la fecha de nacimiento	birth date
vivir	to live
ya	already

NUMBERS FROM 200 TO 1,000,000	
doscientos (as)	200
trescientos (as)	300
cuatrocientos (as)	400
mil	1000
un millón (de)	1,000,000

MONTHS	
enero	January
febrero	February
marzo	March
abril	April
mayo	May
junio	June
julio	July
agosto	August
septiembre	September
octubre	October
noviembre	November
diciembre	December

Gustar with Nouns

To talk about the things that people like, use **gustar + noun.**

Singular	Plural
me gusta la sopa	**me gustan** los jugos
te gusta la sopa	**te gustan** los jugos
le gusta la sopa	**le gustan** los jugos
nos gusta la sopa	**nos gustan** los jugos
os gusta la sopa	**os gustan** los jugos
les gusta la sopa	**les gustan** los jugos

Present Tense of –er and –ir Verbs

vender to sell		**compartir** to share	
vendo	vendemos	comparto	compartimos
vendes	vendéis	compartes	compartís
vende	venden	comparte	comparten

Nota gramatical: To ask a question, use an interrogative word followed by a conjugated verb.
¿Cómo está usted? How are you?

Nota gramatical: The verb **hacer** is irregular in the present tense only in the **yo** form (**hago**). In other forms, it follows the pattern for –er verbs.

Possessive Adjectives

In Spanish, **possessive adjectives** agree in number with the nouns they describe. **Nuestro(a)** and **vuestro(a)** must also agree in gender with the nouns they describe.

Singular Possessive Adjectives		Plural Possessive Adjectives	
mi	**nuestro(a)**	**mis**	**nuestro(a)s**
my	*our*	*my*	*our*
tu	**vuestro(a)**	**tus**	**vuestro(a)s**
your (familiar)	*your (familiar)*	*your (familiar)*	*your (familiar)*
su	**su**	**sus**	**sus**
your (formal)	*your*	*your*	*your*
su	**su**	**sus**	**sus**
his, her, its	*his, her, its*	*their*	*thier*

Comparatives

Use with an adjective to compare two things:

más... que

menos... que

tan... como

If no adjective, use these phrases.

más que...

menos que...

tanto como...

Irregular comparative words.

mayor	**menor**	**mejor**	**peor**
older	*younger*	*better*	*worse*

Nota gramatical: Use **de** and a **noun** to show possesion.
el gato de **Marisa** *Marisa's cat*

Nota gramatical: Use **tener** to talk about how old a person is.
¿Cuantos años **tiene** tu amiga? *How old is your friend?*

Nota gramatical: To give the date, use the phrase: Es el + **number** + de + **month.** Hoy es el **diez** de **diciembre.**
Today is the tenth of December.
Es el **primeiro** de **diciembre.** *It is December first.*

Talk About Shopping

el centro comercial	shopping center, mall
¿Cuánto cuesta(n)?	How much does it (do they) cost?
Cuesta(n)...	It (They) cost. . .
el dinero	money
el dólar (pl. los dólares)	dollar
el euro	euro
ir de compras	to go shopping
pagar	to pay
el precio	price
la tienda	store

Describe Clothing

la blusa	blouse
los calcetines	socks
la camisa	shirt
la camiseta	T-shirt
la chaqueta	jacket
feo(a)	ugly
el gorro	winter hat
los jeans	jeans
llevar	to wear
nuevo(a)	new
los pantalones	pants
los pantalones cortos	shorts
la ropa	clothing
el sombrero	hat
el vestido	dress
los zapatos	shoes

COLORS

amarillo(a)	yellow
anaranjado(a)	orange
azul	blue
blanco(a)	white
marrón (pl. marrones)	brown
rojo(a)	red
verde	green

Expressions with tener

tener calor	to be hot
tener frío	to be cold
tener razón	to be right
tener suerte	to be lucky

Discuss Seasons

la estación (pl. las estaciones)	season
el invierno	winter
el otoño	autumn, fall
la primavera	spring
el verano	summer

Other Words and Phrases

durante	during
cerrar (ie)	to close
empezar (ie)	to begin
entender (ie)	to understand
pensar (ie)	to think, to plan
preferir (ie)	to prefer
querer (ie)	to want

Describe Places in Town

el café	café
el centro	center, downtown
el cine	movie theater; the movies
el parque	park
el restaurante	restaurant
el teatro	theater

In a Restaurant

el (la) camarero(a)	(food) server
costar (ue)	to cost
la cuenta	bill
de postre	for dessert
el menú	menu
la mesa	table
el plato principal	main course
la propina	tip

ORDERING FROM A MENU

pedir (i)	to order, to ask for
servir (i)	to serve

FOR DINNER

el arroz	rice
el bistec	beef
el brócoli	broccoli
la carne	meat
la ensalada	salad
los frijoles	beans
el pastel	cake
la patata	potato
el pescado	fish
el pollo	chicken
el tomate	tomato
las verduras	vegetables

Describe Events in Town

el concierto	concert
las entradas	tickets
la música rock	rock music
la película	movie
la ventanilla	ticket window

Getting Around Town

a pie	by foot
la calle	street
en autobús	by bus
en coche	by car
encontrar (ue)	to find
tomar	to take

Other Words and Phrases

allí	there
almorzar (ue)	to eat lunch
aquí	here
dormir (ue)	to sleep
el lugar	place
poder (ue)	to be able, can
tal vez	perhaps, maybe
ver	to see
volver (ue)	to return, to come back

Stem-Changing Verbs: e → ie

For e → ie stem-changing verbs, the e of the stem changes to ie in all forms except nosotros(as) and vosotros(as).

querer *to want*	
quiero	queremos
quieres	queréis
quiere	quieren

Direct Object Pronouns

Direct object pronouns can be used to replace direct object nouns.

Singular		Plural	
me	*me*	nos	*us*
te	*you (familiar)*	os	*you (familiar)*
lo	*you (formal), him, it*	los	*you, them*
la	*you (formal), her, it*	las	*you, them*

Nota gramatical: Use **tener** to form many expressions that in English would use *to be*.
Tengo frío. *I am cold*

Stem-Changing Verbs: o → ue

For o → ue stem-changing verbs, the last o of the stem changes to ue in all forms except nosotros(as) and vosotros(as).

poder *to be able; can*	
puedo	podemos
puedes	podéis
puede	pueden

Stem-Changing Verbs: e → i

For e → i stem-changing verbs, the last e of the stem changes to i in all forms except nosotros(as) and vosotros(as).

servir *to serve*	
sirvo	servimos
sirves	servís
sirve	sirven

Nota gramatical: **Ver** has an irregular **yo** form in the present tense.
Veo un autobús.

Nota gramatical: Use a form of **ir a** + **infinitive** to talk about what you are going to do.

Describe a House

el apartamento	apartment
el armario	closet; armoire
bajar	to descend
la casa	house
la cocina	kitchen
el comedor	dining room
el cuarto	room; bedroom
la escalera	stairs
ideal	ideal
el jardín (pl. los jardines)	garden
el patio	patio
el piso	floor (of a building)
la planta baja	ground floor
la sala	living room
subir	to go up
el suelo	floor (of a room)

Furniture

la alfombra	rug
la cama	bed
la cómoda	dresser
las cortinas	curtains
el espejo	mirror
la lámpara	lamp
los muebles	furniture
el sillón (pl. los sillones)	armchair
el sofá	sofa, couch

Describe Household Items

la cosa	thing
el disco compacto	compact disc
el lector DVD	DVD player
el radio	radio
el televisor	television set

el tocadiscos compactos	CD player
los videojuegos	video games

Ordinal Numbers

primero(a)	first
segundo(a)	second
tercero(a)	third
cuarto(a)	fourth
quinto(a)	fifth
sexto(a)	sixth
séptimo(a)	seventh
octavo(a)	eighth
noveno(a)	ninth
décimo(a)	tenth

Plan a Party

bailar	to dance
cantar	to sing
celebrar	to celebrate
dar una fiesta	to give a party
decorar	to decorate
las decoraciones	decorations
la fiesta de sorpresa	surprise party
el globo	balloon
los invitados	guests
invitar a	to invite (someone)
salir	to leave, to go out
el secreto	secret
venir	to come

Talk About Chores and Responsibilities

acabar de...	to have just . . .
ayudar	to help
barrer el suelo	to sweep the floor
cocinar	to cook
cortar el césped	to cut the grass
darle de comer al perro	to feed the dog
deber	should, ought to
hacer la cama	to make the bed
lavar los platos	to wash the dishes
limpiar (la cocina)	to clean the kitchen
limpio(a)	clean
pasar la aspiradora	to vacuum
planchar la ropa	to iron
poner la mesa	to set the table
los quehaceres	chores
sacar la basura	to take out the trash
sucio(a)	dirty

Talk About Gifts

abrir	to open
buscar	to look for

envolver (ue)	to wrap
el papel de regalo	wrapping paper
recibir	to receive
el regalo	gift
traer	to bring

Other Words and Phrases

decir	to say, to tell
hay que	one has to, one must
poner	to put, to place
si	if
todavía	still; yet

More Irregular Verbs

Dar, decir, poner, salir, traer, and **venir** are all irregular.

decir *to say, to tell*		venir *to come*	
digo	decimos	vengo	venimos
dices	decís	vienes	venís
dice	dicen	viene	vienen

Some verbs are irregular only in the **yo** form of the present tense.

dar	poner	salir	traer
doy	pongo	salgo	traigo

Affirmative tú Commands

Regular **affirmative tú commands** are the same as the **él/ella** forms in the present tense.

Infinitive	Present Tense	Affirmative tú Command
lavar	(él, ella) lava	¡**Lava** los platos!
barrer	(él, ella) barre	¡**Barre** el suelo!
abrir	(él, ella) abre	¡**Abre** la puerta!

There are irregular **affirmative tú commands.**

decir	hacer	ir	poner	salir	ser	tener	venir
di	haz	ve	pon	sal	sé	ten	ven

Nota gramatical: When you want to say that something has just happened, use the verb **acabar de** + infinitive.

Acabamos de comprar el pastel para la fiesta.
We just bought the cake for the party

Ser or estar

Ser and **estar** both mean *to be.*

Use **ser** to indicate origin.
Use **ser** to describe personal traits and physical characteristics.
Ser is also used to indicate professions.
You also use **ser** to express possession and to give the time and the date.
Use **estar** to indicate location.
Estar is also used to describe conditions, both physical and emotional.

Ordinal Numbers

When used with a noun, an **ordinal number** must agree in number and gender with that noun.

Ordinals are placed before nouns.
Primero and **tercero** drop the **o** before a masculine singular noun.

Sports

el básquetbol	basketball	
el béisbol	baseball	
el fútbol americano	football	
nadar	to swim	
la natación	swimming	
patinar	to skate	
patinar en línea	to in-line skate	
el tenis	tennis	
el voleibol	volleyball	

el partido	game	
peligroso(a)	dangerous	
perder (ie)	to lose	

Locations and People

los aficionados	fans
el (la) atleta	athlete
el campeón (pl. los campeones), la campeona	champion
el campo	field
la cancha	court
el equipo	team
el estadio	stadium
el (la) ganador(a)	winner
el (la) jugador(a)	player
la piscina	pool

Sports Equipment

el bate	bat
el casco	helmet
el guante	glove
los patines en línea	in-line skates
la pelota	ball
la raqueta	racket

Talk About Sports

comprender las reglas	to understand the rules
favorito(a)	favorite

Talk About Staying Healthy

enfermo(a)	sick
fuerte	strong
herido(a)	hurt
levantar pesas	to lift weights
la salud	health
sano(a)	healthy

PARTS OF THE BODY

la boca	mouth
el brazo	arm
la cabeza	head
el corazón (pl. los corazones)	heart
el cuerpo	body
el estómago	stomach
la mano	hand
la nariz (pl. las narices)	nose
el ojo	eye
la oreja	ear
el pie	foot
la piel	skin
la pierna	leg
la rodilla	knee
el tobillo	ankle

Make Excuses

doler (ue)	to hurt, to ache
Lo siento.	I'm sorry.

Other Words and Phrases

anoche	last night
ayer	yesterday
comenzar (ie)	to begin
terminar	to end
¿Qué hiciste (tú)?	What did you do?
¿Qué hicieron ustedes?	What did you do?

Outdoor Activities

el bloqueador de sol	sunscreen
bucear	to scuba-dive
caminar	to walk
hacer esquí acuático	to water-ski
el mar	sea
la playa	beach
tomar el sol	to sunbathe

The Verb jugar

Jugar is a stem-changing verb in which the **u** changes to **ue** in all forms except **nosotros(as)** and **vosotros(as)**.

jugar *to play*	
j**ue**go	jugamos
j**ue**gas	jugáis
j**ue**ga	j**ue**gan

When you use **jugar** with the name of a sport, use **jugar a + sport.**

The Verbs saber and conocer

Both **saber** and **conocer** mean *to know* and have irregular **yo** forms in the present tense.

saber *to know*		conocer *to know*	
sé	sabemos	conozco	conocemos
sabes	sabéis	conoces	conocéis
sabe	saben	conoce	conocen

- Use **saber** to talk about factual information you know. You can also use **saber + infinitive** to say that you know how to do something.
- Use **conocer** when you want to say that you are familiar with a person or place. You also use **conocer** to talk about meeting someone for the first time.

Nota gramatical: When a specific person is the direct object of a sentence, use the personal **a** after the verb and before the person.
No conozco **a** Raúl. *I don't know Raúl.*

Preterite of Regular –ar Verbs

To form the **preterite** of a regular **–ar** verb, add the appropriate preterite ending to the verb's stem.

nadar *to swim*	
nadé	nadamos
nadaste	nadasteis
nadó	nadaron

Preterite of -car, -gar, -zar Verbs

- Regular verbs that end in **-car, -gar, or -zar** have a spelling change in the **yo** form of the preterite.

bus**c**ar	c	becomes → qu	(yo) bus**qu**é
ju**g**ar	g	becomes → gu	(yo) ju**gu**é
almor**z**ar	z	becomes → c	(yo) almor**c**é

Nota gramatical: To express what hurts, use **doler (ue)** followed by a definite article and a part of the body.
Me **duele la cabeza.** *My head hurts.*